CREATIVE
MALADY

CREATIVE MALADY

Illness in the Lives and Minds
of
Charles Darwin
Florence Nightingale
Mary Baker Eddy
Sigmund Freud
Marcel Proust
Elizabeth Barrett Browning

GEORGE PICKERING

New York   Oxford University Press   1974

To my three Carolas

Author's Preface

Everyone knows from his own experience, or that of his acquaintances, that illness is an evil episode, which, rightly, evokes sympathy and commiseration. Few people know that it can occasionally be of benefit not only to the victim but to society. To explore this in some detail is the central theme of this book.

My own experience of the usefulness of illness goes back to childhood. Illness to me brought a comfortable bed, a glowing, flickering fire, and seclusion. I can still recall the impression made on me by the books I read at the time. School reinforced this. Hugh Walpole's *Mr Perrin and Mr Trail*, read in the sick-bay, has since been one of my most vivid memories. So is my stay of three weeks with chickenpox in the sanatorium, where my incarceration led me to the first original scientific concept that I formed. To find subsequently that others had had similar ideas before me did nothing to dim, but indeed quickened the excitement of this first intellectual adventure.

Since I became a professor, and particularly since I became a public servant on bodies such as the University Grants Committee, the Medical Research Council, and the Council for Scientific Policy, I have found it increasingly difficult to find time to call my own. Like so many in my position, I find that I am constantly needed at this meeting or that; I am given to understand that the affairs of the nation will come to a stop without me;* besides I have a conscience, and deliberate absence brings guilt. What suffers then is creative work, by which I mean anything which is essentially my own, whether it be original observations at the bedside or in the laboratory, or an original idea or method, or a new way of looking at an old problem. All kinds of accidents have, from time to time, put

* This is, of course, nonsense, but it is the kind of nonsense purveyed by administrators who want someone to do a job for them.

leisure in my way: fishing holidays when I could not fish (e.g. because the Tweed was frozen or the Thurso River gin-clear), long train journeys, Atlantic crossings, and even the daily commuting. But in the last ten years I have found another ally. I have had a pair of osteo-arthritic hips. When they get intolerably painful I put them to bed. In bed I cannot attend committees or see patients or entertain visitors. But I can read or write or dictate. My wife and family are attentive, thoughtful and kind, my secretaries most accommodating. These are the ideal conditions for creative work; freedom from intrusion, freedom from the ordinary chores of life, ready accessibility of the tools needed for the job.*

Added to these were my experiences as a physician, which I relate briefly in Chapter 1. So I was receptive to the idea that illness, including psychological illness, might occasionally be an asset and not an unmitigated disaster. Such was the start of this intellectual adventure, and the book resulting from it.

* Since writing this I have had both my hip joints totally removed and replaced by metal prostheses. Though it is blissful to be freed from pain and to be no longer crippled, I cannot help regretting the passing of my old friend.

Oxford,
1974

Acknowledgments

I have been helped immensely by many of my friends. Chief amongst these is my wife, who has read my various manuscripts with great care and made drastic but helpful suggestions. Next comes Dr Charles Whitty, who has done the same, and who has also contributed from a knowledge of the subject more detailed and extensive than mine. My secretary, Miss Sheila Hatton, has not only typed the many drafts, but has made the subject her own and supplied me with many books and articles of whose existence I was not aware. Sir Clive Fitts of Melbourne, Dr Thomas Hunt of London, Professor Leslie Witts and Dr Juel-Jensen of Oxford, and non-medical friends, Mr and Mrs Anthony Sampson and Mr Donald Tyreman, have read the manuscript and improved it.

Like all students of Charles Darwin, I am deeply grateful to him and his son Francis for the lucid records of his life and illness. In one respect at least, Darwin would have agreed with the interpretation here made of his illness. He had no doubt that it had been useful to his work. I am also deeply grateful to his grand-daughters, Lady Barlow and Lady Keynes, who were kind enough to read my manuscript and made helpful suggestions. Lady Keynes indeed lent me the correspondence between Sir Clifford Allbutt, Regius Professor of Physic at Cambridge, and her father, Sir George Darwin. Allbutt diagnosed Darwin's case as 'gastric neurosis' which was treated by emptying the stomach through a tube. Sir Hedley and Lady Atkins, the present incumbents of Down House, kindly entertained us there and made us familiar with the physical surroundings of Darwin's work. Sir Alister Hardy also read my manuscript and pointed out to me that it was the British Resident in the Galapagos who told Darwin that he could recognise from which island a reptile or bird had come. It was he, too, who awakened my interest in Wallace.

Miss Nightingale too left a mass of material. This has been sifted and made available particularly by Sir Edward Cook and Mrs Woodham-Smith. I have related in Chapter 1 how it was the reading of her biography that made me realise how similar was Miss Nightingale's illness to that of Mr Darwin. She and Sir Douglas Hubble, who first interpreted Darwin's illness as a good physician should, were the real instigators of this book. Mrs Woodham-Smith's lucid and scholarly text has made it easy to portray Miss Nightingale, her problems and their relation to her illness, in what I hope is a realistic account. I am grateful to her and her publishers in allowing me to quote from her book. Sir Harry Verney, the successor in Claydon to Miss Nightingale's rejected suitor and brother-in-law, and perhaps the only person alive who knew Miss Nightingale before senility set in, kindly showed my wife and me over Claydon, and read my manuscript. I am most grateful to the Director of the British Museum for allowing me access to the Nightingale papers which, however, had been thoroughly culled by Mrs Woodham-Smith.

Concerning Mary Baker Eddy, I am indebted to Mr Colin Roberts, who lent me H. A. L. Fisher's book, the Librarian of Dartmouth College, New Hampshire, who gave me access to their excellent collection of material relevant to Mrs Eddy, to the Director of the British Museum for similar access, and to Mrs Gilbert Mudge, who drove me to see Mrs Eddy's birthplace and the town of Tilton, whither her family removed. I am also grateful to the Librarian of the Hall Library, Tilton, who put me in contact with the Trustees of the Brown family, who owned Mrs Eddy's portrait, which I am able to reproduce, thanks to the Christian Science Board of Directors. They have been most helpful in every way.

The late Robert Baldick of Pembroke College, Oxford, read my manuscript on Proust, as did his pupil, Mr Wakefield. They made some valuable suggestions.

Part of this book was written, and the whole was drastically revised and greatly improved, while my wife and I were guests of the Rockefeller Foundation at its Villa Serbelloni in Bellagio. In expressing our deep gratitude to them I would like to explain that they provide the ideal conditions for scholarship. With all material wants graciously met, and stimulated by the presence of acute minds with totally different backgrounds, my wife and I have been able to give our whole minds to our problem. I hope I shall not be misunderstood when I say that the Foundation provides at its Villa the same ideal conditions for scholarship that Charles Darwin and Florence Nightingale provided for themselves by illness. It was John Marshall, the resident director of the Villa at our first visit, who suggested the inclusion of Elizabeth Barrett and Marcel Proust. His wife, Charlotte, kindly typed part of my manuscript. They both made many helpful suggestions.

I wish to express my gratitude to the following for permission to reproduce quotations and illustrations:

Victor Gollancz Ltd (extract from *Darwin's Century* by Loren Eiseley).

The C. V. Mosby Company (extract from *Psychopathology* by Edward J. Kempf).

The Lancet (extract from 'Charles Darwin and Psychotherapy' by Douglas Hubble).

Hamish Hamilton Ltd (extract from *Florence Nightingale* by Cecil Woodham-Smith).

Ernest Benn Ltd (extracts from *Our New Religion* by H. A. L. Fisher).

Alfred A. Knopf Inc. (extract from *Mary Baker Eddy: The Truth and the Tradition* by E. S. Bates and John V. Dittemore).

The Hogarth Press and Mrs Katherine Jones (extracts from *Sigmund Freud: Life and Works* by Ernest Jones).

Hutchinson Publishing Group Ltd (extracts from *Marcel Proust: Letters to his Mother* translated and edited by George D. Painter).

Chatto and Windus Ltd (extracts from *Marcel Proust: A Biography* by George D. Painter).

George Allen and Unwin Ltd (extracts from *History of Western Philosophy* by Bertrand Russell).

Granada Publishing Ltd (extracts from *Essays in Biography* by John Maynard Keynes).

The Mansell Collection (Plate 1(a)).

The Radio Times Hulton Picture Library (Plates 1(b), 3(a), 7 and 8(b)).

The National Portrait Gallery (Plate 3(b) and watercolour of Florence Nightingale painted by J. Barrett in 1856 used on the jacket).

The Illustrated London News (Plate 4).

The Christian Science Board of Directors (Plate 5).

Sigmund Freud Copyrights Ltd (Plates 6(a) and 6(b) and the picture of Freud used on the jacket).

The Royal College of Surgeons (Plate 2 and the watercolour of Charles Darwin in 1840 used on the jacket).

Mr E. R. Moulton-Barrett (Plate 8(a)).

Madame Mante Proust (Portrait of Proust by Jacques Emile Blanche, 1892, used on the jacket).

I am grateful to my wife, Miss Hatton, Dr Juel-Jensen, and Dr Nicholas Mann, for reading the proofs.

Contents

Illustrations

Chapter 1

CREATIVE ILLNESS

Creative illness may seem a very odd subject. No doubt it is. But then the idea which is here explored seems to be a novel one, namely that illness, and particularly psychological illness, may sometimes be an aid to creative work, indeed essential in the cases here described.

In the preface I have related how the idea that illness can be useful to creative work arose from my personal observation. The idea was supported by experience of others. Wilfred Trotter* was perhaps the greatest and most original mind that I have been privileged to meet. It was illness in his youth, and the enforced solitude that it brought, that made him savour the pleasures of meditation which so enriched his writing. One pupil of mine was an undistinguished scholar until he developed pulmonary tuberculosis, which took him into a sanatorium for a year. He read and he thought, and he emerged a completely changed man, who made original contributions to knowledge.

It became evident to me that an illness that is not debilitating or disabling, or threatening to life, may provide the ideal circumstances for creative work. Its only rival is prison. Of that I have as yet no first-hand experience, but Bunyan made the most of it, as did Bertrand Russell.

To use physical illness when it is thrust upon one to secure conditions for creative work is sensible. But to rely on it to produce the right conditions over a lifetime would not be. It would be like depending for one's income on winning prizes

* Trotter, Wilfred (1872–1939), M.Ch., F.R.C.S., F.R.S. Surgeon to University College Hospital and Serjeant-Surgeon to H.M. King George V, was a most distinguished and highly respected surgeon, who was elected to the Royal Society for his contributions to psychology. His *Instincts of the Herd in Peace and War* first established the concept of the herd instinct. He married Ernest Jones' sister and attended Freud for his cancer of the palate after he came to England.

from lotteries. In this respect, psychological illness turns out to be much superior. It develops to meet a need in a particular set of circumstances, and so long as those remain more or less stable, the illness does its job. Should circumstances change, the illness may cease to have a function and disappear.

My mind was thus receptive when I read a fascinating article by Douglas Hubble on Charles Darwin and psycho-therapy.[1] His thesis was that the obscure illness from which Darwin suffered for most of his life was a psychoneurosis, whose purpose was to protect Darwin from the trivialities of social intercourse. Illness provided him with the solitude and the leisure needed to develop and support his revolutionary concept of evolution, as Darwin himself recognised. Hubble's thesis was not well received, particularly by biologists, who preferred the explanation that Darwin was physically ill from an infection which he acquired in Brazil. The nature of Darwin's illness is still the subject of controversy. But the more I read of Darwin's own account of himself and his illness, the more convinced I became of the correctness of Hubble's view.

I was aware of another distinguished invalid who had also produced a revolution in her lifetime and afterwards, Miss Florence Nightingale. But I was only acquainted with her through a source that was distorted. Lytton Strachey's delight-ful and provocative essay[2] treats Miss Nightingale from the point of view of medieval superstition, picturesque undoubt-edly, but hardly conducive to understanding. In his attitude to Miss Nightingale's behaviour, Lytton Strachey had not pro-gressed much from that of his ancestors and mine, who, six centuries earlier, had burnt Joan of Arc as a witch. He pointed out that Miss Nightingale was not the saintly, self-sacrificing woman that facile fancy had painted. 'She worked in another fashion, and towards another end; she moved under the stress of an impetus which finds no place in the popular imagination. A Demon possessed her.' In describing her refusal to accept her doctors' injunctions to rest when she became severely ill after returning from the Crimea, he wrote: 'No; she had work to do; and, come what might, she would do it. The doctors protested in vain; in vain her family lamented and entreated, in vain her friends pointed out to her the madness of such a course. Madness? Mad—possessed—perhaps she was. A demoniac frenzy had seized upon her.' It was not until I read Mrs Woodham-Smith's lucid life of Florence Nightingale[3] that it became clear to me that here too was a psychological illness with a purpose. And the purpose was to enable Miss Nightingale to achieve the object of her burning passion: to avenge her murdered children, the British soldiers who had died in the Crimea. This vengeance required no less than a complete reform of the War Office.

My collector's appetite having now been whetted by two perfect specimens, I looked around for more. Four satisfied my definition of creative illness, Joan of Arc, Mary Baker Eddy, Sigmund Freud, and Marcel Proust. But in them the role of illness was different. In these four, the illness was an essential part of the act of creation rather than a device to enable that act to take place; in the last three of them, the creative work and the illness had a common source in mental torment.

There was another creative artist, Elizabeth Barrett Browning, who also had an illness, in part psychological. Examination of her case showed yet another situation. In her, creativity seems to have been largely independent of that illness. Thus she provides an interesting contrast to the others that I have studied. I suppose I could have continued my search further. Blake, of whom Edith Sitwell said he was cracked but that was where the light came through, Dostoevsky, Nietzsche, are all candidates for inclusion. But the examples I have chosen are enough to illuminate the problem.

Three reasons can be given why the thesis developed in this book has been neglected in the past. The first reason is the difficulty in distinguishing an illness of the body from one of the mind. It is still perhaps the most difficult of all the problems that face a physician. At the time when most of my subjects were alive, the diagnosis of psychological illness could not be made at all. Freud said of himself in the period 1882–1885 when he was a junior hospital physician in Vienna:

> On one occasion I introduced to my audience a neurotic suffer-
> ing from a persistent headache as of chronic meningitis; they
> quite rightly rose in revolt against me, and my premature
> activities as a teacher came to an end. By way of excuse I may
> add that this happened at a time when greater authorities than
> myself in Vienna were in the habit of diagnosing neurasthenia
> as cerebral tumours.[4]

As it happens, this problem is one in which I have been interested ever since I qualified as a doctor, and in which I have had a fair amount of practical experience. In a way, then, this book reflects one of my own interests in medicine and people.

The second reason for neglect is ignorance of the nature and causation of mental illness. Since the Renaissance, the method of science had revolutionised knowledge and understanding of natural phenomena. Objects and events are described and classified, and their relations simplified into a hypothetical causal sequence. The longer a hypothesis persists without being disproved, the more probable it becomes. It is termed first a theory, and ultimately a 'Law'. These laws are quantitative and mathematical, and are now known to be laws of probability. Their formulation and their testing depends on experiment, and on measurement, particularly the latter. Such, briefly, is the method which has revolutionised physical and biological science. The method has given man his mastery of nature and modern medicine its extraordinary power to cheat death by preventing and curing disease. But one group especially eludes us, the disorders of the mind. This state of affairs is partly due to the fear of them that was so common until quite recently, and partly to the fact that the phenomena being studied here are of a totally different order from those of the physical world, including physical illness. It is possible to measure the functional capacity of the lungs, of the heart, of the kidneys, and the reflex activities of the central nervous system. But when we come to the mind we find entities are difficult to distinguish one from another and at present impossible to measure. They are subjective and not objective. So we know much less about causal sequences and their interdependence in the case of the mind than in the case of the body. Though progress has been made in understanding animal behaviour, particularly through the experiments of Pavlov and his school, and the observations of Konrad Lorenz and his pupils on birds, mammals and fish, human psychiatry is still largely in the descriptive phase. The reason why we have made so little progress in the field of mental disease is similar to the reason why the study of the genetics of behaviour has not progressed very far. About this Medawar wrote:

. . . the problem is very, very difficult. Goodness knows how it is to be got at. It may be outflanked or it may yield to attrition, but probably not to direct assault. No scientist is admired for failing in the attempt to solve problems that lie beyond his competence. The most he can hope for is the kindly contempt earned by the Utopian politician. If politics is the art of the possible, research is surely the art of the soluble. Both are immensely practical-minded affairs.[5]

The third reason is the extent to which society has feared, and still fears, mental illness. My life as a physician has taught me that what fills the mind of man with the most abject terror is the unknown and the unknowable. So it has been with mental disease until quite recently.

Illness of the mind is apt to result in behaviour that is unpredictable and is socially, at best, inconvenient, at worst, outrageous. The doctors had no insight into its causation, could not foretell it, prevent it, or cure it. It was not unnatural that society behaved abominably to the victims. The worst afflicted, called lunatics, were put away in gaunt Victorian edifices, situated in the depths of the country in huge grounds surrounded by high walls. Some of this state of affairs lingers. Conditions in a few of these hospitals and the attitude of a few of the staff to their patients are occasionally so contrary to humanitarianism that they are the subject of public outcry and official investigation. In recent years there have been notable improvements. Bit by bit, knowledge and understanding has come to doctors and scientists, and with it a more tolerant and sympathetic attitude by the public. Indeed, to some, mental illness seems almost desirable. In some circles of advanced thought in the City of New York, to have one's psychiatrist is as much *de rigueur* as it is to have one's own tailor among men of fashion. Nevertheless, most people in Europe still regard disorders of the mind as shameful episodes, to be hidden and if possible forgotten. In Cambridge, undergraduates could seek psychiatric advice at No. 4 Benet Place,* as it was accurately and discreetly called, without informing their tutor or their relatives, or even their family doctor of what to them may have seemed a shameful dilemma.

The idea that symptoms of patients with mental disease have meaning was, according to Freud, first put forward by Breuer in 1880. That causal sequences operate in disorders of the mind may, nowadays, seem no more than a glimpse of the obvious. But it was a revolutionary concept in its day; indeed, its adoption by Freud was the chief reason why his writings appealed to a young scientist like myself forty-five years ago. It is now generally accepted that a disorder of the mind is the result of a sequence of events, often beginning in the remote, and continuing into the recent, past. It is also generally held that functional nervous disorders, the psychoneuroses, have a function or purpose; they bring the sufferer nearer to some evident or concealed wish.† Often the purpose of a psychoneurosis is of

---

* Now (1973) closed for lack of clients.

† The clearest example of a purposive psychological illness I have seen was in my son, then aged about seven. He used to wake with what he called a 'funny tummy', and wanted to stay in bed. He looked ill, in the sense that he was pale and inactive. I would take his temperature, exclude neck rigidity and abdominal tenderness, and say, 'All right, you can get up and have your breakfast and I'll

no, or negative, social value. The victim of hysterical fits, whose purpose is to attract attention to the patient himself, is not an asset to society. Hysterical paralysis, and similar dramatic episodes, such as complete loss of memory and personal identity, that were such a striking feature of the war neuroses, may have the purpose of hiding the intolerable conflict from the patient and the world, but have no tangible benefit for society. The minor psychoneuroses may bring the patient a degree of consideration and of favour that those in more robust health are denied.

There is no *a priori* reason why the purpose of a psychoneurosis should not indirectly benefit society at large as well as benefiting its victim. But until Hubble analysed Charles Darwin's illness, the idea had never, to my knowledge, been put forward. My examination of the personalities here considered, their achievements and their illnesses, has led me to conclude that the world is indebted to their illnesses for the great contributions they made to their own times and to posterity. Without that illness, the great work would not have been done, or done in such splendid style. That is what I mean by creative illness.

Perhaps this essay showing the occasional usefulness of psychological illness may induce a more tolerant attitude to it by society. I should add, in case I am misunderstood, that I have written this book, not in any missionary spirit, but for the intellectual pleasure that always attends a venture into the unknown.

---

take you to school.' The diagnosis unfolded thus: my wife discovered the attacks were periodic and coincided with maths at school. He was top, or nearly so, in everything except maths, in which he was bottom. One Sunday morning I got him to bring me his maths prep. He could not subtract, and as a consequence could not do long division. When asked about this, he burst into tears and explained that he had been ill when subtraction was taught and had not liked to ask. I informed his form master; the defect was repaired; the attacks ceased and never recurred; maths became one of his best subjects. This syndrome is well known, and technically termed 'school refusal'. In most of its victims the cause of the psychoneurosis is never discovered.

Chapter 2
WHAT IS MENTAL ILLNESS?

To help the reader to understand more fully the problems presented by the eminent people with which this book is concerned, a very brief outline of mental illness is here given. I shall pay particular attention to the psychoneuroses and to the variety from which Charles Darwin and Florence Nightingale seem to have suffered.

The whole subject is difficult, partly for the reasons outlined in the first chapter and partly because the dividing lines between mental health and mental illness are by no means clear cut or agreed; nor are the divisions between the classes into which mental illness is commonly divided.

The difficulties in diagnosis are illustrated by the following. A film of a psychiatric interview with an attractive woman in her middle twenties was shown to two American and one British group of psychiatrists, who were asked to make a diagnosis. In the first group, 14 diagnosed the patient as neurotic and 21 as psychotic. In the second group, one third diagnosed schizophrenia; one third a neurosis, and one third a personality disorder. The British group of psychiatrists behaved very differently. Not one diagnosed schizophrenia, and over 75% diagnosed a personality disorder. The Americans had found pronounced apathy in the patient which the British had not.[1]

Mental disorders are divided into the more severe, the psychoses, and the less severe, the psychoneuroses.

THE PSYCHOSES

The psychoses, the most severe disorders of the mind, are distinguished from the less severe psychoneuroses by the patient being out of touch with reality; he is frequently unable to take care of himself, and may be a danger to himself and to others. He is, in the legal sense, insane. Some of these disorders are quite transient and due to an obvious physical cause, such as the delirium of high fever, and the acute confusional state that follows an overdose of insulin. More prolonged, but still reversible, is the delirium tremens of severe and prolonged over-indulgence in alcohol. But the causes of the commonest two psychoses are at present unknown and treatment is still unsatisfactory.

Manic depressive psychosis is a condition in which a mood of extreme exaltation and intense energy is followed by a mood of deep depression and inactivity; in between are varying periods of normal behaviour. In the manic stage, ideas follow one another with extraordinary rapidity. These ideas, combined with the intense energy, may lead to achievements and creations of the first rank. But, in the true maniac, reality is so remote that action may be disastrous. Depression is characterised by deep gloom; the subject feels that he is guilty of all kinds of errors of commission and omission; that he is utterly incompetent, and incapable of performing any useful service; suicide is not uncommon.

Schizophrenia may be the commonest psychosis. One person in five admitted to mental hospitals in the United States is given this diagnosis. It begins with a failure of social adjustment, which may seem only one exaggeration of manifest difficulties. It proceeds to a complete disintegration of personality.

The psychoses are in general outside the scope of this book because they are destructive not creative. Van Gogh was a schizophrenic. While the phase of his illness is apparent from the nature of his canvases, his earlier work shows that his creative ability was in no way due to his illness.

Many readers will recognise in the description of manic depressive psychosis at least a hint of their own, or their friends' behaviour. Many of those who achieve distinction are hypomanics in whom mood swings from one of energy, exuberance and confidence, to one of the reverse. Freud was an example. Such people are quite sane, and, as long as circumstances do not press too hard, are in no danger and often achieve great things.

THE PSYCHONEUROSES

The psychoneuroses comprise a group of abnormalities of behaviour extending from the normal at one end to the psychoses at the other. They differ from the latter in that touch with reality is not lost, though the hold may be tenuous, and the patient is able to look after himself. Whereas in the common psychoses, manic depression and schizophrenia, the illness seems to be a manifestation of an inner disorder, perhaps chemical, the psychoneuroses are usually precipitated, and are much influenced, by environmental events. However, different individuals react in different degrees. Some seem to require quite a small departure from the optimum environment to precipitate a psychoneurosis; these are often called unstable or highly strung. Others require an extreme disturbance; they are called stable.

Because it is so often difficult to identify, isolate and measure the influence of different factors in causation of human disease, recourse is often had to experiments on animals. In the context of the psychoneuroses, the relevant experiments come from the great Russian physiologist, Ivan Petrovich Pavlov, who discovered, and developed, the idea of the conditioned or conditional reflex.[2] Pavlov was studying the secretion of saliva by a dog when it was fed. It had long been known that the display of food to a dog would lead to the secretion of saliva, the so-called psychic secretion. Pavlov found that if the giving of food was accompanied by another event, such as the ringing of a bell, then, after the two had been presented together sufficiently often, ringing a bell alone would cause the dog to salivate. Salivation in response to food is an inborn, or unconditioned, reflex. Salivation induced in this way by ringing a bell is an acquired, or conditioned, reflex. Pavlov and his pupils proceeded to extend and to analyse experiments based on this very simple one. They showed, for example, that conditioned reflexes are of two kinds—excitatory, where the stimulus excites something like the flow of saliva, and inhibitory, where the stimulus prevents it. Stimuli become exciting when they are repeatedly exhibited in association with food, inhibitory when they are repeatedly exhibited in the absence of food. A very interesting set of experiments established excitation to a circle and inhibition to an ellipse. Successively the circle was altered to make it more elliptical and the ellipse to make it more circular. A stage arrived when the two were almost indistinguishable. The whole behaviour of the animal altered:

> The hitherto quiet dog began to squeal on its stand, kept wriggling about, tore off with its teeth the apparatus for mechanical stimulation of the skin and bit through the tubes connecting the animal's room with the observer, a behaviour which had never happened before. On being taken into the experimental room the dog now barked violently, which was also contrary to its usual custom; in short it presented all the symptoms of a condition of acute neurosis.[2]

Pavlov also found that it was much easier to establish an experimental neurosis in some dogs than others.

These experiments, and others like them, show that an animal can be guaranteed to display signs of anxiety and a profound alteration of behaviour and appearance if it is presented with a conflict that it can neither escape nor resolve. I agree with Pavlov, and Adler* and Ross,† that this is also the essential

---

* See Chapter 12.

† Ross, Dr T. A., distinguished as a common-sense psychiatrist and one of the first to use statistics in psychiatry.

cause of the psychoneuroses in man. The variety of conflicts, and the circumstances of their origin, are, of course, infinitely more complex in the ordinary rough and tumble of human life than in the case of dogs being conditioned in a Pavlov chamber. As in the dog, so in the human, susceptibility to neurosis varies from one individual to another.

Students of animal behaviour have made us familiar with two generalised responses of the animal which are fundamental to all behaviour. The first is the orienting reaction, or curiosity reflex. The second is the defence reflex. In most ways the second is an exaggeration of the first. When a new object moves into the sight or hearing of a dog, cat, or horse, its former occupation is interrupted, the head is lifted, the eyes and ears directed to the source, and the body tensed. The heart rate quickens, respiration quickens and deepens, and the arterial pressure rises. In the defence reflex, these responses are greater; in addition the pupils dilate, the hair is raised, the teeth are bared, and the body put into a position prepared for fight (aggression) or flight (submission). These two actions are correlated with two emotive responses, anger and fear, which are accompanied by the same bodily changes.

These responses begin to be exhibited in man in the first year and continue throughout life, becoming dimmed, as all do, in old age. They are evoked hundreds of times each day. Two important attributes deserve notice. In the first place they are preparatory for action. Should the stimulus prove to be less interesting or harmful than it might have been, then no action takes place. Repetition of the stimulus provokes a smaller response, and finally none at all. In the second place, the reflex can be conditioned, that is to say an otherwise ineffective stimulus may, through chance linkage with an effective one, become of itself effective. I once witnessed this in my son. At the age of a year he was sitting on the kitchen floor, which was covered by linoleum of black and white checks approximately two inches square. Beside him was a cocker spaniel. The butcher's boy rang the bell, which was an old-fashioned swinging bell about eight feet from the child; the dog barked, and the child cried. For some weeks afterwards whenever the child was put on the kitchen floor he cried. This response slowly diminished and finally disappeared.

Anxiety neurosis is one of the commonest forms of psycho-neurosis. As its name implies, the manifestations are those accompanying fear or anxiety—rapid heart action, increased respiration, sweating, sometimes goose skin, sometimes head-ache, a feeling of sickness, and, less commonly, actual vomiting. These disturbances disappear during sleep and are character-istically exaggerated, or even only manifest, when a circum-stance arises which is strongly associated in the patient's mind with the object of fear.* This may include the doctor, as I shall shortly relate.

My teacher of psychiatry was an admirer and disciple of Freud. To him, anxiety neurosis had only one cause, sexual desire without gratification. This is a common cause, as my patients have taught me, but it is a special example of the general. I believe that an anxiety neurosis may arise when there is an apparently unresolvable conflict between any very powerful desire and its fulfilment. This conflict arouses anxiety, if the whole situation is unclear to the patient; it arouses fear, if the object precipitating the conflict can be clearly identified.

Soldier's Heart or Da Costa's syndrome. Da Costa described, in the American Civil War, a new disease which caused the physicians of the Union Army much anxiety. This became a major problem in World War I. In the British Army over 70,000 reported sick with this diagnosis and 44,000 received pensions.

The young soldier complains of pain over the heart, breath-lessness, palpitations, giddiness, sweating and other less com-

* Beautifully displayed in Miss Nightingale's case by an attack being brought on whenever her mother or sister visited her.

mon symptoms. When he is examined, his heart rate is raised
and he is usually overbreathing. Often he shows a flush over his
face and neck. Sighing is common. These symptoms are always
exaggerated by exercise which, indeed, normally is accompanied by similar changes in heart and respiration; as a result
exercise is limited. Hence the young soldier breaks down. He
falls out of the marches, the barrack square drill, and particularly the battle practice. He has to be returned to a base camp.
In the First World War he was often sent to hospital for treatment because it was hoped, in view of its shortage, to add him to
the cannon fodder at the front. The doctors were not successful.

I first stumbled on the cause of this disease when I was doing
Sir Thomas Lewis's* work when he was on vacation. On two
successive Thursdays the same doctor sent to outpatients two
young women with the same story. Each had had rheumatic
fever. At that time it was taught that an elevated heart rate
meant the heart muscle was affected by the disease, which I
had just satisfied myself to be untrue. Rest in bed was *de rigueur*
to encourage healing. Week after week the doctor had visited
the patient; asked her to lift her nightdress so that he could
count her heart rate; found the rate still fast; looked at the
patient with a worried expression, and said, 'Well, your heart is
still not normal so you will have to stay in bed.' Each patient
had been in bed for a year.† Each had Da Costa's syndrome,
and each patient was terrified that she had a heart condition
which was going to make her an invalid, prevent marriage and

---

* Lewis, Sir Thomas (1881–1945), M.D., F.R.S., Physician to University
College Hospital, London, was the greatest authority on heart disease and one
of the greatest experimental physiologists of his day. He established the scientific
basis, and the clinical usefulness, of electrocardiography. Soldier's heart was
causing such immense casualties in the British Army in the 1914–18 war that
Lewis was commissioned to study it. He was misled into considering it to be
infectious in origin. Lewis is the father of clinical science. He was a first-rate
clinician, but he had no understanding of, or indeed interest in, mental illness.
It was my privilege to work with him from 1930 to 1939.
† This, of course, is what happened to Florence Nightingale, who, at the beginning of her illness, wrote to Dr Sutherland (5 September 1857): 'The man here
. . . told me not to move and to take no solid food till my pulse calmed down.'

other exciting rewards of life. In each case it was the doctor who was first frightened, and communicated his fear to the patient. The rapid pulse was a manifestation of anxiety or fear and not of active heart disease.

The view that this condition is a psychoneurosis, an anxiety state whose manifestations have become centred on the heart, was put on a solid basis by Paul Wood in World War II.[3] He found that many soldiers with Da Costa's syndrome had a family history of nervous breakdowns and that all these patients had been told at one time or another by a physician that they had heart disease. If soldiers were told by a physician that they had heart disease and would have to rest, many of those who followed instructions developed Da Costa's syndrome; whereas most of those who disobeyed did not develop the disease. Thus the disease represents a pattern of behaviour designed to protect the patient, and particularly against exercise, which is, in the lay mind, as it used to be in the medical mind, the chief danger in heart disease. Sir Thomas Lewis, towards the end of his life, wrote of it: 'To diagnose heart strain in these patients and, on this or other ground, to forbid exercise or enjoin rest, is to cripple these patients and to bring them to a state of partial or complete invalidism.'[4] This was what happened to Charles Darwin and Florence Nightingale.

The condition is not peculiar to war. War displays the disease because of the obligatory exercise and the additional fear of hardship, discomfort and death.

A most interesting aspect of anxiety neurosis in general, and Da Costa's syndrome in particular, is overbreathing. We meet this particularly in Miss Nightingale. The respirations are very rapid and sometimes increased in depth. This washes the carbon dioxide out of the blood. The *acapnia*, as it is called, may induce faintness or loss of consciousness, tingling, weakness, or spasm in feet and hands. Nowadays the physician stops it by getting the patient to breathe in and out of a paper bag, or, if he is prepared to be brutal as I am, by telling the patient not to behave like that but to breathe normally.

Psychoneuroses may take many other forms which fortunately do not concern us. The range of symptoms is due, of course, to the variety of circumstances in which the causal disturbance, usually associated with fear, arose; and to the great resources of the human mind in effecting concealment (repression) and disguise. White, in *The Abnormal Personality*,[5] defines a neurosis as a series of stereotyped reactions to problems which the patient has never solved in the past and is still unable to solve in the present. Not a few of the psychoneuroses seem to be an attempt to hide or disguise these problems so that they cannot easily be recognised by the world, or, indeed, by the patient.

The more intense the conflict, the more securely it tends to be hidden in the mind, and the more profound the psychoneurosis. Unless the doctor can help the patient to detect and resolve that conflict, the psychoneurosis will continue though its symptoms may change. It was to lay bare that hidden conflict, and by exposing it in its naked simplicity to enable the patient to solve it, that Freud developed the psychoanalytic method. The variety of hypotheses of the cause of psychoneurosis which that method has brought, and which are touched on in Chapter 12, testifies to the uncertainty of our present understanding.

What has been said about the role of the doctor in Da Costa's syndrome holds for the other psychoneuroses. Many of the psychoneuroses are difficult to distinguish from organic disease of the body. Some organic diseases may kill the patient, if neglected, and are curable if detected. So the doctor is trained especially to recognise them and to treat them with respect. Sometimes, too, a disease of the body gives rise to an added psychoneurosis. This develops through fear that an ardent wish to accomplish something, to love someone, or simply to live, seems likely to be frustrated through disability or death. This psychoneurosis may be much more disabling than the underlying organic disease. It is especially difficult to decide how much of a patient's disability is due to the disease of the body and how much to the added psychoneurosis, as in the case of Elizabeth Barrett Browning.

The distinction between organic disease and a psychoneurosis, which simulates it, is thus one of the most difficult of all the tasks facing a physician. A century ago, when the characters portrayed in this book were alive, it was impossible. Charles Darwin and Florence Nightingale were treated as suffering from organic disease throughout their lives, as was Elizabeth Barrett until Robert Browning had the perspicacity to see more clearly than the doctors what was the true state of affairs. Nor are the penalties of misdiagnosis all one on side. The serious risk of failing to diagnose organic disease at a stage when it is curable is self-evident. What is not so obvious is the danger of treating a psychoneurosis as though it were a disease of the body.

The symptoms of the psychoneurosis are the patient's own answer to his otherwise intolerable conflict. If the doctor treats them as having an organic basis and advises rest, particularly rest in bed, the avoidance of what is exciting, interesting, exacting, and enjoyable, the patient's own natural tendency to regard the illness as disabling is reinforced by outside authority. The oftener this happens and the longer it goes on, the more profound the disability. Unless the reader fully appreciates this he will not understand the extraordinary contrast between the vigour and the invalidism that characterised the earlier and later periods of the lives of Charles Darwin and Florence Nightingale.

To pronounce that a patient has no organic disease and that the symptoms are those of a psychoneurosis, or that the patient is not so sick as he or she thinks, and should do more for himself or herself, requires more courage and determination than any other decision that I know in medicine. The price of error is high, and the response of the patient is deep resentment. It is an issue that most doctors like to avoid, and it demands the highest degree of professional skill.

Chapter 3
CHARLES DARWIN
The Vigorous Naturalist

Charles Darwin is perhaps the most celebrated scientist of the last century. His book, *The Origin of Species*, completely transformed man's outlook on the living world. It put forward the thesis that species were not separately created, but had evolved, the more advanced from the less advanced, by a process of natural selection. As a boy Darwin was undistinguished and engaged almost entirely in vigorous outdoor pursuits. Then he became an exploring naturalist of great energy and endurance. Between the ages of thirty and thirty-three he became an invalid recluse, which he remained till he died. Before this illness he conceived, and during this illness he perfected, the idea on which his fame depends, and wrote a prodigious number of other learned books. The nature of his illness has given rise to much speculation and four serious hypotheses. We may begin with the facts.

As we shall see, the cause of Darwin's illness is controversial. It is therefore of great importance that the source of the facts should be clear. The sources quoted are: first, his *Autobiography*, labelled (A); second, his *Diary of the Voyage of the Beagle*, labelled (D); and third, the second edition of *A Naturalist's Voyage round the World*, labelled (J). The *Diary* alone was contemporary in the sense that it was written during, and not after, the voyage of the *Beagle*.

Charles Robert Darwin was born at Shrewsbury on 12 February 1809, the youngest but one of six children. His grandfather was the great Erasmus Darwin, a physician of Lichfield, who wrote poetry, which is good enough to provide aimless arts students with a subject for a Ph.D., and whose mechanical devices to aid easier living are reminiscent of those of Thomas Jefferson. Erasmus was a member of the celebrated Lunar Club, and had an imaginative mind which foresaw the aeroplane and the submarine; he put forward a theory of evolution in *Zoonomia*. His grandson wrote: 'At this time (while at Edinburgh) I greatly admired the Zoonomia; but on reading it a second time, after an interval of ten or fifteen years, I was much disappointed; the proportion of speculation being so large to the facts given.' (A)

His father was Dr Robert Darwin, who began to practise with £20 in his pocket and prospered so well that he left his children financially independent. He was a big man weighing 24 stone and being 6 ft 2 in. tall. He died at 82. Robert married Susannah Wedgwood, daughter of the great potter. Mrs Darwin died when Charles was eight and left him with few memories.

The boy early displayed a passion for natural history, and for collecting such objects as shells, seals, coins and minerals. 'The passion for collecting which leads a man to be a systematic naturalist, a virtuoso, or a miser, was very strong in me, and was clearly innate, as none of my sisters or brothers ever had this taste.' (A) His other great passion as a little boy was angling.

In the summer of 1818 he went to Dr Butler's great school in Shrewsbury and remained there till he was sixteen. 'Nothing could have been worse for the development of my mind than Dr Butler's school, as it was strictly classical, nothing else being taught, except a little ancient geography and history. The school as a means of education to me was simply a blank. During my whole life I have been singularly incapable of mastering any language.' (A)

When he left school he was considered a very ordinary boy. Indeed his father said to him one day, to Charles's deep mortification, 'You care for nothing but shooting, dogs and rat-catching, and you will be a disgrace to yourself and all your family'. However, he had strong tastes and recorded the intense satisfaction that he got from the clear geometrical proofs of Euclid as expounded by a private tutor, and the principles of a barometer vernier explained by his uncle, the father of Francis Galton. He enjoyed reading, especially Shakespeare and the recently published poems of Byron and Scott. He continued his collecting and helped his brother in a chemical laboratory which they made in a tool house in the garden.

As he was doing no good at school his father wisely took him away and sent him to Edinburgh to begin his medical studies with his brother who was completing his. Both boys had guessed that their father would leave them enough to subsist in comfort and did not over-exert themselves. Neither completed the course. Darwin wrote:

> The instruction at Edinburgh was altogether by lectures, and these were intolerably dull, with the exception of those on chemistry by Hope; but to my mind there are no advantages and many disadvantages in lectures compared with reading. Dr Duncan's lectures on Materia Medica at 8 o'clock on a winter's morning are something fearful to remember. Dr Munro made his lectures on human anatomy as dull as he was himself, and the subject disgusted me. It has proved one of the greatest evils in my life that I was not urged to practise dissection, for I should soon have got over my disgust, and the practice would have been invaluable for all my future work. This has been an irremediable evil, as well as my incapacity to draw. (A)

After spending two sessions in Edinburgh, his father perceived, or heard from his sisters, that Charles did not like the thought of being a physician. His father proposed he should become a clergyman. 'He was very properly vehement against my turning into an idle sporting man, which then seemed my probable destination.' (A) Charles asked for time to consider the idea, since he had scruples in declaring his belief in all the dogmas of the Church of England. After reading *Pearson on the Creed* and a few other books, and since he did not 'doubt the strict and literal truth of every word in the Bible' (A) he accepted.

After suitable cramming in Latin and Greek he entered Christ's College, Cambridge, early in 1828.

During the three years which I spent at Cambridge my time was wasted, as far as the academical studies were concerned, as completely as at Edinburgh and at school. I attempted mathematics . . . but I got on very slowly. The work was repugnant to me, chiefly from my not being able to see any meaning in the early stages of algebra. This impatience was very foolish, and in after years I have deeply regretted that I did not proceed far enough at least to understand something of the great leading principles of mathematics, for men thus endowed seem to have an extra sense. . . .

From my passion for shooting and hunting, and, when this failed, for riding across country, I got into a sporting set, including some dissipated low-minded young men. We used often to dine together in the evening, though these dinners often included men of a higher stamp, and we sometimes drank too much, with jolly singing and playing at cards afterwards. I know that I ought to feel ashamed of days and evenings thus spent, but as some of my friends were very pleasant, and we were all in the highest spirits, I cannot help looking back to these times with much pleasure. . . .

But no pursuit at Cambridge was followed with nearly so much eagerness or gave me so much pleasure as collecting beetles. It was the mere passion for collecting, for I did not dissect them. . . . In the autumn my whole time was devoted to shooting, . . . Upon the whole the three years which I spent at Cambridge were the most joyful in my happy life; for I was then in excellent health, and almost always in high spirits. (A)

At Cambridge he became well acquainted with Professor Henslow.*

* Henslow, John Stevens (1796–1861) F.R.S., Professor of Botany, Cambridge University, 1827–61.

. . . and during the latter half of my time at Cambridge took long walks with him on most days; so that I was called by some of the dons 'the man who walks with Henslow'; and in the evening I was very often asked to join his family dinner. His knowledge was great in botany, entomology, chemistry, mineralogy and geology. His strongest taste was to draw conclusions from long-continued minute observations. His judgment was excellent, and his whole mind well-balanced; but I do not suppose that any one would say that he possessed much original genius. (A)

In August 1831, Darwin returned from a geological tour in North Wales with Professor Sedgwick* and found that letters had come from Professor Henslow and Mr Peacock† telling him that Captain FitzRoy was willing to give up part of his own cabin to any young man who would volunteer to go with him without pay as a naturalist on a voyage to be undertaken for the Admiralty by H.M.S. *Beagle*. Darwin gave this account of the momentous decision.

I immediately said I would go; but the next morning finding my Father so much averse to the whole plan, I wrote to Mr Peacock to refuse his offer. On the last day of August I went to Maer,‡ where everything soon bore a different appearance. I found every member of the family strongly on my side, that I determined to make another effort. In the evening I drew up a list of my Father's objections, to which Uncle Jos wrote his opinion and answer. This we sent off to Shrewsbury early the next morning and I went out shooting. About 10 o'clock Uncle Jos sent me a message to say he intended going to Shrewsbury and offering to take me with him. When he

* Sedgwick, Adam (1785–1873) F.R.S., Woodwardian Professor of Geology, Cambridge University, 1818.
† Peacock, George (1791–1858) F.R.S., Lowndean Professor of Astronomy, Cambridge University, 1838–58, was consulted on the appointment of a naturalist for the *Beagle*, and applied to Henslow.
‡ The home of his uncle Josiah Wedgwood and his future wife Emma.

arrived there, all things were settled, and my Father most kindly gave his consent.

I shall never forget what very anxious and uncomfortable days these two were, my heart appeared to sink within me, independently of the doubts raised by my Father's dislike to the scheme. I could scarcely make up my mind to leave England even for the time which I then thought the voyage would last. (D)

THE 'BEAGLE' AND ITS COMMANDER

The *Beagle* was a ten-gun brig of 242 tons. She was 90 ft long and 24 ft 8 in. in beam. From 1826 to 1830 she had made a voyage to South America surveying the coast of Tierra del Fuego and the Straits of Magellan. During the last two years she had been commanded by Captain Robert FitzRoy, R.N.*

FitzRoy had again been asked to command the *Beagle* at the request of the hydrographer of the Navy. The voyage was to complete the survey of the coasts of Patagonia, Tierra del Fuego, Chile and Peru, to visit some Pacific Islands and to carry a chain of chronometrical stations round the world. Captain FitzRoy had greatly regretted the absence of a geologist who could inquire into the possible presence of valuable metals in the unexplored mountains of Tierra del Fuego and who could, incidentally, provide further evidence to confute the geological sceptics who disputed the strict and literal truth of every statement in the Bible. He was a deeply religious man and was later to be bitterly ashamed and resentful of the heretical ideas that Darwin had conceived while a member of his crew. He was a manic depressive and committed suicide while deeply depressed, at the age of fifty-nine.

* FitzRoy was a grandson of the Duke of Grafton, who was descended from Charles II through the lovely Barbara Villiers, Duchess of Cleveland. FitzRoy was only twenty-six at this time. His rapid promotion was, of course, not hindered by his ancestry, but was largely due to his devotion and ability. He eventually achieved the rank of Vice Admiral and Governor of New Zealand, where his uncompromising personality led to difficulties with the civil administration.

THE VOYAGE OF THE 'BEAGLE'

Darwin went on board the *Beagle* in Devonport harbour on 25 October 1831. The ship was still being fitted out, and he did not sleep on board till 4 December. Because of bad weather and Christmas celebrations, the *Beagle* did not put to sea till 27 December. The following days were wretched. He was sick and most despondent. 'I often said before starting, that I had no doubt I should frequently repent of the whole undertaking, little did I think with what fervour I should do so. I can scarcely conceive any more miserable state than when such dark and gloomy thoughts are haunting the mind as have today pursued me,' (D) he wrote on 30 December. His spirits did not recover till they reached Tenerife on 6 January.

Darwin, the only non-naval officer, shared Captain Fitz-Roy's cabin for meals and worked in the poop cabin where he kept his books and next to which the carpenters had built a set of drawers for his specimens. In the subsequent five years he was to send back his collections of minerals, animals and plants to Henslow as often as convenient transport allowed.

The still intending clergyman was thrilled with the adventure before him. While still in harbour at Devonport he wrote in his diary:

Dec. 13: If I have not energy enough to make myself steadily industrious during the voyage, how great and uncommon an opportunity of improving myself shall I throw away. May this never for one moment escape my mind and then perhaps I may have the same opportunity of drilling my mind that I threw away whilst at Cambridge. (D)

The voyage of the *Beagle* is described in detail in three texts. Darwin kept a diary (D) which was edited by his grand-daughter, (Lady) Nora Barlow and published in 1933. After his return home Darwin went through his collection with experts. The Zoology was published in five volumes, beginning with *Mammalia* by Waterhouse in 1839, and *Fossil Mammalia* by

Richard Owen in 1840, each of which was edited and introduced by Darwin. Darwin himself prepared his journal for publication in 1837, the publication actually taking place in 1839. Its title was *Journal of Researches into the Natural History and Geology of the Countries Visited during the Voyage round the World of H.M.S. 'Beagle' under command of Captain Fitz Roy, R.N.* A second edition was written and published in 1845.[4] It is this second edition (J) which has been reprinted time and time again as one of the world's classics. A great change took place between the first and second editions, for in the interval Darwin had become convinced of the probability of evolution, much of the evidence having come from working up the results of the *Beagle* expedition. During the voyage Darwin had probably begun to wonder how animals became extinct and how they started. But it is clear from his diary and the first edition of the *Journal of Researches* that the light dawned subsequently. Alan Moorehead's picturesque account of Darwin and FitzRoy arguing about the origin of species in the first year of the *Beagle*'s voyage is, I fear, a serious distortion of the facts.

Darwin's actions, experiences, thoughts and health are described lucidly and in detail in his diary. He reveals himself there as an extremely vigorous, industrious, observant, inquiring, and intellectually honest young man. He enjoyed geology most and was greatly indebted to Lyell's *Principles of Geology*, which he had taken with him. He collected fossils and rocks and he collected plants. He also collected animals of all classes, briefly describing and roughly dissecting many of the marine ones. He noted that his inability to draw and lack of anatomical knowledge made a great pile of manuscripts about animals almost useless. All these specimens were labelled, packed, and sent home as soon as possible to be examined and identified by the experts.

Darwin got ashore whenever he could, for geology was his major preoccupation. He made frequent journeys on horseback inland when the *Beagle* was in port, or overland if he could rejoin the ship. He never missed an opportunity of climbing a mountain. He proved the fittest and, in many respects, the toughest man on board. On one occasion, near Port St Julian, he set off with FitzRoy and four armed men to explore the country. The wind became strong and they had to beach the boat and continue on foot. They were greatly troubled by thirst and as what appeared to be a lake was seen in the distance, Darwin and one of the men set out for it, only to find it was not water but salt. By the evening, two of the party, including FitzRoy, could go no further, so Darwin and the other then set out for the boat leaving their arms behind. They reached the boat, from where a party with water was sent to the exhausted men and brought them back by midnight. Darwin spent the next two days in bed with fever.

His health and spirits were remarkably good throughout the five years' voyage. He suffered from sea-sickness certainly and this did not improve with experience. But there was no return of the initial despondency. He was occasionally unwell (probably gastroenteritis) and had occasional bouts of fever, and one long one lasting seven weeks (possibly typhoid); he also experienced an infected knee and an infected skin lesion. But it would be difficult to find anyone who roughed it as he did who was less affected by the hazards of the tropics. Of the illness which was later to play so big a part there is no mention during the voyage. He was too active and too busy acquiring new experiences.

Brazil brought Darwin his first experience of tropical forest. He was thrilled. In his first letter to Henslow he wrote:

Here I first saw a Tropical forest in all its sublime grandeur. Nothing but the reality can give any idea, how wonderful, how magnificent, the scene is. If I was to specify any one thing I should give preeminence to the host of parasitical plants. . . . I never experienced such intense delight. I formerly admired Humboldt, I now almost adore him; . . . I am at present red-hot with Spiders, they are very interesting, & if I am not mistaken I have already taken some new genera.[7]

Another episode in Brazil made a deep impression. On a journey of 100 miles into the tropical forest with an Irishman called Lennon to visit his estate (hacienda), he met slavery for the first time. 'I thank God', he wrote later, 'I shall never again visit a slave country. To this day if I hear a distant scream, it recalls with painful vividness my feeling when, passing a house near Pernambuco, I heard the most pitiable moans, and could not but suspect that some poor slave was being tortured, yet knew that I was as powerless as a child to remonstrate.' He also had one of his few attacks of fever, despite which he journeyed on. 'Travelled on till it was dark, felt miserably faint and exhausted; I often thought I should have fallen off my horse. . . . The next morning I nearly cured myself by eating cinnamon and drinking port wine.' (D) Darwin was lucky. Another party from the *Beagle* had gone up river snipe-shooting. All got fever and three of them died.

In the Argentine he made his first discovery of rocks containing numerous shells and the bones of large animals, which he collected for three days. He thought one was related to a rhinoceros. When examined later in England they proved extremely interesting. Six belonged to the great class of edentata which include the sloths, anteaters and armadilloes, which these animals resembled. There was also an extinct horse and two other very strange extinct animals. What was most remarkable, however, was the nature of the shells in which these bones were embedded. 'Of the shells found with remains of a quadruped near Punta Alta, twelve are absolutely identical with living species . . .' now inhabiting 'the sea on the shore of which they are likewise found fossil.' (*Zoology*, Vol. I, 1840) As his diary makes clear, Darwin had no concept at the time of the importance of these discoveries. Later he was to learn by experience how the land could rise and leave the former seabed aloft on shore, as had happened at Punta Alta.

At the end of 1832, they paid their first visit to Tierra del Fuego, during which he proved his remarkable strength and endurance by climbing alone one of the highest peaks, in

ascending which, Mr (Sir Joseph) Banks had lost two men on a
previous expedition. Tierra del Fuego was cold, wet, gloomy
and forbidding. On a subsequent visit Darwin thus described its
inhabitants.

Whilst going on shore, we pulled alongside a canoe with 6
Fuegians. I never saw more miserable creatures; stunted in
their growth, their hideous faces bedaubed with white paint
& quite naked. One full aged woman absolutely so, the rain
and spray were dripping from her body. Their red skins filthy
and greasy, their hair entangled, their voices discordant, their
gesticulation violent and without any dignity. Viewing such
men, one can hardly make oneself believe that they are fellow
creatures placed in the same world. I can scarcely imagine
that there is any spectacle more interesting and worthy of
reflection, than one of these unbroken savages. (D)

After leaving Tierra del Fuego, the *Beagle* returned to
Patagonia and the Argentine. While the party in the ship sur-
veyed the coast, Darwin spent his time ashore, much of it on
horseback, and got mixed up with the revolution of General
Rosas, a man of great courage and infinite cruelty. Most of 1833
was spent in the Argentine and Uruguay. Darwin found a lot
more fossil remains of large animals, including the tooth of a
fossil horse, interesting in view of the horse's being unknown
in North America at the time the Spaniards discovered it. Afterwards, in the 1845 edition of the *Journal*, he wrote: 'The existence in South America of a fossil horse, of the mastodon, possibly
of an elephant, and of a hollow-horned ruminant, are highly
interesting facts with regard to the geographical distribution of
animals.'
　　While North America at that time had several native hollow-
horned ruminants, South America had none. At one time they
must have been joined. 'The more I reflect on this case, the
more interesting it appears: I know of no other instance, where
we can almost mark the period and manner of the splitting up of

one great region into two well-characterised zoological pro-
vinces.' (J)

Darwin's study of natural history included that of man. In
Monte Video (29 November to 4 December) he wrote:

During the last six months I have had some opportunity of
seeing a little of the character of the inhabitants of these pro-
vinces. The gauchos or country men are very superior to those
who reside in the towns. The gaucho is invariably most oblig-
ing, polite and hospitable. I have not met one instance of rudeness or inhospitality. He is modest both respecting himself and
country, at the same time being a spirited bold fellow. On the
other hand there is much blood shed and many robberies
committed. The constant presence of the knife is the chief
cause of the former. . . . Police and justice are quite in-
efficient. If a man commits a murder and should be taken,
perhaps he may be imprisoned or even shot; but if he is rich
and has friends he may rely on it, nothing will happen. . . .
EVERY *public officer* is to be bribed; the head of the post
office sells forged government francs: the Governor and the
prime minister openly plunder the state. Justice, where gold is
in the case, is hardly expected. I know a man (he had good
cause) who went to the chief Justice and said 'here are 200
dollars (sixpences) if you will arrest such a person *illegally*;
my lawyer recommended me to take this step'. The Chief
Justice smiled acquiescence and thanked him; before night the
man was in prison. With this utter want of principle in the
leading men; with the country full of ill-paid, turbulent
officers; they yet hope that a Democratic form of government
will last. In my opinion before many years, they will be trembling under the iron hand of some Dictator. I wish the country
well enough to hope the period is not far distant. (D)

The *Beagle* made its way back to Tierra del Fuego, and then
back to the Falklands. After repairing the ship at Rio Santa
Cruz, the *Beagle* made a hazardous voyage through the Straits

of Magellan and reached Valparaiso on 23 July 1834. Darwin as usual spent most of his time ashore while the Beagle was charting the coast. On 20 February 1835, he was lying in a wood hut to rest himself when the ground rocked for two minutes. He saw the effects of this terrible earthquake at Concepcion, where the city, including the cathedral, was almost totally destroyed and its port of Talcahuano devasted by a tidal wave. But what fascinated Darwin was the consequent permanent elevation of the land. 'At the island of St Maria, . . . Captain FitzRoy found beds of putrid mussel shells still adhering to the rocks, ten feet above high-water mark.' This correlated with evidence of past elevations which he found in the Andes. 'It is an old story but not the less wonderful to hear of shells which were once crawling on the bottom of the sea, now standing nearly 14,000 feet above its level. . . . Daily it is forced home on the mind of the geologist that nothing, not even the wind that blows, is so unstable as the level of the crust of the earth.' (*Journal of the Voyage of the Beagle*, 19 March 1935). On 30 March he saw further evidence in the petrified remains of a forest, covered first by sedimentary deposits and then by submarine lava. These were now at 7,000 feet in the Uspallata range.

In Chile, Darwin had his only prolonged illness of the trip. He set out on a geological expedition into the Andes on 14 August 1834. On 19 September he felt unwell. He rode on, feeling very ill and exhausted, reaching Mr Corfield's house in Valparaiso by carriage on 27 September. 'Here I remained in bed till the end of October. It was a grievous loss of time, as I had hoped to have collected many animals. Capt. FitzRoy very kindly delayed the sailing of the Ship till the 10th November, by which time I was quite well again.' Six weeks' illness without remarkable presenting features is most likely to have been typhoid fever.

On 18 March 1835, Darwin set off to cross the Cordillera. On 25 March, 'I experienced an attack (for it deserves no less a name) of the *Benchuca*, a species of Reduvius, the great black bug of the Pampas.' (D) He returned to Valparaiso on 17 April.

From Chile the *Beagle* sailed up the coast to Lima in Peru, and then to the Galapagos Islands, which were to play the decisive part in the theory of evolution. These islands, lying some 600 miles from the coast and belonging to Ecuador, were volcanic in origin, black and relatively barren. 'The country was compared to what we might imagine the cultivated parts of the infernal regions to be.' (D) But what was extraordinary was the fauna. There were no mammals. The dominant species were reptiles, huge tortoises and lizards.

As I was walking along I met two large tortoises, each of which must have weighed at least two hundred pounds: one was eating a piece of cactus, and, as I approached, it stared at me and slowly stalked away; the other gave a deep hiss, and drew in its head. These huge reptiles, surrounded by the black lava, the leafless shrubs, and large cacti, seemed to my fancy like some antediluvian animals. (D)

The birds too were greatly different from those on the mainland.

Of land-birds I obtained twenty-six kinds, all peculiar to the group, and found nowhere else, with the exception of one lark-like finch from North America. (D)

The natural history of these islands is eminently curious, and well deserves attention. Most of the organic productions are aboriginal creations, found nowhere else; there is even a difference between the inhabitants of the different islands; yet all show a marked relationship with those of America, though separated from that continent by an open space of ocean between 500 and 600 miles in width. The archipelago is a little world within itself, or rather a satellite attached to America, whence it has derived a few stray colonists, and has received the general character of its indigenous productions. Considering the small size of these islands, we feel the more astonished at the number of their aboriginal beings, and at their confined range. Seeing every height crowned with its crater, and the boundaries of most of the lava streams still distinct, we are led to believe that within a period geologically recent the un-broken ocean was here spread out. Hence, both in space and time, we seem to be brought somewhat near to that great fact —that mystery of mysteries—the first appearance of new beings on this earth. (J)

Interestingly enough, Darwin might have missed the full import of the message from these islands had it not been for Mr Lawson, the Vice-Governor. He had found that the tor-toises were peculiar to each island, and if brought a tortoise he could tell from which island it had come.

From the Galapagos Islands the *Beagle* crossed the Pacific to Tahiti, New Zealand and Australia, which Darwin enjoyed but had no desire to settle in. The Cocos and Keeling Islands provided him with the data on which he based his theory of coral reefs and coral islands. FitzRoy had sounded with a line 7,200 feet long and found no bottom at a distance of but little more than a mile from the shore.

Hence if we imagine such an Island, after long successive intervals to subside a few feet, in a manner similar, but with a movement opposite to the continent of S. America; the coral would be continued upwards, rising from the foundation of the encircling reef. In time the central land would sink beneath the level of the sea & disappear, but the coral would have completed its circular wall. Should we not then have a Lagoon Island?—Under this view, we must look at a Lagoon Isd as a monument raised by miriads of tiny architects, to mark the spot where a former land lies buries in the depths of the ocean. (D)

The *Beagle* called at the Cape of Good Hope and at St Helena and Ascension, then back to South America to check some chronometric measurement, and so back to England.

Darwin, as we have seen, began the voyage with no reason to question the literal truth of the Biblical account of creation. The experiences he had had were, at a later date, to be the instrument of a remarkable change of attitude which is of course his chief claim to fame. But he was so busy collecting and writing on the *Beagle* that new knowledge and leisure had yet to catalyse his mind. The nearest he gets to a change of ideas is in the following remarks written on a farm in New South Wales on 18 January 1836, less than a year before the voyage ended.

A little time before this I had been lying on a sunny bank and was reflecting on the strange character of the animals of this country as compared to the rest of the World. An unbeliever in everything beyond his own reason might exclaim, 'Surely two distinct Creators must have been at work; their object, however, has been the same and certainly the end in each case is complete. Whilst thus thinking, I observed the conical pitfall of a Lion-Ant:—a fly fell in and immediately disappeared; then came a large but unwary Ant. His struggles to escape being very violent, the little jets of sand described by Kirby (Vol. 1, p. 425) were promptly directed against him.—His fate, however, was better than that of the fly's.* Without doubt the predaecious Larva belongs to the same genus but to a different species from the European kind.—Now what would the *Dis*-believer say to this? Would any two workmen ever hit on so beautiful, so simple, and yet so artificial a contrivance? It cannot be thought so. The one hand has surely worked throughout the universe. A geologist perhaps would suggest that the periods of Creation have been distinct and remote the one from the other; that the Creator rested in his labor. (D)

Darwin had no doubt that the Voyage of the *Beagle* was the most important event of his life and had in fact determined his

* N.B. The pitfall was not above half the size of the one described by Kirby (C.D.).

whole career. And yet it had, as he well realised, nearly been abandoned because of his father's opposition. Of its effects on him he wrote:

The above various special studies were, however, of no importance compared with the habit of energetic industry and of concentrated attention to whatever I was engaged in, which I then acquired. Everything about which I thought or read was made to bear directly on what I had seen or was likely to see; and this habit of mind was continued during the five years of the voyage. I feel sure that it was this training which has enabled me to do whatever I have done in science.

Looking backwards, I can now perceive how my love for science gradually preponderated over every other taste. During the first two years my old passion for shooting survived in nearly full force, and I shot myself all the birds and animals for my collection; but gradually I gave up my gun more and more, and finally altogether, to my servant, as shooting interfered with my work more especially with making out the geological structure of a country. I discovered, though unconsciously and insensibly, that the pleasure of observing and reasoning was a much higher one than that of skill and sport. That my mind became developed through my pursuits during the voyage is rendered probable by a remark made by my father, who was the most acute observer whom I ever saw, of a sceptical disposition, and far from being a believer in phrenology; for on first seeing me after the voyage, he turned round to my sisters, and exclaimed, 'Why, the shape of his head is quite altered'. (A)

The *Beagle* anchored at Falmouth on 2 October 1836. Darwin was surprised that the first sight of the shores of England filled him with 'no warmer feelings than if it had been a miserable Portuguese settlement'. (D) The same night he left by mail for Shrewsbury. He reached home on the 4th and one of his first

acts was to write to his uncle Josiah Wedgwood, whose inter-
cession with his father had been instrumental in making the
voyage possible. He was overjoyed to be back. Indeed he wrote:
'I am so happy I hardly know what I am writing'. (D)

Darwin described the two years and three months, from his
return to his marriage, as the most active in his whole life,
though he was 'occasionally unwell and so lost some time'. (A)
His letters to Henslow make it clear how hard and systematic-
ally he worked. The career of a clergyman seems quietly to
have been dropped during the *Beagle*'s voyage, as Darwin's
letters home and his diary indicated his increasing preoccupation with science. Darwin's own change of intention was clear.
'I remember when in Good Success Bay in Tierra del Fuego
thinking, and I believe I wrote home to that effect, that I could
not employ my life better than in adding a little to Natural
Science.' (A)

Darwin's collections had been sent to Henslow in Cambridge. There he settled on 13 December. He stayed in Cambridge for three months getting all his minerals named by
Professor Miller.

On 7 March 1837 he took lodgings in Great Marlborough
Street in London, where he remained till he was married. During this time he worked at his collections, finished his *Journal*,
read several papers before the Geological Society, began preparing the manuscript of his *Geological Observations*, and
arranged for the publication of the *Zoology of the Voyage of the
Beagle*.

In July 1837 occurred a momentous event. 'I opened my first
note-book for facts in relation to the *Origin of Species*, about
which I had long reflected, and never ceased working for the
next twenty years.' He went a little into society and acted as
one of the two honorary secretaries of the Geological Society.
He undertook only one long excursion, to Glen Roy, whose
parallel roads he attributed in a paper in the *Philosophical
Transactions* of the Royal Society to the action of the sea. This
was subsequently shown to be wrong. T. F. Jamieson showed

the roads were the raised beaches of a glacial lake which had more than one level. Darwin wrote to him: 'Your arguments seem to me conclusive. I give up the ghost. My paper is one long gigantic blunder.' (A) Only the greatest scientists are prepared to be so humble.

Because he was unable to work all day at science, he read a good deal. Milton's *Paradise Lost* was replaced by Wordsworth's and Coleridge's poetry as his chief delight.

Chapter 4

CHARLES DARWIN
The Invalid Recluse

On 29 January 1839 Darwin married his cousin Emma, the daughter of Uncle Josiah Wedgwood, who had already played so decisive a part in his life. The marriage was a long and happy one, and Darwin always spoke in terms of gratitude and affection of his devoted wife. Their children agreed that their parents' life together was one of great sweetness, understanding and calm.

Marriage provoked a pronounced change in Darwin's behaviour. From now on he was to suffer increasingly from bouts of illness that interfered with his work and dictated a complete and profound change in his way of life. He became, in fact, an invalid and a recluse. What actually happened is of the utmost importance to understanding the nature of his illness. Two passages from Darwin's writings are revealing. In a letter to Henslow (14 October 1837) he refused the offer of the Secretaryship of the Geological Society on three grounds, his ignorance of English geology, his ignorance of foreign languages, and that the work would interfere with his completing his own papers. Finally he explained how he had been unwell, how anything that flurried him made him ill, and that the Secretaryship would be the source of more trouble than anything else. However he ultimately accepted the office and was Secretary from February 1838 to February 1841.

In his *Autobiography* he wrote: 'During the three years and eight months whilst we resided in London, I did less scientific work, though I worked as hard as I possibly could, than during any other equal length of time in my life. This was owing to frequently recurring unwellness, and to one long and serious illness.'* He was, however, able to complete *Coral Reefs*, which he had begun before his marriage; he read two papers before the Geological Society; and continued to superintend the publication of the *Zoology of the Voyage of the Beagle*. 'Nor did I ever intermit collecting facts bearing on the origin of species; and I could sometimes do this when I could do nothing else from illness.'

The contrast between the Darwin aged thirty-three and the vigorous young man of the *Beagle* six years before is vividly displayed by this:

In the summer of 1842 I was stronger than I had been for some time, and took a little tour by myself in North Wales, for the sake of observing the effects of the old glaciers which formerly filled all the larger valleys. I published a short account of what I saw in the *Philosophical Magazine*. This excursion interested me greatly, and it was the last time I was ever strong enough to climb mountains or to take long walks such as are necessary for geological work. (A)

During the early part of our life in London, I was strong enough to go into general society, and saw a good deal of several scientific men and other more or less distinguished men. . . . Whilst living in London, I attended as regularly as I could the meetings of several scientific societies, and acted as secretary to the Geological Society. But such attendance, and ordinary society, suited my health so badly that we resolved to live in the country, which we both preferred and have never repented of. (A)

After several fruitless searches in Surrey and elsewhere, the Darwins found a house that suited them at Down in Kent. Darwin's father paid £2,200 for it. The Darwins moved in on

* I have been quite unable to trace this illness. I have not found it in Emma Darwin's letters.[8] His grand-daughters, Lady Barlow and Lady Keynes, have been unable to help.

14 September 1842, nine days before the birth of their third child, who only lived three weeks. Down House was subsequently bought by Sir Buckston Browne who gave it to the Royal College of Surgeons of England, who preserve the house and grounds. Darwin's study remains as he used it.

What attracted the Darwins to Down, apart from the house and grounds, was its situation, the diversity of the vegetation of a chalk district, and its extreme quietness and rusticity. Although it was only sixteen miles from London, it was difficult of access, being five miles from Orpington, the nearest railway station, and not near a main road.

Although, according to Francis Darwin, lack of money had somewhat restricted his parents' choice of property, their life at Down showed no evidence of financial stringency. Charles received an allowance from his father of £2,000 a year. He was a careful manager of money and a shrewd investor. Though he often expressed his anxiety lest his children should not have enough to eat, as he did about his health, his fortune which he passed on to them amounted to some £180,000. He kept meticulous accounts, even down to the tips given to porters. Emma managed all the domestic arrangements, including the conduct of the garden and grounds in which, however, Darwin took a continued deep interest and delight.

Of his life at Down, Darwin said this:

Few persons can have lived a more retired life than we have done. Besides short visits to the houses of relations, and occasionally to the seaside or elsewhere, we have gone nowhere. During the first part of our residence we went a little into society, and received a few friends here; but my health almost always suffered from the excitement, violent shivering and vomiting attacks being thus brought on. I have therefore been compelled for many years to give up all dinner-parties; and this has been somewhat of a deprivation to me, as such parties always put me into high spirits. From the same cause I have been able to invite here very few scientific acquaintances.

My chief enjoyment and sole employment throughout life has been scientific work, and the excitement from such work makes me for the time forget, or drives quite away, my daily discomfort. I have therefore nothing to record during the rest of my life, except the publication of my several books. (A)

Sir Francis Darwin's reminiscences of his father have provided a detailed account of his way of life.

After breakfasting alone about 7.45, he went to work at once, considering the 1½ hour between 8 and 9.30 one of his best working times. At 9.30 he came into the drawing room for his letters—rejoicing if the post was a light one and being sometimes much worried if it was not. He would then hear any family letters read aloud as he lay on the sofa.

The reading aloud, which also included part of a novel, lasted till about half-past ten, when he went back to work till twelve or a quarter past. By this time he considered his day's work over, and would often say, in a satisfied voice, '*I've* done a good day's work'. He then went out of doors whether it was wet or fine. . . . .

My father's mid-day walk generally began by a call at the greenhouse, where he looked at any germinating seeds or experimental plants, which required casual examination, but he hardly ever did any serious observing at this time. Then he went on for his constitutional—either round the 'Sand-walk',* or outside his own grounds in the immediate neighbourhood of the house. . . .

Luncheon at Down came after his mid-day walk; . . . After his lunch he read the newspaper, lying on the sofa in the drawing room. . . . After he had read his paper, came his time for writing letters. These, as well as the MS. of his books, were written by him as he sat in a huge horsehair chair by the fire, his paper supported on a board resting on the arms of the chair. . . . When letters were finished, about three in the

* About one mile.

afternoon, he rested in his bedroom, lying on the sofa, smoking a cigarette, and listening to a novel or other book not scientific. He only smoked when resting, whereas snuff was a stimulant, and was taken during working hours. . . .

He came down at four o'clock to dress for his walk, and he was so regular that one might be quite certain it was within a few minutes of four when his descending steps were heard.

From about half-past four to half-past five he worked; then he came to the drawing room, and was idle till it was time (about six) to go up for another rest with novel reading and a cigarette.

Latterly he gave up late dinner, and had a simple tea at half-past seven (while we had dinner), with an egg or a small piece of meat. After dinner he never stayed in the room, and used to apologise by saying he was an old woman who must be allowed to leave with the ladies. This was one of the many signs and results of his constant weakness and ill-health. Half an hour more or less of conversation would make to him the difference of a sleepless night and of the loss perhaps of half the next day's work.

After dinner he played backgammon with my mother, two games being played every night. For many years a score of the games which each won was kept, and in this score he took the greatest interest. He became extremely animated over these games, bitterly lamenting his bad luck and exploding with exaggerated mock-anger at my mother's good fortune.

After playing backgammon he read some scientific book to himself, either in the drawing-room, or, if much talking was going on, in the study.

In the evening—that is, after he had read as much as his strength would allow, and before the reading aloud began—he would often lie on the sofa and listen to my mother playing the piano. . . .

He became much tired in the evenings, especially of late years, and left the drawing room about ten, going to bed at

half past ten. His nights were generally bad, and he often lay
awake or sat up in bed for hours, suffering much discomfort.
He was troubled at night by the activity of his thoughts, and
would become exhausted by his mind working at some problem which he would willingly have dismissed. . . .

It was a sure sign that he was not well when he was idle at
any times other than his regular resting hours; for, as long as
he remained moderately well, there was no break in the
regularity of his life. Weekdays and Sundays passed by alike,
each with their stated intervals of work and rest. It is almost
impossible, except for those who watched his daily life, to
realise how essential to his well-being was the regular routine
that I have sketched: and with what pain and difficulty anything beyond it was attempted. Any public appearance, even
of the most modest kind, was an effort to him. In 1871 he went
to the little village church for the wedding of his elder
daughter, but he could hardly bear the fatigue of being present
through the short service. The same may be said of the few
other occasions on which he was present at similar cere-
monies. . . .

When, after an absence of many years, he attended a meeting of the Linnean Society, it was felt to be, and was in fact, a
serious undertaking; one not to be determined on without
much sinking of heart, and hardly to be carried into effect
without paying a penalty of subsequent suffering. In the same
way a breakfast party at Sir James Paget's,* with some of the
distinguished visitors to the Medical Congress (1881), was to
him a severe exertion.[1]

In his later years the picture changed. In his reminiscences of
his father, Francis noted:

During the last ten years of his life the state of his health was

---

* Paget, Sir James, Bt. (1814–1899) F.R.S., President of the Royal College of
Surgeons, 1875; Serjeant-Surgeon to H.M. Queen Victoria, 1877.

a cause of satisfaction and hope to his family. His condition showed signs of amendment in several particulars. He suffered less distress and discomfort and was able to work more steadily.[1]

Francis went on to say:

Scattered throughout the last pages are one or two references to pain and uneasiness felt in the region of the heart. How far these indicate that his heart was affected early in life I cannot pretend to say; in any case it is certain that he had no serious or permanent trouble of this nature until shortly before his death.

However, in 1879 (aged seventy) he noted in a letter to Sir James Sullivan that his scientific work tired him. He noted the same in a letter to Hooker in 1881: 'I have not the heart or strength to begin any investigation lasting years, which is the only thing which I enjoy, and I have no little jobs which I can do.'

In the autumn of 1881 he had the first of a series of attacks which later became more frequent. During the last week of the next February, and first week of March, attacks of pain in the region of his heart with irregularity of the pulse became frequent, coming on indeed nearly every afternoon. Such an attack when walking alone marked the last time he was able to reach his favourite 'Sand-walk'. On 15 April, while seated at dinner, he was seized with giddiness and fainted in an attempt to reach his sofa. During the night of 18 April, about a quarter to twelve, he had a severe attack which passed into a faint. 'He seemed to recognise the approach of death, and said "I am not in the least afraid to die". All the next morning, he suffered from terrible nausea and faintness, and hardly rallied before the end came. He died at about four o'clock on Wednesday, 19 April 1882.'

There is no doubt that Darwin at seventy had come to feel the decline of his powers that inevitably comes, sometimes later, sometimes sooner, as men grow older. There is equally no doubt that the attacks which began in December 1881, and which killed him in April 1882, were completely different from his earlier illness. It is especially to be noted that these later attacks were not precipitated by the same incidents as were the earlier. They came, as it were, out of the blue. These attacks were almost certainly caused by death of parts of the heart muscle, and in particular those which regulate the rhythm of the heart. This in turn was due to the arteries supplying the heart becoming stopped up. The technical names for these processes are myocardial infarction and coronary artery thrombosis. This remains one of the commonest modes of death in a man of seventy-three.

Living and working thus, this invalid recluse had an extraordinary output of original, informative, and extremely influential articles and books. Of these works, the *Origin of Species* is by far the most important. Nearly all his books sold well, and some, like *Origin of Species*, very well indeed (16,000 in England by 1876). Its history is described by Darwin thus:

During the voyage of the *Beagle* I had been deeply impressed by discovering in the Pampean formation great fossil animals covered with armour like that on the existing armadillos; secondly, by the manner in which closely allied animals replace one another in proceeding southwards over the Continent; and thirdly, by the South American character of most of the productions of the Galapagos archipelago, and more especially by the manner in which they differ slightly on each island of the group; none of the islands appearing to be very ancient in a geological sense.

It was evident that such facts as these, as well as many others, could only be explained on the supposition that species gradually become modified; and that neither the action of the surrounding conditions, nor the will of the organisms (especially in the case of plants), could account for the innumerable cases in which organisms of every kind are beautifully adapted to their habits of life—for instance, a woodpecker or a tree-frog to climb trees, or a seed for dispersal by hooks or plumes. I had always been much struck by such adaptations, and until these could be explained it seemed to me almost useless to endeavour to prove by indirect evidence that species have been modified.

After my return to England it appeared to me that by following the example of Lyell* in Geology, and by collecting all facts which bore in any way on the variation of animals and plants under domestication and nature, some light might perhaps be thrown on the whole subject. My first note-book was opened in July 1837. I worked on true Baconian principles, and without any theory collected facts on a wholesale scale, more especially with respect to domesticated productions, by printed inquiries, by conversation with skilful breeders and gardeners, and by extensive reading. When I see the list of books of all kinds which I read and abstracted, including whole series of Journals and Transactions, I am surprised at my industry. I soon perceived that selection was the keystone of man's success in making useful races of animals and plants. But how selection could be applied to organisms living in a state of nature remained for some time a mystery to me.

In October 1838, that is, fifteen months after I had begun my systematic enquiry, I happened to read for amusement Malthus on *Population*, and being well prepared to appreciate the struggle for existence which everywhere goes on from long-continued observance of the habits of animals and plants, it at once struck me that under these circumstances favourable variations would tend to be preserved, and unfavourable ones to be destroyed. The result of this would be the formation of a new species. Here, then, I had at last got a theory by which to work; but I was so anxious to avoid prejudice, that I determined

---

* Lyell, Sir Charles, Bt. (1767–1849) F.R.S., Secretary, and later President, of the Geological Society.

not for some time to write even the briefest sketch of it. In June 1842 I first allowed myself the satisfaction of writing a very brief abstract of my theory in pencil in 35 pages; and this was enlarged during the summer of 1844 into one of 230 pages, which I had fairly copied out and still possess.

But at the time I overlooked one problem of great importance; and it is astonishing to me, except on the principle of Columbus and his egg, how I could have overlooked it and its solution. This problem is the tendency in organic beings descended from the same stock to diverge in character as they become modified. That they have diverged greatly is obvious from the manner in which species of all kinds can be classed under genera, genera under families, families under suborders, and so forth; and I can remember the very spot in the road, whilst in my carriage, when to my joy the solution occurred to me; and this was long after I had come to Down. The solution, as I believe, is that the modified offspring of all dominant and increasing forms tend to become adapted to many and highly diversified places in the economy of nature.

Early in 1856 Lyell advised me to write out my views pretty fully, and I began at once to do so on a scale three or four times as extensive as that which was afterwards followed in my *Origin of Species*; yet it was only an abstract of the materials which I had collected, and I got through about half of the work on this scale. But my plans were overthrown, for early in the summer of 1858, Mr Wallace,* who was then in the Malay archipelago, sent me an essay *On the Tendency of Varieties to depart indefinitely from the Original Type*; and this essay contained exactly the same theory as mine. Mr Wallace expressed the wish that if I thought well of his essay I should send it to Lyell for perusal.

The circumstances under which I consented at the request of Lyell and Hooker† to allow of an abstract from my MS,

---

* Biographical note (see end of chapter).
† Hooker, Sir William Jackson (1758–1865) F.R.S., Regius Professor of Botany, Glasgow University; Director of Kew Gardens.

together with a letter to Asa Gray,* dated September 5, 1857, to be published at the same time with Wallace's Essay, are given in the Journal of the Proceedings of the Linnean Society, 1858, p. 45. I was at first very unwilling to consent, as I thought Mr Wallace might consider my doing so unjustifiable, for I did not then know how generous and noble was his disposition. The extract from my MS. and the letter to Asa Gray had neither been intended for publication, and were badly written. Mr Wallace's essay, on the other hand, was admirably expressed and quite clear. Nevertheless, our joint productions excited very little attention, and the only published notice of them which I can remember was by Professor Haughton of Dublin, whose verdict was that all that was new in them was false, and what was true was old. This shows how necessary it is that any new view should be explained at considerable length in order to arouse public attention.

In September 1858 I set to work by the strong advice of Lyell and Hooker to prepare a volume on the transmutation of species, but was often interrupted by ill-health, and short visits to Dr Lane's delightful hydropathic establishment at Moor Park. I abstracted the MS. begun on a much larger scale in 1856, and completed the volume on the same reduced scale. It cost me thirteen months and ten days' hard labour. It was published under the title of *Origin of Species*, in November 1859. Though considerably added to and corrected in the later editions, it has remained substantially the same book. (A)

The impact of the *Origin of Species* would not have been so early and so intense had it not been for the meeting of the British Association in Oxford in 1860. The opportunity was seized for an attack on Darwin and his views by the Bishop of Oxford, Samuel Wilberforce† ('Soapy Sam'), who made it clear he was bent on destruction. The meeting was in the University

---

* Professor of Natural History, Harvard University.
† Wilberforce, Samuel (1805–1872), Bishop of Oxford and later of Winchester; son of William Wilberforce, the anti-slavery leader.

Museum, recently built to John Ruskin's specification. It was attended by the notables who had come for the kill. Amongst those present was T. H. Huxley* who had not come expecting or prepared to speak, but was so enraged that he got up and pulverised Wilberforce. From now the battle was on between the new idea and the forces of reaction who believed in the literal interpretation of Holy Writ; the latter included most elderly scientists and most of what would now be called 'The Establishment'. Darwin characteristically took no part in the public controversy, which he would have hated, because he knew it would have made him very ill. Those prominent in the battle were Huxley ('Darwin's Bulldog'), Lyell and Hooker. Oddly enough, Richard Owen,† who had worked up *Fossil Mammalia* for Darwin, was prominent on the other side.

DARWIN'S RELIGIOUS VIEWS

It was ironical that the man who had been designed for the clergy and who, with characteristic honesty, had examined and approved Christian dogma, had now become the spearhead in the attack on the literal interpretation of the Bible. This was not, of course, of Charles's seeking. It had happened. And it is of great interest to inquire further how it happened. Fortunately once again Darwin had left behind a lucid account of how his views changed and his eventual reconciliation between the idea of evolution and the religious idea of God.

During these two years‡ I was led to think much about religion. Whilst on board the *Beagle* I was quite orthodox, and I remember being heartily laughed at by several of the officers (though themselves orthodox) for quoting the Bible as an unanswerable authority on some point of morality. I

* Huxley, Thomas Henry (1825–1895), President of the Royal Society 1883–1885.
† Owen, Sir Richard (1804–1892) F.R.S., Superintendent of Natural History Collections of British Museum.
‡ October 1836 to January 1839.

suppose it was the novelty of the argument that amused them. But I had gradually come by this time, i.e. 1836 to 1839,* to see that the Old Testament was no more to be trusted than the sacred books of the Hindoos. The question then continually rose before my mind and would not be banished,—is it credible that if God were now to make a revelation to the Hindoos, he would permit it to be connected with the belief in Vishnu, Siva, etc., as Christianity is connected with the Old Testament? This appeared to me utterly incredible. . . .

Although I did not think much about the existence of a personal God until a considerably later period of my life, I will give here the vague conclusions to which I have been driven. The old argument from design in Nature, as given by Paley,† which formerly seemed to me so conclusive, fails, now that the law of natural selection has been discovered. We can no longer argue that, for instance, the beautiful hinge of a bivalve shell must have been made by an intelligent being, like a hinge of a door by man. There seems to be no more design in the variability of organic beings, and in the action of natural selection, than in the course which the wind blows. . . .

Another source of conviction in the existence of God, connected with the reason and not with the feelings, impresses me as having much more weight. This follows from the extreme difficulty or rather impossibility of conceiving this immense and wonderful universe, including man with his capacity of looking far backwards and far into futurity, as the result of blind chance or necessity. When thus reflecting, I feel compelled to look to a First Cause having an intelligent mind in some degree analogous to that of man; and I deserve to be called a Theist. This conclusion was strong in my mind about the time, as far as I can remember, when I wrote the *Origin of Species*, and it is since that time that it has very gradually,

---

* Note that this is *after* he returned from the *Beagle* voyage.

† Paley's *Evidences of Christianity*. In the nineteenth century, candidates for Cambridge University had to satisfy the examiners on their knowledge of this book before matriculating.

with many fluctuations, become weaker. But then arises the doubt—can the mind of man, which has, as I fully believe, been developed from a mind as low as that possessed by the lowest animals, be trusted when it draws such grand conclusions?

I cannot pretend to throw the least light on such abstruse problems. The mystery of the beginning of all things is insoluble by us, and I for one must be content to remain an Agnostic. (A)

DARWIN'S OTHER MAJOR WORKS

Darwin produced at Down several major works arising out of the *Beagle* voyage, including *Geological Observations on South America* (1846) and his two volume work on *Cirripedia* (1854). This took eight years, of which two were occupied by illness. From then on he was chiefly engaged in arranging his notes and experiments on the transmutation of species. After the publication of the *Origin of Species* and its several revisions, he began work on 1 January 1860 on *Variation of Animals and Plants under Domestication*, a theme which had long interested him and indeed formed one of the threads braided into the *Origin*. It was again an immense collection of facts obtained from various sources. It cost him '4 years and two months' hard labour', and was published in 1868. His other books were all germane to his life-long interest in the origin of species, except perhaps the last. They were:

The Structure and Distribution of Coral Reefs (1842)
On the Various Contrivances by which British and Foreign Orchids are Fertilised by Insects (1862)
The Descent of Man, and Selection in Relation to Sex (1871)
The Expression of the Emotions in Man and Animals (1872)
Insectivorous Plants (1875)
On the Movement and Habits of Climbing Plants (1875)
Effects of Cross- and Self-Fertilisation in the Vegetable Kingdom (1876)

The Different Forms of Flowers (1877)
The Power of Movement in Plants (1880)
The Formation of Vegetable Mould through the Action of Worms
  (1881)

Of these I propose to mention two to illustrate the manner in which his interest was aroused and the subject pursued.

He wrote of *Expression of the Emotions in Man and Animals*:

My first child was born on 27 December 1839, and I at once commenced to make notes on the first dawn of the various expressions which he exhibited, for I felt convinced, even at this early period, that the most complex and fine shades of expression must all have had a gradual and natural origin. During the summer of the following year, 1840, I read Sir C. Bell's admirable work on expression, and this greatly increased the interest which I felt in the subject, though I could not at all agree with his belief that various muscles had been specially created for the sake of expression. From this time forward I occasionally attended to the subject, both with respect to man and our domesticated animals. (A)

Insectivorous Plants originated thus:

In the summer of 1860 I was idling and resting near Hartfield, where two species of (Sundew) abound; and I noticed that numerous insects had been entrapped by the leaves. I carried home some plants, and on giving them insects saw the movements of the tentacles, and this made me think it probable that the insects were caught for some special purpose. Fortunately a crucial test occurred to me, that of placing a large number of leaves in various nitrogenous and non-nitrogenous fluids of equal density; and as soon as I found that the former alone excited energetic movements, it was obvious that here was a fine new field for investigation. (A)

Darwin's observations on Earthworms proved of the greatest

value to his great contemporary Louis Pasteur. The earth-worm's part in mixing earth by feeding below and excreting on the surface was the key to understanding how anthrax could be transmitted from a dead buried animal to a living animal grazing above it.

NOTES ON WALLACE

Alfred Russel Wallace was by origin a vastly different person from his co-discoverer.[9] He was born the son of poor parents in 1824 and he left school at the age of thirteen and went to work. He was thus entirely self-educated. So to a large extent was Charles Darwin, for while he had been to a great school and two great universities, he had failed as a medical student, and his formal education for the Church at Cambridge did nothing to make him the great scientist he became. Wallace became an assistant to his elder brother, who was a land surveyor working on the railways, then springing up all over England. He had inexhaustible curiosity. His work took him constantly into new country. He bought a shilling book on botany and was astonished to learn that order lay behind the very different appearances of plants and flowers. He taught himself geology, the theoretical counterpart to his practical work in surveying. He met a youth of his own age, H. W. Bates, who was an enthusiastic collector of butterflies, so Wallace began to collect them too. By twenty-five, Wallace had quite an extraordinary knowledge of the natural history of the countryside. But alas, the railway boom had ended and Wallace lost his job. Bates and he decided to go up the Amazon River collecting for museums and private collectors. There they went in 1848. Wallace and Bates collected with great assiduity. In two months they sent home 550 winged insects, 350 beetles, and 400 other varieties to stock collectors' cabinets. Wallace brought out his younger brother who unfortunately died of yellow fever within a year.

After that he decided to travel alone up the Amazon to

Manaos at the mouth of the Rio Negro. Thence he set off up the river till he reached Uaupes, which no European had properly explored. He passed three years alone in these explorations and collecting. Being trained as a surveyor, he made careful observations of the geography and made his name as a geographical explorer. He contracted dysentery and was deserted by his native crew, but Wallace got through. He had malaria and at Para he developed yellow fever, from which he also recovered. He set out for home but, alas, his ship caught fire and most of his specimens were lost, including some birds, insects and orchids which had never been discovered before.

Back in London he had become famous, but he was restless. Inspired by travellers' tales and a catalogue of birds, he set off for the Malayan archipelago, arriving in Singapore in 1851. Before long, 1000 specimens of insects were on their way to London. He crossed to North Borneo where Rajah Brooke was in control of Sarawak. Wallace was in camp near the mouth of the Sarawak River alone with a Malay cook when he let his thoughts drift around the many varieties of new species he had found. 'I was quite alone with one Malay boy as cook and during the evenings and wet days I had nothing to do but to look over my books and ponder over the problem which has rarely been absent from my thoughts.'

The result was a paper published in the *Annals and Magazine of Natural History* in 1855, *On the law which has regulated the introduction of new species*, based on his own observations and his knowledge of the natural distribution of fossils in rocks. He concluded that every species had come into existence coincident both in space and time with a pre-existing closely allied species. What caused this was a mystery.

The paper had a poor reception but Darwin read it and wrote: 'I can plainly see that we have thought much alike and to a certain extent have come to similar conclusions.'

In 1858 Wallace was confined to his hut in Ternate in the Moluccas with intermittent fever. He spent several hours every day lying down. His thoughts went back to Malthus, whom he had read when he was a schoolmaster in Leicester. Animals reproduce themselves on an extravagant scale. Why do only some survive ? 'Then it suddenly flashed upon me that this self-acting process would necessarily improve the race because in every generation the inferior would inevitably be killed off and the superior would remain—that is the fittest would survive.' That night and the succeeding two evenings he wrote *On the tendency of varieties to depart from the original type*. He had to write quickly because the mail was leaving. He sent it to Darwin with the consequences related above.

Wallace remained in the Malayan archipelago in which he made his great discovery, Wallace's line, between Bali and Lombok. On the west side the fauna and flora were essentially those of Asia, and on the east those of Australia. This was one of the more important pieces of evidence supporting his and Darwin's hypothesis. But he was nearly wrecked in 1860 when he was sailing between the islands. He lost boats and anchors, and ran out of water and even out of oil, but not out of courage. He read with increasing admiration the *Origin of Species*.

When Wallace returned home he married and built himself a succession of houses in which he planned and developed exciting gardens. Unfortunately he did not get the position of curator of a museum for which he craved, and was so superbly suited. He did not know the right people. He was one of nature's rebels, a vegetarian who dabbled in mesmerism, and professed to cure asthma by taking care of his food. He was a spiritualist. His profession had shown him how wastefully men used the land. Spencer and Mill led him to the idea of land nationalisation and thus to socialism.

Wallace generously gave all of the credit for their joint discovery to Darwin. As Wallace said, his essay had been written in three nights whereas Darwin's took eighteen years. He wrote a book on Darwinism. He died in 1913 in his ninety-first year, looking forward to his new alpine garden.

Chapter 5

DARWIN'S ILLNESS

Darwin's own account of his life, and the letters he wrote, give a picture of a long and troublesome illness, beginning in 1837, when he was twenty-eight, and continuing until his death in 1882. The illness was accentuated after his marriage, but was notably absent in the vigorous young naturalist of the *Beagle* voyage of 1831-36. Although according to its victim the illness interfered with his work, it did not prevent the enormous output of learned and novel books. In the last decade of his life his health improved, and his work was less interrupted by illness. He died of coronary heart disease at the age of seventy-three.

Darwin's illness has been a great source of controversy for many years. The controversy now centres around the issue of whether Darwin suffered from a chronic infection or a psychoneurosis. I have carefully examined all the evidence I can find, particularly Darwin's own meticulous records of his experience. In my view, the case for a chronic infection does not withstand critical examination. Conversely, that for a psychoneurosis becomes ever more probable, the more closely the evidence is examined. The theory that Darwin's illness was a psychoneurosis, whose purpose was to protect him from social intercourse and thus allow him to write the *Origin of Species* was first put forward by Hubble in 1943.[24]

The case for a psychoneurosis is first that the symptoms suggest it, and, taken in their entirety, they fit nothing else. Second, there is no evidence that any physical signs were ever found as they should have been after forty years of organic disease, and Darwin consulted the best physicians of his day, including Sir Andrew Clark,* Brinton, and Bence Jones. Third,

---

* Not to be confused with Sir James Clark, who helped Miss Nightingale to visit Queen Victoria.

the circumstances precipitating the attacks are right. Fourth, the illness got better towards the end of his life, which is quite unlike organic disease. Lastly, no other diagnosis that has been proposed, or that I can think of, fits all the facts.

Of all the features of an illness, its onset is by far the most helpful in diagnosis. At the beginning, illness presents in its pure form, later it tends to become complicated by secondary factors. In Darwin's case, we are particularly fortunate in having a collector who observed carefully and set down and kept his observations. Nor was he uninterested in illness; he came, after all, from a long line of doctors and was a one-time medical student, who had diagnosed and treated patients under the supervision of his father.

The illness began while he was waiting for the *Beagle* to sail.

These two months (Oct. 24 to Dec. 27 1831) at Plymouth were the most miserable which I ever spent, though I exerted myself in various ways. I was out of spirits at the thought of leaving all my family and friends for so long a time, and the weather seemed to me inexpressibly gloomy. I was also troubled with palpitations and pain about the heart, and like many a young ignorant man, especially one with a smattering of medical knowledge, was convinced that I had heart disease. I did not consult any doctor, as I fully expected to hear the verdict that I was not fit for the voyage, and I was resolved to go at all hazards. (A)

This description is typical of Da Costa's syndrome. Darwin suggests a reasonable cause for it. Neither the *Diary* nor the *Autobiography* contains any hint of a recurrence of symptoms during the six years of the *Beagle*'s voyage.

Darwin's letters to Henslow[7] give a splendid insight into his state of mind during the voyage and after his return. In his last letter of the voyage, written from St Helena, he wrote prophetically: 'Oh the degree to which I long to be once again living quietly, with not one single novel object near me.' After his return home his letters are those of an extremely enthusiastic and extremely hard working and busy young man, somewhat nostalgic for the past. On 28 March 1837 he wrote: '. . . though I sadly miss a good walk in the country I am pretty well resigned to my fate (living in London)', and after seeing the *Beagle* in May, 'If it was not for the sea sickness, I should have no objection to start again.' The first mention of illness after his return is on September of that year. 'I have not been well of late with an uncomfortable palpitation of the heart, and my doctors urge me *strongly* to knock off all work and go and live in the country for a few weeks. . . . I feel I must have a little rest, else I shall break down.' After this he was never entirely well again.

The next mention of illness is contained in a letter to Henslow dated 14 October 1837 in which he refused the Secretaryship of the Geological Society. The general purport of the letter has been noted. It goes on:

> My last objection is that I doubt how far my health will stand the confinement of what I have to do without any additional work. I merely repeat that you may know that I am not speaking idly, that when I consulted Dr Clark in town he at first urged me to give up entirely all writing and even correcting press for some weeks. Of late anything which flurries me completely knocks me up afterwards and brings on a violent palpitation of the heart. Now the Secretaryship would be a periodical source of more annoying trouble to me than all the rest of the fortnight put together.

This letter is of great importance. It tells us that his symptoms were troubling him sufficiently to lead him to consult one of the most eminent physicians of the day, Sir Andrew Clark; and that Sir Andrew did not set his mind at rest; indeed, he confirmed the seriousness of his illness by counselling a reduction in work. Finally, the events precipitating these attacks could not be more explicitly stated.

As we saw in Chapter 3, doctors play a very important part in establishing the psychoneuroses, particularly Da Costa's syndrome. Darwin had suspected that his heart was affected; Sir Andrew had confirmed the gravity of his illness. His father (also a physician) added his opinion. In 1841, Darwin wrote to Lyell: 'My father scarcely seems to expect that I shall become strong for some years.'

The events precipitating the attacks have a remarkable consistency. In the account of his life we have seen how scientific meetings, going out into society, dinner parties, having guests in the house, precipitate an attack. So is perfected the routine of Down House, in which everyone is a slave (probably a willing slave) to Darwin's illness. Any infringement of the rules evokes an attack, e.g. his daughter's wedding, and breakfast with Sir James Paget; his father's funeral is not to be attempted. Here are some examples.[6]

> *28 March 1843 (to a Mr Fox describing*
> *life at Down)*
> I am *very* much stronger corporeally but am little better in being able to stand mental fatigue, or rather excitement, so that I cannot dine out or receive visitors except relations with whom I can pass some time after dinner in silence.

> *31 March 1843 (to FitzRoy)*
> I find most unfortunately for myself that the little excitement of breaking out of my quiet routine so generally knocks me up that I am able to do scarcely anything when in London.

When Darwin wrote these letters he was thirty-four. It was only seven years since the same young man had eagerly faced every new adventure on the *Beagle*.

> *1847 (to Hooker)*
> I have been bad enough these last few days having had time to think and write too much about Glen Roy. . . . Mr Milne having attacked my theory which made me horribly sick.

The symptoms in his attacks change with time. Gradually the 'accursed stomach' plays a bigger part.

During the first part of our residence (at Down) we went a little into society; but my health almost always suffered from the excitement, violent shivering and vomiting attacks being thus brought on. I have therefore been compelled to give up all dinner parties. (A)

Palpitations and breathlessness would scarcely have been an appropriate protest against a dinner party. Vomiting was exactly right. And it was an appropriate expression of his rejection of Mr Milne.

I believe I have not had one whole day or rather night without my stomach having been grossly disordered during the last three years and most days great prostration of strength; thank you for your kindness; many of my friends, I believe, think me a hypochondriac.

Here we have a departure from the former episodic illness. It has become more continuous. Could this be something else, such as a duodenal ulcer, which is prone to give pain and vomiting at night, after which he would feel exhausted? It obviously could be. But peptic ulcer is also typically episodic, each episode lasting weeks or months with similar intervals of freedom. 'Three years without one whole day or rather night' would be uncommon in peptic ulcer. Cancer of the stomach is excluded by the subsequent course.
A series of new symptoms appear.

> *28 March 1849 (to Hooker, written at Malvern where he was undergoing Dr Gully's water cure)*

On the 13th November, my poor dear father died. . . . I was at the time so unwell that I was unable to travel, which added

to my misery. Indeed, all this winter I have been bad enough
. . . and my nervous system began to be affected, so that my
hands trembled, and head was often swimming.

12 October 1849 (to Hooker)
I am going on very well, and am certainly a little better every
month, my nights mend much slower than my days. I have
built a douche, and am to go on through all the winter, frost or
no frost. My treatment now is lamp five times per week, and
shallow bath for five minutes afterwards; douche daily for
five minutes, and dripping sheet daily. The treatment is
wonderfully tonic, and I have had more better consecutive
days this month than on any previous ones. . . . I am allowed
to work now two and a half hours daily, and I find it as much
as I can do; for the cold-water cure, together with three short
walks, is curiously exhausting; and I am actually *forced* to go
to bed at eight o'clock completely tired. I steadily gain in
weight, and eat immensely, and am never oppressed with my
food. I have lost the involuntary twitching of the muscle, and
all the fainting feelings etc.—black spots before the eyes, etc.
Dr Gully thinks he shall quite cure me in six or nine months
more.

The new symptoms could have been due to overbreathing,
another feature of anxiety neurosis; in view of their transience
they could not have been those of organic nervous disease.

The principle enunciated long ago by William of Occam*
and now termed the principle of the paucity of hypotheses, is
generally accepted as the basis for sound medical diagnosis.
If everything can be accounted for by one diagnosis then that is
most likely to be correct. Only one diagnosis covers all these
manifestations—a psychoneurosis. The alternative is a collection of disparate and improbable hypotheses.

Charles Darwin consulted many physicians, some of them
of the greatest distinction. No record of their diagnoses has

* Occam's razor: '*Essentia non sunt multiplicanda praeter necessitatem*'.

come down to us. Da Costa did not describe his syndrome till 1862, and it was unknown in Britain till the first world war. Darwin records that he was suspected of hypochondria, and indeed he displayed all its symptoms.

The term hypochondria is a relic of a previous age. In the sixteenth and seventeenth centuries, the seat of melancholy was believed to be the liver, gallbladder and spleen, hence the term hypochondria (below the ribs). It was a popular diagnosis in Darwin's day. In his grandfather Erasmus's view, hypochondria consisted of indigestion and consequent flatulence, with anxiety and a want of pleasurable sensation. Nowadays it is defined in the Oxford English Dictionary as 'a disorder of the nervous system, generally accompanied by indigestion, but chiefly characterised by the patient's unfounded belief that he is suffering from some serious bodily disease'.

Sir Arthur Keith, a medical man who lived at Down, considered that Darwin was a hypochondriac, a very real one. He explained this. 'The voluntary part of his brain seemed to have too easy and too free an access to his involuntary part. Therein, I believe, lies the source of all his ills.' Keith was an anatomist, and no doubt this anatomical explanation satisfied him. It has no meaning to me. Hypochondriasis would be the conclusion to draw from the six years of careful daily records that Darwin kept of his health, and which can still be inspected at Down House. In his second article, *The Life of the Shawl*,[10] Hubble concluded that Darwin was a hypochondriac. He supported this by the frequency of illness, with no proved organic basis, in the Darwin family.

Hypochondria, or hypochondriasis, is not now to be found in the index of any textbook of medicine. It is regarded as one of the many manifestations of a psychoneurosis. Moreover, to apply the term hypochondria to Darwin's illness is to leave unexplained the major fact about it—the amazing contrast between the vigorous young naturalist in his twenties and the invalid recluse in his early thirties.

W. C. Alvarez considered that Darwin suffered from depression, a diagnosis which he supported by the family history, as Hubble did his hypochondria. He wrote:

> If a geneticist were to read that a man with Darwin's probably poor genes married his cousin who had a badly depressed brother, he would expect most of their children to be depressed or odd or eccentric or mentally retarded, and this is exactly what *did* happen. Anyone who wants to learn of Charles and Emma Darwin's children should read that delightful book, *Period Piece*, by Mrs Gwen Raverat, Charles Darwin's granddaughter. According to her, of Charles Darwin's 10 children, almost all suffered from nervous difficulties.[11]

I have read as many of Darwin's letters as I could find, as well as the *Diary* and *Autobiography*, and I only find two occasions on which I can capture some of the mood of depression. The first was on 30 December 1831 (see p. 40) when he was seasick, had just left home and was suffering the inevitable reaction to an adventurous decision taken against parental opposition. The other was in his old age in a letter to Wallace: 'We have just returned home after spending five weeks on Ullswater; the scenery is quite charming, but I cannot walk, and everything tires me, even seeing scenery. . . . What I shall do with my few remaining years I can hardly tell. I have everything to make me happy and contented, but life has become very wearisome to me.' Again, this is a perfectly natural reaction of a sentient human being. They were episodes of dejection rather than depression. Emma, writing of Charles's illness in 1840 (which Alvarez interpreted as a depression) wrote:

> It is a great happiness to me when Charles is most unwell that he continues just as sociable as ever, and is not like the rest of the Darwins, who will not say how they really are; but he always tells me how he feels and never wants to be alone, but continues just as warmly affectionate as ever so that I feel I am a comfort to him.[8]

I happen to be extremely familiar with the mood of a depressed patient, partly from vicarious, partly from personal, experience. Its most disturbing feature is the feeling of utter hopelessness, and the complete divorce between what the patient feels about his achievements and prospects and what an ordinary man would think. I remember being first struck with this when a house physician was rescued from his bath where he had tried to drown himself. He was the most brilliant boy of his year and had a charming and attractive wife. He moaned, 'Why didn't you let me do it? You know I'm no good.' To which his wife replied, 'Don't be silly, darling.' What was so impressive to me was that he himself was in deadly earnest, and indeed he later succeeded in killing himself.

I have known an exactly similar state of mind in three non-medical colleagues of the highest intelligence, achievement and reputation. And I have experienced the same during the two weeks when I had a depression following influenzal pneumonia. Despair, guilt, a knowledge of one's own incompetence, and an inability to put one's hand to anything, is the terrible experience of a depressive. This does not emerge in Darwin's case. The other characteristic of depression, an inability to do anything during a prolonged period of depression, was absent. He was frequently incapacitated for a few days, a day or a night, but rarely for weeks. Some of these could have been depressive, but we have no real evidence. As for the inheritance which Alvarez quotes, three of Charles's sons became Fellows of the Royal Society. The Darwins became, and remain, the most celebrated of the Cambridge dynasties. It is a very odd concept of 'poor genes'.*

Kohn, in his review,[12] considers several more possibilities: the chronic infection, brucellosis; suppressed gout, which was supposed to have been one of the diagnoses made in Darwin's lifetime; migraine; diaphragmatic hernia; chronic arsenical poisoning; but he could, and I can, find no evidence for any of

* Lady Keynes has drawn my attention to a large number of inaccuracies in Alvarez's account of the Darwin family.

these. Paroxysmal tachycardia, suggested by Dent,[13] would account for the attack in Devonport Harbour but not for his prolonged ill health. The only serious alternative to a psychoneurosis is Chagas's disease.

Chagas's disease is due to *trypanosoma cruzi* transmitted by various blood-sucking insects. The initial lesion is usually in the eye or in the skin. In the skin it starts as a small painful hot red spot which enlarges, reaching a diameter of about seven centimetres in a week, the surrounding tissues being indurated. After two weeks or so the spot crusts over, then regresses slowly, leaving a pigmented scar. This may be associated with intermittent fever and other symptoms. The disease follows a chronic course with a great variety of manifestations. The most frequent late development is in the heart, resulting in heart failure.

The idea that Darwin's illness was due to Chagas's disease was first put forward by S. W. Adler in 1959.[14]

Adler knew that Darwin had been bitten by the *Benchuca* (*Triatoma Infestans*), the great black bug of the Pampas (on 25 March 1835), the most important vector of *trypanosoma cruzi*. After listening to papers on the protean nature of Chagas's disease and its frequent termination in heart failure, it occurred to him that here was the explanation of Darwin's mysterious illness. He concluded 'Darwin was therefore definitely exposed to infection at least on one occasion.' His case, therefore, is that Darwin was bitten by the right bug and that the disease could have been Chagas's disease.

After being bitten by the *Benchuca* in March 1835, Darwin did not record a sore of any kind. He was in the midst of an exacting crossing of the Cordillera, which he successfully accomplished. He wrote: 'From this day (9 April) till I reached Valparaiso (on 17 April) I was not very well, and saw nothing and admired nothing.' On 27 April he had recovered sufficiently to begin a long journey into the interior which lasted till 5 July. For the rest of the voyage he was in remarkably good health.

His illness began after he returned home, lasted for years, but got better towards the end of his life. Had it been a chronic infection gradually killing him, it should have got worse. While he did die of heart failure, this was almost certainly due to myocardial infarction and not to myocarditis. He had undoubted angina pectoris before he died. The case for Chagas's disease therefore seemed to me to be a flimsy one.

It is not surprising that non-medical biologists eagerly embraced Adler's hypothesis. Infection was understandable and a well-founded concept while some of the suggestions of the psychiatrists were, to say the least, far fetched. de Beer wrote:

> The conclusion of the specialist on Chagas's disease is that Darwin could not, in view of the evidence, have avoided decoming infected by the *trypanosoma*. Whether he also suffered from neurotic tendencies is a question that must be left unanswered except to suggest that if he was suffering from a disease like Chagas, which his doctors were unable to diagnose or treat, it would not be surprising if he shunned society and sheltered under the care of his wife.[15]

Huxley and Kettlewell came to a similar conclusion: 'In fact, it is probable that he suffered from both infection and neurosis. The predisposing cause for his neurosis seems to have been the conflict and emotional tension springing from his ambivalent relations with his father, Robert, whom he both revered and subconsciously resented.'[16]

Medawar concurred:

> I believe that Darwin was organically ill (the case for his having been a victim of Chagas' disease is clearly a strong one) but was also the victim of a neurosis; and that the neurotic element in his illness may have been caused by the very obscurity of its origins; by his being genuinely ill, that is to say, and having nothing to show for it—surely a great embarrassment to a man whose whole intellectual life was a marshalling and assay of hard evidence.[17]

Medawar also put the doctors in their place. Hubble was easily dismissed: 'There is no refuting Hubble's argument, for there is no argument; the case is merely presented as an asseveration.' And Darwin's own medical attendants received a severe reproof:

> If this interpretation (Chagas's disease) represents any large part of the truth, the physicians who inclined to think Darwin a hypochondriac cannot be held blameless. . . . Perhaps Darwin's physicians should have been more on their guard against an interpretation of his illness that gave him so much less comfort than it gave themselves.

The views just quoted represent a crescendo of pontification without real evidence. The question at issue was not whether Darwin's illness could have been Chagas's disease, but was it? What may appear odd to non-medical scientists is that diseases do have attributes which enable them to be identified with varying degrees of probability. This Adler did not even attempt to do, and the other scientists merely accepted Adler's authority.* I have already given the reasons which led me to reject the hypothesis that his long illness in England was due to Chagas's disease.

However, my speciality is not tropical medicine. Professor Woodruff's is and he has disposed once and for all of the diagnosis of Chagas's disease.[18] Adler considered that because the infection was so common in the Argentine, Darwin was definitely infected when he was bitten by the bug. Woodruff pointed out that it is not the bite of these insects which causes infection, but contamination of the wound with their excreta. Woodruff also found that the frequency of a positive diagnostic test for Chagas's disease in the Mendoza district was so small that 'the majority of persons who developed such infection had been exposed, we can say for certainty, not just for a few weeks

* The motto of the Royal Society, to which they and I belong, is *Nullius in Verba*.

but for several years'. Woodruff then applied the clinical test. Were the attributes of Darwin's illness those of Chagas's disease ? Woodruff's answer was no, and for the following valid reasons.

First, his symptoms were brought on by emotionally charged situations. Second, if in 1842 heart failure had been the cause of his giving up high mountain walking, it is inconceivable that he could have lived till 1882 without developing overt signs of heart failure. Moreover, his capacity for exercise was remarkably good. His daily turn round the Sand-walk was measured by Woodruff as about a mile. His son, Francis, described how sometimes he would do this several times, walking rapidly with a swinging gait and carrying a heavy stick. Fourth, the nausea and flatulence which Darwin noted, occur in Chagas's disease with heart failure, but not in its absence. Fifth, neither Sir Andrew Clark nor Dr Bence Jones found any physical signs. 'It is beyond credulity that Chagas's disease could produce symptoms of cardiac insufficiency for between forty and fifty years and not produce some physical signs.' Sixth, although Darwin persuaded one of his colleagues to volunteer to be bitten by the *Benchuca* bug, no other member of the crew was affected by Chagas's disease. Finally, if Darwin's weakness and other symptoms were to be explained by organic damage brought about by Chagas's disease, it would have had to cause a very curious form of myocardial degeneration—in his thirties and at intervals during middle life, and then to have become naturally better during his last decade. Woodruff concluded: 'Each of these would cause doubts, and some of them grave doubts, about a diagnosis of Chagas's disease, but taken collectively they make an overwhelming case against it.' Woodruff's personal diagnosis was an anxiety state with obsessional features and psychosomatic manifestions, with which I agree.

THE CAUSE OF DARWIN'S PSYCHONEUROSIS

Darwin's life is one of great contrast between youth and mature age. On the one hand, the young naturalist, active, fit, usually in the open air, and on the other, after his marriage, the invalid recluse, still in his early thirties. His last entry of substance in the *Beagle* diary reads: 'But I have too deeply enjoyed the voyage not to recommend to any naturalist to take all chances, and to start on travels by land if possible, if otherwise, on a long voyage.' The ardent young traveller never travelled again. What happened?

Darwin's prolonged and distressing illness seems to have begun in 1837. His letters of September and October of that year have already been noted (p. 53). The illness became fully established after his marriage on 29 January 1839. Two events of great importance to Darwin happened during these two years: he came to realise that evolution would explain his extraordinary findings, and he married.

Darwin had gone to work on his specimens immediately after his return. His various experts had been busy. Part II of *Zoology*, *Mammalia*, was published in 1839, and Part I, *Fossil Mammalia*, by Richard Owen in 1840. The idea of evolution seems to have occurred to him in March 1837. In 1837 he wrote in his pocket book: 'In July opened first notebook on "transmutation of species". Had been greatly struck from about month of previous March on character of South American fossils and species of Galapagos Archipelago. These facts origin of all my views.'[5] From that time on, the whole idea seems to have consumed him. As he himself said, 'the subject haunted me.' He noted that when he was too ill to do anything else, he could always work on the new theory. Every other occupation and every irrelevant distraction was abandoned and outlawed. Thus the birth of the idea of the transmutation of species, and its development, coincided closely in time with the beginning and development of his prolonged illness.

Evolution was not a new idea. Empedocles, the greatest of the early Greek philosophers, had had it, as had many others.

> Great Empedocles, that ardent soul,
> Leapt into Etna, and was roasted whole.

Darwin had at first admired his grandfather's *Zoonomia*, in which the concept was outlined, but thought it too speculative on second reading. Saint-Hilaire and Lamarck in revolutionary Paris had developed the hypothesis and were professors in the university. But revolutionary anticlerical Paris was one place, Victorian Anglican England was another. The educated and un-educated, scientists and non-scientists, had all been brought up as their forefathers had, to an unquestioning faith in the Holy Writ. Darwin had searched his own mind before agreeing to enter Holy Orders and had satisfied himself as to the tenets and teaching of the Church, and he had not, at least in his conscious mind, changed his views during the voyage.

Here he was then, in March 1837, convinced that evolution would explain the phenomena he had recorded, described, lived with, and puzzled over for six years, and whose meaning had become clear as the fossil bones had been identified and classified. He was a passionate man, as his autobiography and, above all, his letters make clear; a passion for shooting, then a passion for collecting, then a passion for natural history, and the final passion for science which drove all else, music, poetry and literature, from his mind. And he passionately hated speculation.

It is not easy for us living in the second half of the twentieth century to appreciate how deeply a man of Darwin's scientific integrity in the early nineteenth century would hate hypothesis. It was only a little over a century since the great god of British science, Isaac Newton, had written '*hypotheses non fingo*'. In 1785 Thomas Reid had written, 'The world has been so long fooled by hypotheses in all parts of philosophy that we must learn to treat them with just contempt as the reveries of vain and fanciful man.'[19]

As this unconventional and even, at that time, outrageous idea seeded itself and grew in his mind, he saw as a scientist that the case for it was largely void. We have seen how the explanation of the mechanism, that of natural selection, suddenly flashed into his mind in October 1838 as he read Malthus for 'amusement'. After reading Babbage's *Ninth Bridgewater*

Treatise,* which contained a letter of Herschel's,† Darwin wrote in his note book on 2 December 1838: 'Herschel calls the appearance of new species the mystery of mysteries and has grand passage upon the problem. Hurrah—intermediate causes.' We have seen how another obstacle disappeared as he got the solution to divergence when riding in his carriage. Judging by the vast amount of evidence he had collected in the twenty-two years elapsing till the premature publication of the *Origin of Species*, Darwin must have realised the enormity of the task that lay in front of him if he were to avoid repeating the fault of his grandfather in producing merely another speculative work, as he was determined not to do. As his letter of 14 October 1837 showed, he feared that social obligations such as the Secretaryship of the Geological Society would interfere with his work. Going out into society always produced an attack. Thus we need seek no further for the cause of Darwin's psychoneurosis. It was the conflict between his passionate desire to collect convincing evidence for his hypothesis and the threat imposed on his work by social intercourse.

He had to proceed diligently, collecting any evidence bearing on the idea, and cautiously, so that the new concept was fully documented. He allowed himself to prepare a brief abstract of his theory in June 1842, enlarged during the summer of 1844. He felt so passionately about his idea that that summer he wrote to his wife as follows:

I have just finished my sketch of my species theory. If as I believe my theory in time be accepted even by one competent judge it will be a considerable step in science. I therefore write this in case of my sudden death, as my most solemn and last

---

* Charles Babbage, *Bridgewater Treatises*: Works on The Goodness of God, as manifested in the creation for which the eighth Earl of Bridgewater left the sum of £8,000. Babbage (1792–1871) F.R.S., Lucasian Professor of Mathematics, Cambridge University, 1828–39; inventor of mechanical calculating machine, the forerunner of the modern computer.

† Herschel, Sir John Frederick William, Bt. (1792–1871) F.R.S., astronomer; Master of the Mint, 1850–55.

request which I am sure you will consider the same as if legally entered in my will that you will devote £400 to its publication or through Hensleigh* take trouble in promoting it.[5]

He appended a list of the scientists in order of preference to whom she might entrust the task. They were also to be given all his notes and all the books in his library, which had been annotated for this purpose. Darwin was then only thirty-five.

We have already seen the intense anguish that the receipt of Wallace's letter caused him, and how he was forced to publish, as he thought, precipitously though it was twenty-one years after the idea had occurred to him and since he had begun to devote himself to it. Finally, we have seen how he was quite unable to bring himself to enter into public controversy. That he left to Huxley and others.

Darwin's letters to Henslow make it clear how much of his mind was occupied by the species problem in these intervening years. He wanted to see if, by experimental selection, he could alter species, or whether they remained true to type. He had by no means decided between these two when Wallace's essay precipitated the publication of the *Origin*. Later the Law of Ancestral Inheritance, namely that physical make-up is decided by parents (one half; grandparents—one quarter; and by great-grandparents—one eighth, and so *ad infinitum*) put forward by Fleeming Jenkin (a Professor of Engineering) and adopted by Galton, seemed to destroy the mechanism. And Darwin accepted the criticism. It was only with the rediscovery of Mendelian inheritance that the theory once more became plausible. So Darwin's anxiety about his theory was fully justified and not allayed in his lifetime.

The other factor in producing his prolonged illness was almost certainly his wife. His marriage to Emma Wedgwood formed a watershed in Darwin's life. Before that he had occasional illnesses. After it he became an invalid, unable to live in

* Mrs Darwin's half-brother.

London, unable to attend scientific meetings, to go out to entertainments at other people's houses, or to have more than occasional visitors in his own, and then only briefly. The routine of the household became laid down, and its central purpose was to allow Darwin to collect, in his own way, the relevant scientific facts, and his mind to become 'a kind of machine for grinding general laws out of large collections of facts'. (A)

Emma was Charles's cousin. Her father had been instrumental in overcoming parental opposition to the *Beagle* voyage. They were old and close friends. She must have known and understood Charles's passionate purpose and the extent to which it was threatened by social intercourse. Here was the instrument to hand. Social intercourse made Charles ill. What more sensible than to live a secluded life in the country? Besides, they could afford it. And Emma loved looking after invalids.

Such an interpretation receives strong support from her granddaughter, Gwen Raverat, who describes her childhood and her family with insight and wit in *Period Piece*.[20] Mrs Raverat had just been discussing Henrietta, Charles and Emma's second daughter, who, at the age of fifteen, was ordered by her doctor to have breakfast in bed, and had it in bed every day till she died at the age of eighty-five. She remarks of her aunt:

She had been an invalid all her life; but I don't know what (if anything) had originally been the matter with her. . . . I am quite sure that, with her iron will, she could have ignored and controlled her ill health . . . if only she had been set off in the right way when young. The trouble was that in my grandparents' house it was a distinctive and a mournful pleasure to be ill. This was partly because my grandfather was always ill . . . and partly because it was so delightful to be pitied and nursed by my grandmother. . . . I have sometimes thought that she must have been rather too sorry for her family when they were unwell. . . . The attitude of the whole Darwin family to sickness was most unwholesome. At Down, ill health was considered normal.

Darwin's illness presented a splendid challenge to the disciples of Freud, which they gratefully accepted. He was, after all, an iconoclast like the Master, and the cause of his illness was still unknown. Kempf[21] was one of the first. Darwin's illness was a reflection of an anxiety neurosis relating to his

. . . complete submission to his father whereby he deprived himself of all channels of self-assertion in his relations with his father or anything that pertained to him. Free assertions for his rights might have led to a mortal father-son conflict, because both had irrepressible affective cravings that contended for the idealisation of the same love-object. This would, perhaps, as it so often does, have terminated in Darwin becoming a paranoic, if not an invalid. His search for the secrets of nature and his mother's love would then have become hopelessly aborted by hate. Through the renunciation of all envy and all competitive interests in life, such as ambition for priority, and the unreserved acceptance of his father's word and wisdom, Darwin, by adroitly selecting diversions, succeeded in keeping suppressed all disconcerting affective reactions with no more inconvenience that that of producing nutritional disturbances, uncomfortable cardiac and vasomotor reactions, vertigo and insomnia.

The theme was taken up by Good:

. . . there is a wealth of evidence that unmistakably points to these symptoms as a distorted expression of aggression, hate, and resentment felt, at an unconscious level, by Darwin towards his tyrannical father, although at a conscious level we find the reaction-formation of the reverence for his father which was boundless and almost touching.[22]

Phyllis Greenacre believed that Darwin suffered from a severe confusion of sexual orientation and that he turned to science because of his ambivalent identification with his father and grandfather, '. . . but even more from reactions to sado-masochistic fantasies concerning his own birth and his mother's death'.[23] Ernest Jones believed that both Darwin and Wallace paid the penalty for committing unconscious patricide, while Darlington suggested that it was Mrs Darwin's disapproval of some of her husband's work that might have caused his illness.

The case of Sigmund Freud and his view, formed as a result of analysing himself, that psychological illness is generally due to an Oedipus complex are discussed in Chapter 12. Good and Kempf and Greenacre have done their best to fit Darwin to Freud's Procrustean* bed. The thesis could be stated thus. Darwin's illness was a reaction against his frightening father. The *Beagle* voyage was a running away from his father and therefore a relief of anxiety. On his return he was anxious to preserve his dearest possession, his scientific work, at all costs (castration complex). His concept of evolution caused un-conscious, as well as conscious, alarms because it unseated the father figure, Jehovah. Finally, in psychological terms, his marriage could have represented the murder of his father, and his replacement by the son as a sexual partner of his mother.

To me, such an explanation is no more than a fairy tale, cap-able neither of proof nor disproof. I am profoundly sceptical of this rigid application of Freud's theories. The Freudian hypo-thesis would explain just as well as the hypothesis here presented the temporal relationship between the growing obsession with the hypothesis of evolution and the onset and development of Darwin's illness. But apart from my prejudice against a hypo-thesis which is incapable of being refuted by evidence, as is the Freudian hypothesis, I find that the evidence, such as it is, does not support it.

After a careful reading of Darwin's autobiography and letters, I find no evidence of real antipathy to his father, of whom Darwin writes with affection and respect. Moreover, his

*Procrustes, in legend, was a robber who fitted his victims to his only bed. If too long they were reduced by amputation. If too short they were stretched on the rack.

father bought Down and was generous enough to make Darwin financially independent at about the time when his illness began. Nor can I find any evidence of antipathy to his grandfather, though there was antipathy to his grandfather's hypothesis being unsupported by evidence and too speculative. Of his mother he wrote: 'My mother died in July 1817, when I was a little over eight years old, and it is odd that I can remember hardly anything about her except her deathbed, her black velvet gown, and her curiously constructed work-table.' (A) This is hardly evidence for an Oedipus complex. Moreover, I am sure that it was not putting forward the evolutionary hypothesis that Darwin feared. After all, this had been done by his father's father, the prime source of the family's position and distinction. What he was afraid of was putting forward a hypothesis which he had come to know in his bones was right, but for which anything resembling scientific proof was lacking. He would have been dismayed if he had, like his grandfather, put forward a hypothesis which was largely speculative. That this is the correct explanation is supported by the way in which he put off publication, while he patiently collected evidence, for more than twenty years, which would have been longer if it had not been for Wallace.

We have already noted the extraordinary contrast between the young adventurer who never missed a new challenge, who was never put off by hardship or difficulty, and who enjoyed nearly every minute of his five years of foreign travel, and the young recluse, who never left the confines of his own domain. The change in his mind was by no means so abrupt. Nevertheless, it was conspicuous. As usual, Darwin has recorded the change himself in words that cannot be improved.

I have said in one respect that my mind has changed during the last twenty or thirty years. Up to the age of thirty, or beyond it, poetry of many kinds, such as the works of Milton,

Gray, Byron, Wordsworth, Coleridge, and Shelley, gave me great pleasure, and even as a schoolboy I took intense delight in Shakespeare, especially in the historical plays. I have also said that formerly pictures gave me considerable, and music very great delight. But now for many years I cannot endure to read a line of poetry; I have tried lately to read Shakespeare, and found it so intolerably dull that it nauseated me. I have almost lost my taste for pictures or music. Music generally sets me thinking too energetically on what I have been at work on, instead of giving me pleasure. I retain some taste for fine scenery, but it does not cause me the exquisite delight which it formerly did. On the other hand, novels, which are works of the imagination, though not of a very high order, have been for years a wonderful relief and pleasure to me, and I often bless all novelists. . . .

This curious and lamentable loss of the higher aesthetic tastes is all the odder, as books on history, biographies, and travels (independently of any scientific facts which they may contain), and essays on all sorts of subjects interest me as much as ever they did. My mind seems to have become a kind of machine for grinding general laws out of large collections of facts, but why this should have caused the atrophy of that part of the brain alone, on which the higher tastes depend, I cannot conceive. . . .

On the favourable side of the balance, I think that I am superior to the common run of men in noticing things which easily escape attention, and in observing them carefully. My industry has been nearly as great as it could have been in the observation and collection of facts. What is far more important, my love of natural science has been steady and ardent.

This pure love has, however, been much aided by the ambition to be esteemed by my fellow naturalists. . . .

My habits are methodical, and this has been of not a little use for my particular line of work. Lastly, I have had ample leisure from not having to earn my own bread. Even ill-health, though it has annihilated several years of my life, has saved me from the distractions of society and amusement. (Darwin, at last, realised the function or purpose of his illness.)

Therefore, my success as a man of science, whatever this may have amounted to, has been determined, as far as I can judge, by complex and diversified mental qualities and conditions. Of these, the most important have been—the love of science—unbounded patience in long reflecting over any subject—industry in observing and collecting facts—and a fair share of invention as well as common-sense. With such moderate abilities as I possess, it is truly surprising that I should have influenced to a considerable extent the belief of scientific men on some important points. (A)

That Darwin joined the *Beagle* was 'a nice run thing', as Wellington described Waterloo. Had he not gone, there is little doubt that we should not have had *The Origin of Species*, and probably not the illness. It seems quite likely that he would have become a country clergyman with an intense interest in Natural History, probably a steady contributor to scientific journals. He would possibly have become a Fellow of the Royal Society. But the facts that impressed themselves on his mind in South America, and particularly in the Galapagos Islands, would have remained inaccessible. And without the urgency which all this instilled into Darwin's mind, his illness would have lacked a function or purpose, and most likely never have happened.

Darwin's illness was not diagnosed, at least in a form we should now recognise, during his lifetime. It is thus not surprising that he wandered from doctor to doctor without much benefit. Dr Gully of Malvern was celebrated for his water-cure. So Darwin went to Malvern and derived so much benefit that he rigged up a douche of his own with the butler as bath-man. But the effect wore off. Moreover, while Dr Gully's ideas about the water-cure were plausible enough, his views about other matters were not acceptable. 'It is a sad flaw, I think, in my

beloved Dr Gully, that he believes in everything. When Miss
—— was very ill, he had a *clairvoyant* girl to report on internal
changes, a *mesmerist* to put her to sleep—an *homœopathist*, viz.
Dr ——, and himself as *hydropathist*! and the girl recovered.'
Dr Lane's water-cure establishment at Moor Park was also
patronised for a while. Dr Bence-Jones prescribed horse-riding
and a quiet cob called Tommy was procured. But Darwin
found that riding took much attention, and that he could not
give his mind to his scientific work as he could when walking;
then Tommy fell on him, and that ended it. Thereafter he returned to Sir Andrew Clark, whom he had first consulted years
before. Of him Francis Darwin wrote: 'It was not only for his
generously rewarded service that my Father felt a debt of
gratitude towards Sir Andrew Clark. He owed to his cheerful
personal influence an often-repeated encouragement, which
latterly added something real to his happiness. . . .'

It is of great interest to inquire how Darwin would have
been treated today had his illness been diagnosed as a psychoneurosis, and he been sent to a psychiatrist for treatment. Here
I cannot improve on what Hubble wrote in 1943.

Treatment which would have been simple at Devonport had
become impossible fifteen years later. How then to treat
Charles Darwin in 1943 ? It would be tempting to explain to
the author of *Expression of the Emotions in Man and Animals*
that his own illness displayed the autonomic disturbance
characteristic of emotional expression in man. It would be
easy for the author of the *Origin of Species* to understand that
his illness might represent an unfavourable adaptation to
environment. Then the course would be set for an investigation of the nature of the unresolved conflicts that at once profoundly disturbed his somatic functions and deeply impelled
his scientific genius. Could one relieve the one without imped-
ing the other ? Restore the healthy naturalist with his tastes
for shooting and Milton without at the same time destroying
the *Origin of Species* ? No one in his senses would attempt the

perilous task. 'The chamber is swept and garnished,' quoted Middleton Murry twenty years ago in a passionate protest against psychoanalysis, 'and the seven devils enter in.' With Darwin the danger would be that one might restore the chamber's garnishings and sweep out the only devil that mattered—the devil of single-mindedness. Superficial psychotherapy would be the ineluctable method; reassurance, hope and comfort, in much the same fashion as his Victorian doctors gave them to him. One may regret that he would not wash in the waters of Jordan with Allfrey of St Mary's Cray but preferred the waters of Abana with the pompous Lane and of Pharpar with the self-gulling Gully. Still, his doctors did him pretty well. No one could have reassured him more strongly than the 'cheery and skilful' Brinton, no one could have given him more hope than Lane and Gully, no one could have encouraged and consoled him more adroitly than the courtly Clark. He retained his reason and he wrote the *Origin of Species*. This is his doctors' justification. It is a terrifying thought that the Darwins of today may be known to posterity only in the case-books of the psychiatrists.[24]

RECENT ERRORS OF FACT

The explanation here proposed for Darwin's illness would be untenable if Darwin had actually become convinced of the probable truth of the evolutionary hypothesis during the voyage of the *Beagle*. Two recent writers, Moorehead[25] and Eiseley,[26] imply this.

Moorehead's error has been noted (p. 41). More serious is that of Eiseley, a scholar and an anthropologist. In his book, *Darwin's Century*, Eiseley points out that Darwin must have been thoroughly familiar with the idea of evolution before he started on the voyage. His grandfather had written about it in *Zoonomia*, which Charles had read. At Edinburgh he had a friend, Grant, who had spent some time in Paris, and become attached to Lamarck's teaching. While at the university, an anonymous article had been contributed to the *New Philosophical Journal* setting out the evolutionary theory.[27] Finally the theory had been outlined by three people in the United Kingdom, Willis, Matthew and Robert Chambers. Chambers' *The Vestiges of the Natural History of Creation* was published in 1844, and was so successful that 'four editions appeared in seven months and by 1860 some 24,000 copies had been sold'. Indeed, the evolutionary theory had been debated in 1830 in the French Academy of Sciences by Geoffroy Saint-Hilaire who was for it, and Cuvier who was against it. Cuvier won the debate because Saint-Hilaire had chosen a bad example to explain the transition from invertebrates to vertebrates. All these are noted by Darwin in *The Origin of Species*.

Eiseley proceeds: 'One can, in a sense, regard the voyage of the *Beagle* as a romantic interlude. One can point out that every idea Darwin developed was lying fallow in England before he sailed. One can show that sufficient data had been accumulated to enable a man of great insight to have demonstrated the fact of evolution and the theory of natural selection by sheer deduction in a well-equipped library.' He goes on to show how these ideas actually came during the voyage.

Let us take first the actual day-to-day references in the diary. We need not look for evolutionary statements directly expressed. They would have annoyed Fitzroy, and Darwin's log was part of the official record of the expedition and open by right to Fitzroy. Some of the entries, however, are most provocative. We must also bear in mind as we examine Darwin's remarks that they can be divided into two categories: *those bearing on the proof that evolution has occurred, and those concerned with the actual search for the mechanism by which organic change is produced.* It is the confusion between these two points which is probably responsible for some of Darwin's own contradictory statements of later years. Apparently he came to equate, in some instances, the discovery of natural selection with his belief in the reality of evolution. Actually,

(b) Charles Darwin in old age

1(a) Charles Darwin in 1849, from the painting by T. H. Maguire

2 Darwin's study at Down House, from an etching at Down House

however, the diary and notebooks of the voyage, as well as one of Darwin's own remarks in his autobiography, suggest that he began with an evolutionary suspicion which grew stronger with his continued observations and led, finally, to the discovery of the principle of natural selection and its accompanying law of divergence. . . .

It is possible from the information Darwin has left us, and again making allowance for the educational background that as a naturalist he already possessed, to interpret the successive stages of his thought in the development of the evolutionary hypothesis. There are, as we have earlier shown, two aspects of the problem: the demonstration of evolution itself as a process taking place in time, and, second, the nature of the mechanism controlling it. So far as the voyage is concerned, Darwin succeeded in solving only the first aspect of the problem, that is, the actual demonstration of the likelihood that evolution had taken place. Nevertheless, as we shall see, he came, in the Galapagos, upon a key to the mechanism itself.

If Moorehead's or Eiseley's accounts were correct, the explanation here advanced for Darwin's illness would be groundless. But they are not. We have seen how his *Diary* contains no hint that, during the voyage, he doubted separate creations, though he did begin to wonder; nor does the *Diary* contain any hint of his having discovered the mechanism of evolution during his stay in the Galapagos. His *Autobiography* makes it clear that during the voyage he accepted the Bible literally. His revolutionary ideas concerning his experiences during the *Beagle* voyage appear not in the first, but in the second, edition of the *Journal*, written after the decisive events of March 1837, when the idea occurred to him that the curious phenomena he had observed during the voyage might be due to evolution.

Eiseley's comments are those of an armchair scientist, who believes that revolutionary hypotheses are born in a library. No one who reads Darwin's own writings can doubt that the hypothesis was forced on him by the facts which he had been instrumental in uncovering. Any lingering doubt should be removed by this letter to Hooker written in 1844:

. . . I have been now ever since my return engaged in a very presumptuous work, and I know no one individual who would not say a very foolish one. I was so struck with the distribution of the Galapagos organisms, &c., &c., and with the character of the American fossil mammifers, &c., &c., that I determined to collect blindly every sort of fact, which could bear any way on what are species. I have read heaps of agricultural and horticultural books, and have never ceased collecting facts. At last gleams of light have come, and I am almost convinced (quite contrary to the opinion I started with) that species are not (it is like confessing a murder) immutable. Heaven forfend me from Lamarck nonsense of a 'tendency to progression,' 'adaptations from the slow willing of animals,' &c! But the conclusions I am led to are not widely different from his; though the means of change are wholly so. I think I have found out (here's presumption!) the simple way by which species become exquisitely adapted to various ends. You will now groan, and think to yourself, 'on what a man have I been wasting my time and writing to'. I should, five years ago, have thought so.[6]

And again, this letter to Dr Otto Zacharias in 1877, quoted by Huxley in his obituary of Charles Darwin for the Royal Society:

When I was on board the *Beagle* I believed in the permanence of species, but as far as I can remember, vague doubts occasionally crossed my mind and in July 1837 I opened a notebook to record any facts that might bear on the question. But I did not become convinced that species were mutable until I think two or three years had elapsed.[28]

Chapter 6

FLORENCE NIGHTINGALE
The Young Heroine

Many people, the world over, are familiar with the legendary Florence Nightingale, the high-born lady with the lamp, whose selfless devotion brought comfort, and indeed life, to thousands of sick and wounded British soldiers in the Crimean War, and whose energy and example founded nursing as a skilled and respected profession. Few, however, are aware that this was merely the prelude to what she regarded as, and indeed was, her life's great work. What had happened to the British Army in the Crimea was due to the inept administration of the War Office, and to ignorance of the importance of sanitation. These had to be put right, and that being done led to similar reform for the Army in India. These were her great achievements and they were done from her bed. For, on her return from Scutari, a national heroine at the age of thirty-six, she became first a recluse and then an invalid under sentence of death. She did not re-emerge into the world until she was sixty, to die at ninety.

Florence Nightingale was born in 1820, the younger of the two daughters of W. E. and Fanny Nightingale. Her father was a well-to-do, well connected, well-educated country gentleman of scholarly tastes. Fanny was one of ten children who, when young, 'never thought of anything all day long but our ease and pleasure', as she wrote later. Florence was her father's favourite; she was beautiful, highly intelligent and witty and had an immense zest for life. Her father educated the girls himself, chiefly in Latin, Greek, German, French and philosophy, but so well that in later life, Jowett, the great Master of

Balliol, consulted Florence over his editings and translations of Plato. Fanny had great social plans for her daughters and there were the usual dances, dinner parties and week-ends with the various local gentry, including the Duke of Devonshire, Lord Palmerston, the future Earl of Shaftesbury, and others who were to play an important role in her life. Florence, although seemingly enjoying the social life, wrote: 'I craved for some regular occupation, for something worth doing instead of frittering away my time on useless trifles.' And then as she wrote in her private diary: 'On 7 February 1837, God spoke to me and called me to His service.' Forty years later she wrote that God had spoken four times, once in 1837, the date of her call, once in 1853 before she went to the Hospital for Invalid Gentlewomen; once before the Crimea in 1854, and once after Sidney Herbert's death in 1861.

In the years 1837 to 1839 the family travelled extensively on the continent. Florence kept a dairy, noting amongst other things, the precise hour of departure and arrival and the distance covered by each journey. Her meticulous interest in detail was to pay handsomely later. In 1839, before leaving Paris, she noted that to make herself worthy to be God's servant the first temptation to overcome was the desire to shine in society. On their return to England the social whirl began again with Florence a beautiful, gay and much sought after young lady, or so it seemed on the surface. Underneath was the seriousness of her 'call', but to what? Her first step was to improve herself by learning mathematics. This was bitterly opposed by both W.E.N. and Fanny. All Florence was able to get was a lesson twice a week, fully chaperoned, from a married clergyman in her uncle's library. But later this instruction produced astonishing results. For it was her mathematical approach that saved the British Army at Scutari and which provided the data on which sanitary reform was later to be based.

1842 saw the beginning of Miss Nightingale's fight for an independent life in the service of humanity. It was a year of great suffering and hardship in Britain, one of the 'hungry forties'. She wrote: 'My mind is absorbed with the idea of the sufferings of man.' In 1843 she began to spend the greater part of the day helping the sick poor in their homes. In 1844 she at last knew her vocation; it was in hospitals among the sick. 'Since I was twenty-four,' she wrote later, '. . . there never was any vagueness in my plans or ideas as to what God's work was for me.' Her struggle had begun. From the first that struggle was associated with illness.

Florence was passionately attached to a beautiful young neighbour of her own age, Marianne Nicholson, while Marianne's brother, Henry, was pressing Florence to marry him. The three were in a Christmas house party in 1843 when she had her first illness which took her to bed for several weeks, at the end of which her vocation became revealed to her. In the summer of 1844 she was forbidden to help in the cottages whose occupants had scarlet fever. She was ill for some months. The nature of these illnesses is uncertain. The next spring Henry Nicholson proposed and was refused. Marianne ended her friendship. Florence again became ill and was approaching a mental collapse when her grandmother and her old nurse were successively ill and Florence was allowed to nurse both. She improved at once. She now knew her vocation and at Christmas sought to go to Salisbury hospital to be trained. The Nightingales were horrified, there were scenes and the plan was dropped. At the time this was not surprising, for hospitals, and the sick they contained, were filthy, and nurses a lewd, lecherous and drunken lot. Florence was heart-broken but not ill. She became remote and she began to study secretly. Blue Books,* hospital reports and information from abroad on hospitals, health and mortality were read and carefully abstracted before breakfast and the daily social round. In the autumn of 1847 she again became ill, was taken by Mr and Mrs Bracebridge to Italy to convalesce, and there met Sidney Herbert† and

---

* Government publications of a factual nature, including reports of Commissions.
† Herbert, Sidney (1810–1861), later Baron Herbert of Lea; second son of eleventh Earl of Pembroke; War Secretary 1845–46, 1852–55, and 1859–60.

his wife, who were wintering in Rome. The three immediately became intimate friends, so beginning an association that was to shape all their lives.

In 1849 she refused her second proposal of marriage. Richard Monckton Milnes* was rich and a social reformer. Florence and he had first met at the Palmerstons seven years before and had been very close subsequently. In describing her reaction she wrote:

> I have an intellectual nature which requires satisfaction and that would find it in him. I have a passionate nature which requires satisfaction and that would find it in him. I have a moral, an active, nature, which requires satisfaction and that would not find it in his life. Sometimes I think I will satisfy my passional nature at all events, because that will at least secure me from the evil of dreaming. But would it? I could be satisfied to spend a life with him in combining our different powers in some great object. I could not satisfy this nature by spending a life with him in making society and arranging domestic things.

The family was furious and Florence became ill. She was again saved by her friends, the Bracebridges, who took her abroad. Her diaries are filled with despair at her inability to serve God. On the way home they visited Berlin where Florence began visiting hospitals and charitable institutions. Then came the turning point of her life. She visited Kaiserswerth on the Rhine. She had first heard of Kaiserswerth in 1842 from the Prussian Ambassador, Chevalier Bunsen. There Pastor Fliedner and his wife trained Protestant Deaconesses in the hospital of the Institution to nurse the sick poor. She stayed for a fortnight and was so well on leaving that she wrote a pamphlet of 32 pages in less than a week. This, published anonymously in 1851, was her first printed work.[6]

The return home brought nothing but frustration. Her mother was determined she should only indulge in activities 'proper to

* Later Lord Houghton (1802–1885), President of the London Library 1882–85; Hon D.C.L. Oxford.

her station'. Her elder sister, Parthenope, became insanely jealous of Florence's social success and demanded that her sister should become her slave. To this Florence acceded for the next six months, but escaped to spend some time at Kaiserswerth. She found 'the nursing there was nil, the hygiene horrible. . . . But never have I met with a higher tone, a purer devotion than there. . . . I find the deepest interest in everything here and am so well in body and mind.' When she returned to her mother and sister, 'They would hardly speak to me. I was treated as if I had come from committing a crime.' Although over thirty and with a distinguished circle of friends, her movements were controlled, her letters read, her invitations supervised. She was imprisoned by her affection for her father, her sense of duty and her loyalty to her family. She escaped to Paris in the hope of entering the Maison de la Providence, to be trained as a nurse, but was twice prevented by family illness. In 1853, Mrs Herbert told Florence that her friend, Lady Canning, was looking for a new superintendent for the 'Institution for the Care of Sick Gentlewomen in Distressed Circumstances', which had got into difficulties. Florence was interviewed and appointed. Her mother stormed, her sister had hysterics and had to be put to bed. Her father escaped to London where he took the important step of allowing Florence £500 a year. Florence, despite the lamentations of her family, took rooms in Pall Mall. She wrote to her friend 'Clarkey'* in Paris: 'I have talked matters over with Parthe, not once but thousands of times. . . . It has been, therefore, with the deepest consideration and with the fullest advice that I have taken the step of leaving home, and it is a *fait accompli.*'

Miss Nightingale was not what the Committee of society ladies, who ran the institution, had expected. Her genius was practical. She installed bells with valves that flew open when the patient called, had hot water piped to every floor and sent her committee round to view 'windlass installations', to bring

* Mary Clarke, a cousin of Lord Dalrymple and a protegée of Mme Récamier in Paris; Married Julius Mohl. Florence met her in Paris in 1838.

up the patients' food. Every detail of furnace, of supply of coal, of food, of linen, of furniture, and of medical and surgical equipment was inspected thoroughly and arrangements made to supply the best quality at the lowest prices. The original staff did not survive and were succeeded by people of her own choosing. Her relationship with her ladies is illustrated by this letter to Clarkey:

My Committee refused me to take in Catholic patients, where-upon I wished them good morning, unless I might take in Jews and their Rabbis to attend them. So now it is settled, and in print that we are to take in all denominations whatever, and allow them to be visited by their respective priests and Muftis, provided I will receive (in any case whatsoever that is not of the Church of England) the obnoxious animal at the door, take him upstairs myself, remain while he is conferring with his patient, make myself responsible that he does not speak to, or look at, anyone else, and bring him downstairs again in a noose, and out into the street. And to this I have agreed! And this is in print! Amen.

In six months, she had the place organised and running smoothly, and was beginning to visit hospitals and collect facts to establish a case for reforming conditions for hospital nurses. In the summer of 1854 cholera broke out in Soho and Miss Nightingale went as a volunteer to the Middlesex Hospital to superintend the nursing of cholera patients.

Mrs Gaskell described her:

She is tall; very slight and willowy in figure; thick shortish rich brown hair, very delicate colouring; grey eyes which are generally pensive and drooping, but which when they choose can be the merriest eyes I ever saw; and perfect teeth, making her smile the sweetest I ever saw. . . . She has a great deal of fun and is carried along by that I think. She mimics most capitally, mimics for instance the way of talking of some of the poor Governesses in the Establishment, with their delight at having a man servant, and at having Lady Canning and Lady Mounteagle to do this and that for them. . . . She has no friend—and she wants none. She stands perfectly alone, half-way between God and his creatures.[7]

THE CRIMEA

In March 1854 Britain and France declared war on Russia and in September the allied armies landed in the Crimea with the object of capturing and destroying the newly built Russian base on the Black Sea, Sebastopol. The campaign was to be a disaster, resulting in the destruction of the British Army, not by enemy action, but by disease, exposure and starvation. Cholera was endemic from the start. Transports, supplies, doctors, medicines, everything needed to support an army fighting a war were woefully inadequate. The British headquarters were at Scutari where an enormous Turkish barracks and its attached hospital were handed over to the British. Here came 1,000 cholera cases, followed by the wounded from the battle of Alma. One of the transports, 'the *Kangaroo*, fitted to receive 250 sick, received between 1,200 and 1,500. Cholera cases, battle casualties, were crammed in together. Too weak to move, too weak to reach the sanitary conveniences, they fell on each other as the ship rolled and were soon lying in heaps of filth. Men with amputations were flung about the deck screaming with pain.'[5] At the barracks hospital there were no beds and there was no kitchen, and there were no cups or buckets to bring water in. This scene of misery was faithfully reported to the British Public by the *Times* correspondent, W. H. Russell. The country was outraged. Russell had pointed out how much superior were the medical arrangements of the French, who had also the help of the Sisters of Charity. So a public demand arose for nurses.

Sidney Herbert was Minister at War and responsible for the arrangements for the sick and wounded. On 15 October 1854 he wrote to Miss Nightingale inviting her to go to Scutari at the Government's expense in command of a party of nurses. The letter contained these passages:

The selection of the rank and file of nurses will be very difficult; no one knows it better than yourself. The difficulty of
finding women equal to a task, after all, full of horrors, and
requiring, besides knowledge and goodwill, great energy and
great courage, will be great; . . . and not the least will be the
difficulty of making the whole work smoothly with the medical
and military authorities out there. This it is which makes it so
important that the experiment should be carried out by one
with a capacity for administration and experience. A number
of sentimental enthusiastic ladies turned loose into the
Hospital at Scutari would probably, after a few days, be *mises
à la porte* by those whose business they would interrupt, and
whose authority they would dispute.

My question simply is, Would you listen to the request to
go and superintend the whole thing? You would of course
have plenary authority over all the nurses, and I think I could
secure you the fullest assistance and co-operation from the
medical staff, and you would also have an unlimited power of
drawing on the Government for whatever you thought
requisite for the success of your mission.

Oddly enough, Miss Nightingale had already and independently decided to go and had written to the Herberts for their
approval. Her letter and his crossed in the post. She saw the
issue clearly. It was nothing less than the future of nursing. The
eyes of the nation were focused on Scutari. If the experiment
succeeded, nursing would never again be despised. She decided
to start four days after receiving Sidney Herbert's letter, during
which time nurses had to be engaged, uniforms made, and
tickets and berths reserved. The Bracebridges were to go too
and he undertook the travelling arrangements.

She took thirty-eight nurses, of whom ten were Roman
Catholic nuns, fourteen were Anglican sisters, and fourteen
hospital nurses. After a stormy voyage, they arrived in the
Bosphorus on 3 November. 'Oh Miss Nightingale,' said one of
the party, 'when we land don't let there be any red tape delays,

let us get straight to nursing the poor fellows.' Miss Nightingale, gazing at the gigantic pile of the Barracks Hospital, replied: 'The strongest will be wanted at the wash tub.'

The Times correspondent had not overestimated the gravity of the situation. The Turkish Barracks at Scutari which became the British Hospital was an immense hollow square with towers surmounted by golden domes at each corner. Inside everything was filthy and dilapidated and there was practically no equipment. Worst of all was a total lack of elementary sanitary arrangements. Men who had become sick from exposure and starvation on the heights above Sebastopol were brought to Scutari where they died of cholera or typhus. When the war was over it was discovered that the mortality of each regiment was dependent on the number of men sent to Scutari.

Miss Nightingale and her party were graciously received and conducted to their quarters in the Barrack Hospital. Five small rooms and a kitchen had been allocated to Miss Nightingale and forty nurses. As Miss Nightingale took her eight 'Sellonites' to the upper room which they were to occupy, they found the room already occupied by the body of a dead Russian general. There was no furniture, no food, no means of cooking food, and no beds. The nurses were expected to sleep on the raised wooden platforms called Turkish divans on which the Turks placed bedding. There was, however, no bedding. Miss Nightingale went over to the hospital where she managed to procure tin basins of milkless tea. While her nurses drank Miss Nightingale told them of her discoveries. The hospital was totally lacking in furniture or equipment, even an operating table was wanting; moreover, it was useless to ask for any, as there was none. For the time being the nurses must use their tin basins for everything, washing, eating and drinking. Water was rationed to one pint a day for everything, obtained from a fountain at the end of a corridor. Moreover, the situation was soon expected to get worse as the battle of Balaclava had been fought on 24 October, and transports filled with wounded were on the way.

The doctors ignored Miss Nightingale. She offered her nurses and supplies and they were not accepted. Miss Nightingale realised that the success of her mission depended on winning the confidence of the doctors. She determined not to offer her nurses or stores again but to wait till the doctors asked for help. The nurses were to watch the wounded suffer and to do nothing until officially asked. Perhaps this was the most difficult and courageous of all Miss Nightingale's decisions, particularly since the nurses disliked it.

The sorry state of affairs at the Barracks Hospital at Scutari and the impending disaster, which Miss Nightingale so clearly foresaw, were due to fatal defects in the system by which the health of the British Army was administered. Three departments were concerned, the Commissariat, the Purveyor's Department, and the Medical Department. Forty years of peace, together with the cheese-paring by successive governments, had reduced the staffs of each to a size completely inadequate for the needs of war. Moreover, the responsibilities of each were rigidly defined and circumscribed. Communications between them were made by filling out forms and making requisitions. Once this had been correctly done, responsibility ended. It was no one's duty to ensure that action was taken.

Moreover, each department refused to admit that anything was wrong or defective. Before Miss Nightingale left England she was assured by Dr Andrew Smith, head of the Medical Department, that there was a profusion of every kind of medical supply at Scutari. Miss Nightingale was sceptical and had purchased a great deal at Marseilles on her way out. She now sent the Bracebridges to buy more in the markets of Constantinople. As the stores arrived the nurses were put to work to sort, to count, and put away.

On 6 November, the wounded began to arrive from Balaclava, suffering terribly as they were carried on their bumpy ride to the Barracks Hospital. Days passed and Miss Nightingale did almost nothing; she was not asked. She gained her entrée through the kitchen. The cooking arrangements were hopelessly inadequate, as was the supply of food; at one time one clerk did all the issues for 2,500 patients. No provision existed in the regulations for invalid foods. Miss Nightingale had brought plenty of food and cooking utensils. She was soon supplying invalid diets to the whole hospital, though only on requisition by a doctor.

Then on 9 November the situation was abruptly changed. A flood of sick began to descend on Scutari in such numbers that at last the doctors sought Miss Nightingale's help. Her nurses stopped sorting linen and began to sew up great bags and fill them with straw. These were laid out almost touching one another, not only in the wards but also in the corridors (Plate 4). Day after day the sick poured in until the enormous building was filled. Men lay on the bare boards because the supply of bags was exhausted. The floors were unwashed and everything was crawling with vermin. Amputations were done in the open ward on boards put on two trestles. The filth was incredible. Miss Nightingale estimated that there were over 1,000 patients with diarrhoea in the hospital and only two chamber pots. The privies had been allowed to become unusable. Mr Augustus Stafford said there was liquid filth which floated over the floor an inch deep and came out of the privy itself into the anteroom. Huge wooden tubs stood in the wards and corridors for the men to use. The orderlies disliked emptying them and they frequently remained unemptied for 24 hours. Miss Nightingale wrote: 'We have Erysipelas, fever and gangrene, . . . the dysentery cases have died at the rate of one in two . . . the mortality of the operations is frightful. . . . This is only the beginning of things.' It was. The destruction of the British Army had begun.

The British Army was marooned on the heights above Sebastopol. Thousands of men possessed only what they stood in. Riddled with cholera and in the intense heat of summer, the men had, at their officer's orders, abandoned their packs. There was only one good road to the British base at Balaclava, but that was of little importance since there was no transport. In mid-November a hurricane devastated the Crimea, destroying every ship in Balaclava harbour, including a transport bearing comforts for the men, ripping to pieces the tents in which the men slept and the marquees that formed the field hospital. Such fuel stores and such little forage as the army possessed were destroyed. Winter began, with sleet and snow and driving winds. Dysentery increased. Shipload after shipload of emaciated starving men clad only in rags inundated the hospital at Scutari. Conditions in the hospital got rapidly out of hand, because action was the responsibility of no one. And then all at once it became clear that there was one quarter in which help could be sought with the certainty that it would be given promptly and with precision. Miss Nightingale had wealth at her disposal and had foreseen the need. So she laid in what she thought would prove necessary and issued it, provided it had been properly requisitioned by a doctor. Each day she ascertained what articles were missing from the Purveyor's store, what requisitions had been received and not met. Her agent went into Constantinople and bought the goods which were placed in her store and issued on proper requisition. By the end of December she was purveying the whole hospital. She wrote to Sidney Herbert: 'I am a kind of General Dealer in socks, shirts, knives and forks, wooden spoons, tin baths, tables and forms, cabbages and carrots, operating tables, towels and soap, small tooth combs, precipitate for destroying lice, scissors, bed pans, and stump pillows.' In two months she supplied 6,000 shirts, 2,000 socks, and 500 pairs of drawers. She had the lavatories and the wards cleaned and she rented a house in which she had the patients' clothing washed by soldiers' wives. At the end of December, when the hospital was full, a letter from the Commander in Chief announced the arrival of a further 500 sick and wounded. It was decided to put in order a wing of the barracks that had been damaged by fire before the British arrived. The British Ambassador, given *carte blanche* by Sidney Herbert, failed to get anything done and the military commandant had neither money nor authority. So Miss Nightingale hired the necessary workmen and had it done. Not only did she repair it but she equipped it. 'Orderlies were wanting, utensils were wanting, even water was wanting,' she wrote to Sidney Herbert on 12 December 1854. 'I supplied all the utensils, including knives and forks, spoons, cans, towels, etc. . . . and was able to send on the instant arrowroot in huge milk pails (two bottles of port wine in each) for 500 men.' For the first time the sick and wounded were received with clean bedding and warm food by Miss Nightingale and her nurses. As one of them said, 'We felt we were in heaven'.

This achievement spread Miss Nightingale's fame far and wide. But it also excited the most intense resentment in the service departments. Her difficulties were further increased, when on 14 December, without her consent or indeed her knowledge, a rival group of forty-four nurses suddenly arrived under her friend, Mary Stanley. Miss Nightingale was furious. Her letter to Sidney Herbert set out her position:

I sacrificed my own judgement and went out with forty females, well knowing that half that number would be more efficient and less trouble, and that the difficulty of inducing forty untrained women, in so extraordinary a position as this (turned loose among 3,000 men) to observe any order or even any of the directions of the medical men, would be Herculean. Experience has justified my foreboding. But I have toiled my way into the confidence of the medical men. I have, by incessant vigilance, day and night, introduced something like order into the disorderly operations of these women. And the plan may be said to have succeeded in some measure, as it stands. . . . At this point of affairs arrives at *no one's* requisition, a fresh batch of women, raising our number to eighty-four. You have sacrificed the cause, so near to my heart. You have sacrificed me—a matter of small importance now—you have sacrificed your own written word to a popular cry. . . .

The absence of accommodation in Scutari temporarily

solved the difficulty, and an abject letter from Sidney Herbert re-established her authority. Nevertheless, these additional nurses, not of her choosing, and with a high percentage of Roman Catholics (a religion to which Mary Stanley had recently been converted) were to add enormously to her difficulties. Her position was eased by a letter from the Queen to Sidney Herbert saying: '. . . I wish Miss Nightingale and the ladies would tell these noble wounded and sick men that no-one takes a warmer interest or feels more for their sufferings or admires their courage and heroism more than their Queen.' A week later the Queen's gifts to her soldiers were entrusted to Miss Nightingale, who was asked to suggest something the Queen could do 'to testify her sense of the courage and endurance so abundantly shown by her sick soldiers'. Miss Nightingale suggested first that the amount stopped from pay for sickness be reduced and second that the military cemeteries in Scutari be transferred to the British. Both had been widely supported but nothing had been done. Following Miss Nightingale's letter both were carried through. Her opponents were thus reminded of her powerful connections.

Meanwhile the sick continued to pour in from Sebastopol. Of a consignment of 1,200, Miss Nightingale estimated 85 per cent were suffering from scurvy. The Barracks Hospital overflowed and all the inadequacies so painfully evident before, became more so. Miss Nightingale alone could take decisions and get things done. The purveyor sought her help, the doctors depended on her and the men adored her. As Colonel Sterling wrote: 'Miss Nightingale now queens it with absolute power.' But she had to work for it as few can have done before or since.

Her quarters were called the Tower of Babel. All day long passed in and out captains of transport, doctors, nurses, chaplains, asking for shirts, splints, bandages, stoves and butter, etc., or advice on a course of action. Here she received the requisitions without which she would not supply and the merchants from whom she would purchase. She slept in the sickroom behind a screen. She saw callers in the same room at a little desk at which she wrote between the callers. She wore a black dress with a white collar and cuffs and a white cap under a black silk handkerchief. Here she kept all her records, including those of the free gifts scheme which was to be such a thorn in her flesh; here she wrote her enormous correspondence to Sidney Herbert. Throughout that winter it was desperately cold. There was no heating and she hated cold.

When a flood of sick came in she was on her feet all day. She was known to spend eight hours on her knees dressing wounds, and she would work the clock round. She never let a man she had tended die alone. She estimated that during that winter she witnessed 2,000 deaths. There was never a severe case that escaped her notice. She did her rounds every night carrying her lantern which she would set down before she bent down over any of the patients. 'What a comfort it was to see her pass even,' wrote a soldier. 'She would speak to one, and nod and smile to as many more; but she could not do it all you know. We lay there by hundreds; but we could kiss her shadow as it fell and lay our heads on the pillow again content.' (Plate 4)

Despite the improvements in the Barracks Hospital the mortality climbed because of an outbreak at the end of December of what was variously described as famine fever and Asiatic cholera, but described more accurately by Miss Nightingale as gaol fever, almost certainly typhus. By mid-January the epidemic had claimed not only the sick but also four surgeons, three nurses, and the old Purveyor. Russell's dispatches to *The Times* had brought home to the public the heroism of the British Army and that these heroes were now nearly all dead from starvation, exposure and disease. In Parliament the government was censured and resigned. However, the new Prime Minister was Miss Nightingale's old friend, Lord Palmerston; the new Secretary for War, Lord Panmure, was instructed to show consideration for her wishes and suggestions. Lord Panmure sent out in February a Sanitary Commission which, as Miss Nightingale wrote, 'saved the British Army'. The Commission consisted of Dr John Sutherland of the Board of Health, Mr Rawlinson, a civil engineer, and Dr Milroy, a physician; these were accompanied by the borough engineer and the sanitary inspectors from Liverpool. They were instructed not to rest content with an order but '. . . see instantly, by yourselves or your agents, to the commencement of the work and to its superintendence day by day until it is finished.'

The Commission began work early in March and at once made the most alarming discoveries. The sewers under the Barracks Hospital were cess-pools of filth. Water was stored in tanks next to open privies. The Commission had the sewers cleaned out, cleared the dead animals and filth from the court-yard, lime-washed the walls and removed the Turkish divans which harboured rats, which were so conspicuous a problem of the place. Mortality at once began to fall, by 7 April to 14·5 per cent, and by 19 May to 5·2 per cent. Simultaneously spring returned to the Crimea. The crisis was over. That it had been surmounted was due to Miss Nightingale. In May Miss Nightingale was able to report her first really satisfactory reception of sick. Two hundred men were bathed, cleansed, and put into clean shirts and clean, comfortable beds and given good food.

By the spring of 1855 Miss Nightingale was physically exhausted. Nevertheless, feeling that affairs at Scutari were under reasonable control, she determined to go to the Crimea. Unfortunately her terms of appointment were now seen as defective, since her authority was confined to Turkey and did not extend over the whole theatre of war. The Chief Medical Officer, Dr John Hall, who had been unwise enough to report to the War Office that the hospitals were in excellent condition, was utterly opposed to this interfering woman. Besides, the Sanitary Commission had reported adversely on his hospitals and he had been censured by Lord Raglan, the Commander in Chief. The nurses in the Crimea were the remnants of Mary Stanley's party, who did not in general accept Miss Nightingale's authority.

On 5 May she arrived at Balaclava, and at once went ashore to pay her respects to Lord Raglan. As Lord Raglan was away she decided to visit one of the batteries outside Sebastopol. The sight of a lady mounted on a very pretty mare and surrounded by men in glittering uniform was a new experience. Word went round that the lady was Miss Nightingale. The soldiers rushed from their tents and cheered with three times three. That evening Miss Nightingale was exhausted. The next day she began her inspection. She was viewed with hostility and rudeness and found the hospitals in a most depressing state of filth and confusion. She had decided to give battle when, on the second day, she fainted. Miss Nightingale was suffering from Crimean fever.* For two weeks, nursed by Mrs Roberts, death seemed imminent. Consternation reigned in the British Army and amongst the people at home. Then she started to recover and on 28 May the Queen was 'truly thankful that that excellent and valuable person Miss Nightingale is safe'. She recuperated in Scutari, surviving a plot by Dr Hall to ship her directly to England. On arrival she was emaciated, white-faced and extremely weak. Her hair had been shorn during the fever. By 9 July, she was sufficiently recovered to have decided to return to the Crimea and not to return to England. 'If I go, all this will go to pieces,' she wrote to her sister.

It was not to be easy. During her illness, things had gone from bad to worse in the Crimea and discipline had become lax in Scutari. In September the Bracebridges decided to go home.

Florence was now urgently in need of dependable help. Her Aunt Mai† arrived on 16 September and was horrified by her niece's appearance. 'The public generally imagine her by the soldier's bedside,' she wrote on 18 September 1855, '. . . how easy, how satisfactory if that were all. The quantity of writing, the quantity of talking is the weary work, the dealing with the mean, the selfish, the incompetent.' During her first week Aunt Mai worked from 5 or 6 a.m. till 11 p.m. copying.

Miss Nightingale returned to the Crimea in late September where she again met opposition, every attempt being made to

---

* Probably typhus, possibly typhoid.
† Her father's younger sister, married to Samuel Smith.

humiliate her. Added to that she had to be admitted to hospital with sciatica. She wrote: 'I have now had all that this climate can give, Crimean fever, Dysentery, Rheumatism and believe myself thoroughly acclimatised and ready to stand out the war with any man.' In a week she was working again. At the end of November she was sent for to Scutari where cholera had broken out. Before she left she wrote to Sidney Herbert: 'There is not an official who would not burn me like Joan of Arc if he could, but they know the War Office cannot turn me out because the country is with me—that is my position.'

The cholera epidemic had broken out in German mercenaries who were quartered in a depot that had been condemned by the Sanitary Commission. Not only had she to deal with this, but with two nurses, one accused of ill treating patients and the other of midnight visits. By the end of 1855 she had earache, continual laryngitis and insomnia, and was obsessed by failure. And the cold was again intense. 'Food, rest, temperature never interfere with her doing her work,' Aunt Mai wrote. 'You would be surprised at the temperature in which she lives . . . she who suffers so much from cold. . . . She has attained a most wonderful calm. No irritation of temper, no hurry or confusion of manner ever appears for a moment.' But this was only superficial. After interviews concerning a certain, very troublesome, Miss Salisbury she often seemed about to faint. She lay on the sofa, unable to speak or eat, yet, if business was to be done, she appeared normal.

In January 1856 the Commission of Inquiry into Supplies for the British Army in the Crimea reported to Parliament. The disaster of 1854–55 was a product of indifference, stupidity and inflexible bureaucracy. Lord Panmure directed a Board to allow the accused to defend themselves. The War Office did much white-washing and Hawes* and Hall† were made KCB. Miss Nightingale wrote on 3 March 1856:

---

* Hawes, Sir Benjamin (1797–1862), Under-Secretary for War, 1857–62, incurred Miss Nightingale's wrath by opposing War Office reform, but highly respected by most; caused opening of British Museum on Sundays. Hawes was

I am in a state of chronic rage. I who saw the men come down through all that long dreadful winter, without other covering than a dirty blanket and a pair of old regimental trousers, when we knew the stores were bursting with warm clothing, living skeletons devoured by vermin, ulcerated, hopeless, speechless, dying like the Greeks as they wrapped their heads in their blankets and spoke never a word. . . . Can we hear of the promotion of the men who caused this colossal calamity, we who saw it? Would that the men could speak who died in the puddles of Calamita Bay!

Fitzgerald, the chief Purveyor in the Crimea, had written a 'Confidential Report' on Miss Nightingale to the War Office. It was an incriminating document full of lies and misrepresentation. In February 1856 she was invited by the Chief Medical Officer of the Land Transport Corps to send nurses to the Crimea, but in view of the open criticism of the Chief Medical Officer and the Purveyor she doubted if she should. Sidney Herbert was informed and of the falseness of her position due to his original omission. Other agents too were at work and on 16 March 1856, the Secretary of War's dispatch to the Commander in Chief was made public. It gave her complete authority over the nurses in the military hospitals of the army. Her triumph was complete.

Miss Nightingale arrived in the Crimea on the same day as the despatch establishing her authority. She had brought a party of nurses on the invitation of Sir John Hall. Wisely she had also brought everything they needed, for Mr Fitzgerald saw fit to deprive them of rations. She wrote to Sidney Herbert:

We have now been ten days without rations. . . . I thank

the brother-in-law of the great engineer, Brunel. With his support, Brunel constructed a prefabricated hospital of advanced design which was sent to the Crimea and proved extremely successful. A few months later the war ended.
† Hall, Sir John (1795–1866) M.D., Principal Medical Officer in Crimea, 1854–56.

God my charge has felt neither cold nor hunger. . . . I have, however, felt both. . . . During these ten days I have fed and warmed these women at my own private expense by my own private exertions. I have never been off my horse until 9 or 10 at night, except when it was too dark to ride home over these crags even with a lantern, when I have gone on foot. During the greater part of the day I have been without food necessarily, except a little brandy and water (you see I am taking to drink like my comrades of the Army). But the object of my coming has been attained and my women have neither suffered nor starved.

The hospitals were some five miles in each direction from Balaclava. But there were no roads, only tracks. She went at first on horseback. 'The extraordinary exertions Miss Nightingale imposed on herself . . . would have been perfectly incredible if not witnessed by many and well ascertained. . . . I have seen that lady stand for hours at the top of a bleak rocky mountain near the hospitals, giving her instructions while the snow was falling heavily.' She became exhausted by the long hours of riding without food. So a springless hooded baggage cart was procured. In this she henceforth travelled. This cart is now preserved in St Thomas's Hospital where it is the show-piece of the Nightingale School of Nursing.

On 29 April peace was proclaimed. On 26 July 1856, the last patient left the Barrack Hospital in Scutari and her task was ended.

The task which Miss Nightingale was sent to perform, and which, as has now been told, she performed with such distinction that she became a national and international heroine, did not satisfy this extraordinarily acute and vigorous mind. She saw clearly that the destruction of the British Army, which she had done her best to stem, was the result of the War Office's attitude to, and detached administration of, the British Army. Unless that were reformed, the Crimean campaign would have been for nought. Her views, as they developed, are set out in the thirty odd letters, many of great length, which she wrote to Sidney Herbert in the small hours of the night and in the intervals between callers by day. At the time when Mary Stanley's party arrived, she wrote:

> There is a far greater question to be agitated before the country than that of these eighty-four miserable women— eighty-five including me. This is whether the system or no system which is found adequate in time of peace but wholly inadequate to meet the exigencies of a time of war is to be left as it is—or patched up temporarily, as you give a beggar half pence—or made equal to the wants not diminishing but increasing of a time of awful pressure.

She was largely responsible for the two Commissions to which reference has already been made, the 'Sanitary Commission', and the McNeill and Tulloch 'Commission of Inquiry into the Supplies for the British Army in the Crimea'. But she was also responsible for many small reforms which in sum represented a complete change of attitude to the common soldier. He had been regarded as the scum of the earth, caring nothing but spending his wages on drink, and being utterly unfaithful to his wife, and quite unteachable. Drink and prostitutes were his needs off the battlefield.

Miss Nightingale's first two minor reforms, effected through the good offices of the Queen, have already been noted. In May 1855 she opened a small reading room for men able to walk but not to leave hospital. This was opposed by the authorities on the grounds that it would lead to indiscipline. The conduct of the men was excellent. In November 1855, in a letter thanking the Queen for a brooch designed by Prince Albert, she wrote on the causes of drunkenness in the British Army. A chief cause was the difficulty in remitting money home. The Queen sent it to the Prime Minister who laid it before the Cabinet, who were impressed with the argument. Offices were opened where money orders could be obtained and £71,000 was sent home in six months. When General Storks took command at Scutari, she found an ally. The drink shops were closed and a large recreation hut erected for the army with private funds, the Inkerman Coffee House. A second was opened in the Barracks Hospital. In each newspapers and writing material were paid for by Miss Nightingale. In the spring of 1856, four schools were opened. She wrote:

> The lectures were crowded to excess so that the men would take the door off the hut to hear. Singing classes were formed and the members allowed to sing in the Garrison Chapel. The men got up a little theatre for themselves, for which dresses and materials were lent by a private hand, and this theatre was, I believe, always perfectly orderly. Football and other games for the healthy, dominoes and chess for the sick, were in great request. . . . A more orderly population than that of the whole Command of Scutari in 1855–56, though increased by the whole of the Cavalry being sent down there for winter quarters, it is impossible to conceive.

'She taught,' said an onlooker, 'officers and officials to treat the soldiers as Christian men.'

Miss Nightingale's astonishing achievement at Scutari, duly reported in *The Times*, made her a national heroine. Her illness, her recovery, and her determination to stay at her post, continued to focus attention, respect, admiration and love for this remarkable woman. A public meeting was organised and held on 29 November 1855, with the Duke of Cambridge as chairman; it was decided to collect for a 'Nightingale Fund'. Florence's parents did not go to the meeting, but instead her mother held a reception of notabilities. Her mother wrote: 'The 29th November. The most interesting day of thy mother's life. It is very late, my child, but I cannot go to bed without telling you that your meeting has been a glorious one . . . the like has never happened before, but will, I trust, from your example, gladden the hearts of many future mothers.' Miss Nightingale replied: 'My reputation has not been a boon in my work; but if you have been pleased that is enough.'

Miss Nightingale was informed of the fund and accepted it only on condition that there was great uncertainty as to when she would employ it. The fact is that she had fallen in love again. Her first love was nursing; her second was the British Army. And she had seen her new love die before her eyes. As she prepared to leave the Crimean theatre she wrote: 'Oh my poor men: I am a bad mother to come home and leave you in your Crimean graves—73 per cent in 8 regiments in 6 months from disease alone—who thinks of that now?'

The end of the war brought great hope to her mother and sister, who wrote Aunt Mai many letters about her plans. Would she accept an official reception? Presumably now, with her work done, she would come and enjoy the fruits of her labour at home. The Government offered a man of war to take her home in state and the Mayors of Folkestone and Dover asked Mr Stafford to 'find out privately where Miss Nightingale would first touch English ground in order to rouse the whole community.' Her sister wrote that 'the whole regiments of the Coldstreams, the Grenadiers and the Fusiliers would like to meet her, or failing that they would like to send their bands to play her home wherever she might arrive, by day or night'.

On 28 July she began her journey home with Aunt Mai, travelling incognito as Mrs and Miss Smith. After spending a night in Paris and one in London with the Bermondsey nuns, she took the train northwards. She walked from the station and into her home alone and unannounced.

Chapter 7

FLORENCE NIGHTINGALE
The Tyrannical Invalid

After her return, from what in the eyes of the world had been a triumphal achievement, and the lapse of over a century makes it seem no less, Miss Nightingale's mood and behaviour were most unusual. She refused all invitations, public and private, with which she was inundated, even a reception at Chatsworth* in her honour, to which she was invited by the Duke of Devonshire; she refused to make a public appearance or make a public statement. Indeed, she tried deliberately to destroy her fame so that in two years the public assumed she was dead. She was in a state of mental turmoil. There were tears and prayers and she could be heard pacing her room at midnight. She could never forget those magnificent men in their graves in the Crimea. She wrote again and again on her blotting paper 'I can never forget'. A month after her return she wrote in a private note, 'I stand at the altar of the murdered men, and while I live I fight their cause.' But how was she to ensure that this would never happen again? It meant no less than the reform of the War Office and the administration of the British Army. It was a colossal task, and, as she saw clearly, she considered that she had two special difficulties: she was a woman, and she was a popular heroine. Any scheme which was known to emanate from her would immediately be opposed in official circles. To succeed would consume her whole self, everything else would have to be subordinated. She had not shrunk from Scutari, but

* In Derbyshire. One of the great houses of England, Seat of the Duke of Devonshire.

this was a task of a different order of magnitude and not limited by time or place.

She wrote to Lord Panmure asking for an official interview. He was in Scotland shooting grouse. He replied offering to see her later. Meanwhile 'it will be more pleasant for you to rest a little while'. Lying sick and exhausted on her couch, she wrote letter after letter to Sidney Herbert, imploring him to take action now before it was too late. He was fishing salmon in Ireland. He wrote saying her letters were overwrought and told her family that Florence's state of mind was causing him concern; they should plan some moderate occupation for her.

At the end of August she met Sidney Herbert on his return from Ireland. He was lukewarm about any reform. She was in despair. Early in September the situation was transformed by an invitation from Sir James Clark, Her Majesty's Physician. She was asked to stay at his house near Balmoral* at the express wish of the Queen. Immediately she left her sofa and sprang to work writing to all the authorities and searching all the records so that she would be able to give the Queen, and the Prince Consort, the full evidence on which to persuade them of the need for a Royal Commission. She was weak and emaciated and felt sick at the sight of food. Nevertheless, she worked non-stop, collecting and collating for four days. From Sir James Clark's house she was commanded to Balmoral. 'She put before us,' wrote the Prince in his diary that night, 'all the defects of our present military hospital system and the reforms that are needed. We are much pleased with her; she is extremely modest.' The Queen called on Miss Nightingale several times and went out driving with her alone. She was convinced and decided to ask Lord Panmure (nicknamed the Bison) to Balmoral to meet Miss Nightingale. To accelerate discussion, Miss Nightingale wrote Her Majesty a letter outlining her views on army reform which the Queen received with 'great grace' and forwarded to her minister. The interview took place on 5 October. 'You may like to know,' wrote Mr John Clark, Sir

* In Aberdeenshire. Queen Victoria's favourite Scottish residence.

James's son, 'that you fairly overcame Pan. We found him with his mane absolutely silky; and a loving sadness pervading his whole being.' On 2 November, Sidney Herbert wrote: 'I forget whether I told you that the Bison wrote to me very pleased with his interview with you. He says that he was very much surprised at your physical appearance, as I think you must have been at his. God bless you.' She obtained all she wanted. There was to be a Royal Commission whose instructions were to be drawn up according to her suggestions, and she was to be asked for a Confidential Report by Lord Panmure (War) and Lord Palmerston (Prime Minister) acting jointly. With one or two exceptions, she also got her way with the membership of the Commission, such was the charm that she had now come to exercise over Lord Panmure.

Unfortunately Lord Panmure was still being harassed by the aftermath of the previous commissions. His response to difficulty was inaction. The setting up of the Commission was delayed week after week. Miss Nightingale was distraught. In a private note she wrote:

No one can feel for the Army as I do. These people who talk to us have all fed their children on the fat of the land and dressed them in velvet and silk while we have been away. I have had to see my children dressed in a dirty blanket and an old pair of regimental trousers, and to see them fed on raw salt meat, and nine thousand of my children are lying, from causes which might have been prevented, in their forgotten graves.

Never have murdered children had a mother more determined to dedicate her life to ensure that such could never happen again. She still had her trump card. At the end of February 1857 she wrote to Sidney Herbert:

All that Lord Panmure has hitherto done (and it is just six months since I came home) has been to gain time. . . . He has broken his most solemn promise to Dr Sutherland, to me and to the Crimea Commission. And three months from this day I publish my experience of the Crimea Campaign and my suggestions for improvement, unless there has been a fair and tangible pledge by that time for reform.

This threat and other omens won the day.

On 27 April, Lord Panmure paid an official call on Miss Nightingale at the Burlington Hotel. Such was her position that Lord Panmure brought her the official Draft of the Instructions before submitting it for approval to the Queen. The War Office had submitted a list of Commissioners which would have ruined the urgency. These Miss Nightingale fought with tact but tenacity: and she won. On 5 May, the Royal Warrant was issued. A week later the Commission began work.

From the beginning Miss Nightingale was the Commission. Her rooms in the Burlington Hotel were 'the little War Office', the reformers were the 'band of brothers', and the meals they shared were 'our mess'. Miss Nightingale, Sidney Herbert and Dr Sutherland were the leaders. A letter of her mother's gives an idea of the strain on Miss Nightingale. She spent a morning at Belgrave Square coaching Sidney Herbert for the sitting the next day, and the afternoon at Highgate doing the same for Dr Sutherland,* returning home to work far into the night. Next day she set off for Highgate at 9 a.m., worked there until after dark, then went to work with Dr Farr† and did not get home till very late. Next day she left at 8.30 a.m. for Highgate, worked there until 7.30 p.m. and finding a message from Sidney Herbert, went straight off again to Belgrave Square, returning after 11 p.m. 'By Sidney Herbert's desire,' Miss Nightingale wrote in a reminiscence, 'I saw everyone of the witnesses myself and reported to him what each could tell him as a witness in public.' 'She is the mainspring of the work,' wrote Dr Sutherland to Aunt Mai in May 1857. 'Nobody who has not worked

* Sutherland, John (1808–91) M.D., 1831, sanitarian.
† Farr, William (1807–1883) F.R.S., statistician; studied medicine at Paris 1829–31; President, Statistical Society 1871–72.

with her daily could know her, could have any idea of her strength and clearness of mind, her extraordinary powers joined with her benevolence of spirit. She is one of the most gifted creatures God ever made.' Miss Nightingale herself was the most important witness. Her evidence was written and one of the Commissioners thought, 'It must prove of the most vital importance to the British soldier for ages to come.'

At the same time as she was feeding the Commission with facts, drive and incisiveness, Miss Nightingale was composing her 'Notes on Matters affecting the Health, Efficiency and Hospital Administration of the British Army' of which her evidence to the Commission was a small part. It is an enormous volume, packed with facts and figures. She used the Crimean Campaign. 'It is a complete example (history does not afford its equal) of an army after falling to the lowest ebb of disease and disaster from neglects committed, rising again to the highest state of health and efficiency from remedies applied. It is the whole experiment on a colossal scale.' She collected figures to show that even in peace time, and despite recruits being selected for physical fitness, mortality in the British Army was twice that in the population at large. 'Our soldiers enlist to death in the barracks. . . . 1500 good soldiers are as certainly killed by these neglects yearly as if they were drawn up on Salisbury Plain and shot.'

She finished the notes in July, but owing to the speed at which she had driven the Commission, she had now begun to write its report, so the Notes were only printed privately. By the end of July she saw that the report itself would solve nothing. As she wrote: 'Reports are not self-executive.' So in August, Sidney Herbert wrote to Lord Panmure outlining the main recommendations of the Commission, and the information that the disclosures about the health of the army were so sensational that public opinion would be aroused. He suggested that the government would gain in prestige by announcing the appointment of four sub-Commissions of each of which Sidney Herbert was to be chairman. These would:

(1) put the Barracks in sanitary order;
(2) found a Statistical Department for the Army;
(3) institute an Army Medical School;
(4) completely reconstruct the Army Medical Department, revise the Hospital Regulations, and draw up a new Warrant for the Promotion of Medical Officers.

In mid-August Lord Panmure accepted the suggestions. Miss Nightingale had won the first battle.

MISS NIGHTINGALE BECOMES AN INVALID

During the twelve months following her return from the Crimea, Miss Nightingale was in a highly charged emotional state. She cared deeply about success or failure. The success which was achieved was due above all to the clarity, incisiveness and vigour of her mind and to her unremitting toil. She had arrived home from the Crimea tired and thin. Subsequently she drove herself and her colleagues relentlessly; she ate and slept little. In August 1857, with the first task completed, she collapsed. The circumstances of her collapse were concerned with her mother and sister.

When Miss Nightingale returned from her visit to Scotland where she had had such productive discussions with the Queen, she took rooms in the Burlington Hotel. Her family came too. Her father soon left but her mother, Fanny, and her sister, Parthe, stayed, to enjoy being mother and sister to Miss Nightingale. 'No one,' wrote Miss Nightingale in a private note, 'has enjoyed my reputation more than my own people. . . . I was the same person who went to Harley Street and who went to the Crimea. Nothing was different except my popularity. Yet the person who went to Harley Street was to be cursed and the other blessed . . . this false popularity has made all the difference in the feelings of my family towards me.' In the family suite Miss Nightingale did all her work in her bedroom or in a little drawing-room, while her mother and sister occupied the rest of the suite, entertaining visitors and interrupting Florence as they wished. Fanny and Parthe had a carriage. Florence took a cab or an omnibus or walked, even in wind and rain. 'The whole occupation of Parthe and Mama was to lie on two sofas and tell one another not to get tired by putting flowers into water.' 'You lead a very amusing life,' they said to her. 'It is a scene worthy of Molière,' she wrote, 'where two people in tolerable and even perfect health, lie on the sofa all day, doing absolutely nothing and persuade themselves and others that they are the victims of their self-devotion for another who is dying of overwork.'

In August 1857, the heat was intense and the hotel airless. She had driven herself relentlessly over the report and was faced with unexpected extra work.* She was still plagued by Fanny and Parthe. It was in these circumstances that she collapsed. She had had enough. 'I must be alone, quite alone,' she told Parthe, 'I have not been alone for four years.' She had not eaten any solid food for four weeks and lived on tea. She was so weak that Parthe was frightened. Florence refused to go home or to be nursed. 'She took,' wrote Fanny to W.E.N., 'a sudden resolution to go to Malvern. Nothing would induce her to take anyone but George (a footman). It makes us very unhappy to think of her so forlorn and comfortless.' Dr Sutherland wrote as her physician imploring her to stay at Malvern, pointing out that the Burlington was the worst possible place for anyone in her condition 'whose blood wanted renewing'. She replied angrily.

. . . Had I lived anywhere but handy would Mr Herbert have used me? Had I not been ever at hand could he have used me? . . . Now had I lost the Report what would the health I should have 'saved' have profited me, or what would the ten years of my life have 'advantaged' me exchanged for the ten weeks this summer? Yes, you say, you might have walked, or

---

* This was concerned with a free gifts scheme to soldiers in the Crimea for which she was responsible, and for which there had been accusations of maladministration.

(b) Florence Nightingale at the age of eighty-one

3(a) Florence Nightingale in 1857 after her return from the Crimea

4 The Lady with the Lamp
Illustrated London News, 24 February 1855
'She is a "ministering angel", without any exaggeration in these hospitals, and as she glides quietly along each corridor every poor fellow's face softens at the sight of her. When all the medical officers have retired for the night and silence and darkness have settled down upon those miles of prostrate sick, she may be observed alone, with a little lamp in her hands, making her solitary rounds.'

driven, or eaten meat. Well . . . let me tell you Doctor, that after any walk or drive I sat up all night with palpitation. And the sight of animal food increased the sickness. . . . Now I have written myself into a palpitation. . . . I have been greatly harassed by seeing my poor owl lately without her head, without her life, without her talons, lying in the cage of your canary . . . and the little villain pecking at her. Now, that's me. I am lying without my head, without my claws and you all peck at me. It is *de rigueur, d'obligation*, like the saying something to one's hat when one goes into church to say to me all that has been said to me 110 times a day during the last 3 months. It is the obbligato on the violin, and the twelve violins all practise it together, like the clocks striking twelve o'clock at night all over London, till I say like Xavier Le Maistre '*Assez, je le sais, je ne le sais que trop*'.

Her father came to Malvern and reported to Fanny, 'Her days may be numbered. Her breathing betrays her moments of distress, her power to take food fails her if excited, her nights are sleepless in consequence. . . . Tis a sad tale.'

Aunt Mai was again called in. She expected to return home in a week or two, but she accompanied Florence to the Burlington Hotel at the end of September. From now on Miss Nightingale was an invalid. Mrs Woodham-Smith wrote:

She not only became an invalid; she began to exploit her ill health. From the summer of 1857 she used her illness as a weapon to protect herself from her family. The summer had discouraged Fanny. She had been ill, and she announced that her health would not permit her to 'attempt the Burlington' in the winter. Parthe, however, wrote that she proposed coming to London. Aunt Mai was told to write and tell Parthe not to come. Parthe was furious. Did Florence think her own sister was not capable of doing what was wanted for her? She insisted on coming.

Miss Nightingale's reply was to have an 'attack'. Aunt Mai

wrote in the greatest agitation. After reading Parthe's letter, Florence had been ill all night. Dr Sutherland had been much alarmed and had said he could not sleep for thinking of her. 'It was excessive hurried breathing with pain in the head and the heart.' As a result, Parthe did not come to London. W.E.N. then insisted on coming; he must see Florence and discuss her future plans. She had another 'attack', and he retreated.

It was evident that in the present state of her health, while her life, as Aunt Mai wrote, 'hung by a thread', it was too much for her to see her family. They must keep away from her.

In February 1868, Parthe wrote to say they were coming to London for the season and would stay at the Burlington. The result was another attack. They decided to stay at another hotel. Florence improved instantly.

In the summer of 1857, Sir Harry Verney, a widower, had been paying frequent visits to Florence and later that year asked her to marry him. She refused and he transferred his favours to Parthe, whom he married in the summer of 1858. Henceforth Parthe, and Fanny with her new interest, left Florence alone.

MISS NIGHTINGALE'S LIFE AS AN INVALID

Miss Nightingale, on her return to London, was convinced that she had only a few months to live. This conviction was transmitted to her immediate circle so that the 'cause' for which she struggled received a new urgency. She moved to new rooms in an annexe of the Burlington, three bedrooms and a sitting-room on one floor, a double sitting-room on the floor below. Aunt Mai shut up her house and sent her children and husband to stay with the Nightingales. Her son-in-law, the poet Arthur Hugh Clough, became Florence's slave, visiting the Burlington every day to write notes and act as a messenger, fetching and delivering the letters and reports that his mistress needed. Miss Nightingale, convinced of imminent death, arranged with him all the details of her funeral and wrote several letters to be delivered when she was dead. Sidney Herbert was assigned the sacred task of implementing the reforms. She wrote: 'You have sometimes said you were sorry you employed me. I assure you that it has kept me alive. . . . I hope you will have no chivalrous ideas of what is "due" to my "memory". The only thing that can be "due" to me is what is good for the troops.' To Parthe she gave directions for her burial. She longed to be buried in the Crimea, 'absurd as I know it to be. For they are not there.' She made a will in November 1857 in which her property was to be used to erect a model barrack. The emotional atmosphere was intensified by her concept of the perfect relationship with Aunt Mai as that of 'The Virgin Mother'. Her own maternal feeling for those she had helped was displayed.

Probably there is not a word of truth in the story of the Virgin Mary. But the deepest truth lies in the idea of the Virgin Mother. The real fathers and mothers of the human race are NOT the fathers and mothers according to the flesh. I don't know why it should be so. It 'did not ought to be so.' But it is. Perhaps it had better not be said at all. What is 'Motherhood in the Flesh'? A pretty girl meets a man and they are married. Is there any thought of the children? The children come without their consent even having been asked because it can't be helped. . . . For every one of my 18,000 children, for every one of these poor tiresome Harley Street creatures I have expended more motherly feeling and action in a week than my mother has expended for me in 37 years.

Because she had so little time, she began to work as she had never worked before. The task was now to effect the reforms recommended by the Commission. The great obstacle was the War Office itself, which would have none of it, with her two enemies, Hawes and Dr Andrew Smith, as administrative and medical heads. Miss Nightingale saw that victory depended on which side could frighten Lord Panmure more. So she instituted a press campaign in which the evidence that most deaths in the army, either in peace or war, were due to preventable disease was displayed by coloured diagrams. Miss Nightingale maintained that she had invented this device which is now such common practice. 'Our soldiers enlist to death in the barracks' was the battle cry. And it succeeded. The four sub-Commissions were set up in December 1857. 'With such ample instructions as you may guess them to be, when I tell you they were written by me.' The reforms now had great success so that in May 1858, Sir John McNeill wrote to Miss Nightingale: 'To you more than to any other man or woman alive will henceforth be due the welfare and efficiency of the British Army. I thank God that I have lived to see your success.'

Miss Nightingale's rooms, 'the little War Office', were a hive of industry. She toiled lying on the sofa of her sitting-room, seldom sitting up, rarely going out. Throughout the summer of 1858 she left the Burlington only twice for a week's cure at Malvern. She travelled by train in an invalid carriage, attended by Aunt Mai and Clough. She was carried in a chair as though she were a goddess. The stationmaster and his staff stood bare-headed and curious onlookers were pushed back as she was borne to the carriage. Miss Nightingale had become a legend.

In the summer of 1858 the Indian Mutiny broke out. Miss Nightingale was anxious to go to India to do what she had done in the Crimea, but was dissuaded by Sidney Herbert. It would have been extremely interesting to see what such a venture would have done for her health. As a result of the Mutiny, India passed to the Crown, and Miss Nightingale pressed for a Royal Sanitary Commission to do for the Indian Army what its predecessor was doing for the Army at home. In 1859 she was successful and Sidney Herbert was invited to be its chairman. Then in March the Government fell and in the following general election Lord Palmerston was returned to power. He invited Sidney Herbert to become Secretary of State for War, who wrote to Miss Nightingale:

I must write you a line to tell you I have undertaken the

Ministry of War. I have undertaken it because I believe that in certain branches of administration I can be of use, but I do not disguise from myself the severity of the task, nor the probability of my proving unequal to it. But I know you will be pleased at my being there. I will try and ride down to you to-morrow afternoon. God bless you.

This was a gross understatement. For over a year Sidney Herbert's health had been failing. He was chairman of the four reforming sub-Commissions and of the Sanitary Commission for India, and now had taken on the most exacting job of all. As Miss Nightingale expressed it: 'The War Office is a very slow office, an enormously expensive office, and one in which the Minister's intentions can be entirely negatived by all his sub-departments and those of each of the sub-departments by every other.' In consultation with Miss Nightingale a scheme for reform was prepared. Its objects were 'to simplify procedure, to abolish divided responsibility, to define clearly the duties of each head of a department and of each class of office; to hold heads responsible for their respective departments with direct communication with the Secretary of State'. Both she and Sidney Herbert felt crushed by the work they had undertaken. Miss Nightingale wrote: 'I am being worked on the treadmill.'

The British public had wished to express their appreciation of Miss Nightingale's services in the Crimea, and had subscribed £45,000. Miss Nightingale had indicated that she could not decide at once how to use it. Her decision came indirectly. In her evidence to the Royal Sanitary Commission, Miss Nightingale revealed a startling knowledge of civil as well as military hospitals. She had visited, and made notes on, nearly all. In 1859 two papers she had written on Hospital Construction were expanded and published as a book, *Notes on Hospitals*. Its thesis was that the answer to the high death rate in hospitals was not prayer or self-sacrifice but ventilation, drainage and cleanliness. It was an instant success and Miss Nightingale was flooded with requests for guidance on plans for new hospitals.

Amongst these was St Thomas's, who had also approached her to help them decide whether to sell their site to the South Eastern Railway Company for London Bridge Station, or whether they owed it to the local community to stay where they were. Miss Nightingale asked for figures, which showed that most of their patients were not of local origin. So St Thomas's moved, and the eight huge blocks connected by long draughty corridors exemplify well her 'parlour system'. Because St Thomas's had taken more of her attention than any other, and because her best nurse in the Crimea, Mrs Roberts, had come from St Thomas's, Miss Nightingale decided to establish there a school for training nurses and to endow it with the fund collected for her. The Nightingale School of Nursing was thus established in 1860. Through it came a stream of well-born, well-educated women to be trained according to the standards and ideals of Miss Nightingale. They provided Matrons for most important hospitals. Thus was nursing in Britain raised to the standard at which it has since remained, the envy of the world. The establishment of the School was preceded by the publication of *Notes on Nursing* (1859), in which Miss Nightingale not only revealed herself as a trenchant critic of the 'coxcombries of education' but as a gentle and sympathetic nurse who understood what the patient suffered and why.

The interpolation of this series of episodes into the main stream of events emphasises the extraordinary volume and variety of the contributions to reform of this distinguished invalid during a few short years. And every one of her contributions had style.

At the end of the summer of 1859 Miss Nightingale had another relapse, with fainting, breathlessness, weakness and nausea. She was unable to leave London so she took rooms in Hampstead, to which Sidney Herbert rode daily from Belgrave Square. Her mother described her: 'She would have made a beautiful sketch, lying there reclining upon pillows in a blue drifting gown, her hair so picturesquely arranged, her expression most trusting, hardly harmonising with the trenchant things she sometimes says, her sweet little hands lying there ready for action.'

Florence's life had been 'hanging by a thread' for two years now. Aunt Mai's family grew restive; they liked her and wanted her back; moreover the health of her daughter's husband, Arthur Clough, never robust, was being undermined by the demands of Miss Nightingale. So Aunt Mai's husband, Uncle Sam, did his best to get them to return. Miss Nightingale was very angry. They were necessary for the work. In October she returned to the Burlington with Aunt Mai and Clough in attendance.

SIDNEY HERBERT'S ILLNESS AND DEATH

Sidney Herbert, half-brother and heir presumptive to the Earl of Pembroke, had come to be Miss Nightingale's instrument for effecting her purpose. Handsome, rich, charming, able, and dedicated to a life of service to his country, he was the embodiment of the best in the aristocratic tradition. Florence had met the Herberts when they were all on vacation in Rome in 1847, and had formed a friendship with them, and particularly with Liz Herbert, as charming and good looking as her husband. In 1856 Sidney Herbert had found Florence the agent he needed to right the situation in the Crimea. Her success had been phenomenal. She had returned determined to reform the War Office and the conditions affecting the health of the British Soldiers, her murdered children—Sidney Herbert was cast as her *deus ex machina* to do it. And now when at last he was Secretary of State for War, and perfectly placed to carry out Miss Nightingale's reform, his health (never good) had begun to collapse. In August 1860, Miss Nightingale took rooms in Hampstead again, in order to remain in London. She was very feeble, lying in bed all day in front of open windows. Sidney Herbert, forced by pressure of work to stay in London, was weary and depressed. He complained of headaches, of weakness and nausea, the early symptoms of the renal failure from which he was to die. He rode out daily to see her but he was weary and confessed he had 'a total inability to deal with business', which Miss Nightingale regarded as weakness. 'He shrank from the Herculean task of cleansing the Augean stable.'

Sidney Herbert was in no doubt about his health. 'Every day I keep the War Office with the House of Commons is one day taken off my life.' But both his wife and Miss Nightingale would allow him no respite. Early in December he collapsed and his doctors pronounced him to be suffering from kidney disease in an advanced stage; he must drastically reduce his work. Miss Nightingale and his wife persuaded him to give up the Commons, which he loved, but to keep on the War Office, which he hated. He was to go to the House of Lords. Miss Nightingale persuaded herself and tried to persuade him that the doctors had been too gloomy. 'I hope you will not judge too hardly of yourself from these doctors' opinion,' she wrote on 8 December,

> . . . it is not true that you cannot (sometimes) absolutely mend a damaged organ, almost always keeping it comfortably going for many years, by giving Nature fair play. . . . But I do hope you won't have any vain ideas that you can be spared out of the W.O. You said yourself that there was no one to take your place—and you must know that as well as everybody else . . . I don't believe there is anything in your constitution which makes it evident that disease is getting the upper hand. On the contrary.

And yet she was too intelligent and factual to be utterly oblivious of the truth. 'I see death written in the man's face. And, when I think of the possibility of my surviving him, I am glad to feel myself declining so fast,' she wrote on 13 January 1861. That month the scheme for reform of the War Office was launched against the implacable opposition of the Permanent Under-Secretary, Sir Benjamin Hawes. Miss Nightingale saw clearly that success depended on Sidney Herbert and that he was not as strong as he should be. 'No one appreciates as I do

Mr H's great qualities. But no one feels more the defect in him of all administrative capacity in details.' In March she wrote: 'Though he says he will set about your committee as soon as ever you like, make haste, for he is like the son who said "I go and goeth not".' She and his wife drove him on. 'He is a great deal better, of that there is no doubt,' she wrote to Lady Herbert in March. In May she wrote: 'I am sure the Cid thinks "Oh she does not know how weak I feel and how much worse in general health" . . . but I do. I see it every time I see him and sorrowfully perceive that he is weaker and thinner—and yet I don't think him worse in general health, not materially worse.' In the first week of June he collapsed and wrote to Miss Nightingale on 7 June, telling her he must resign the War Office. She was furious and refused to accept his ill-health as an excuse. 'I believe you have many years of usefulness before you. I have repeated so often my view of your case—and I never felt more sure of any physical fact in my life—that I will not trouble you with writing my letters all over again.' She believed that their project to reform the War Office was wrecked. 'I consider your letter as quite final about the re-organisation of the W. O. And I promise never to speak of it again. Many women will not trouble you by breaking their hearts about the organisation of an office—that's one comfort. . . . Hawes has won. If you will not think me profane I will say "Hell hath gotten the victory".' She refused to see him or write to him further. Poor Sidney Herbert was deeply wounded. He went to face her in her old familiar room in the Burlington Hotel. She was a woman possessed, consumed with grief and rage, who refused to see him as what he was—a dying man. Later she wrote that she told him: 'A Sidney Herbert beaten by a Ben Hawes is a greater humiliation than the disaster of Scutari. No man in my day has thrown away so noble a game with all the winning cards in his hands.' On 9 July he came to say good-bye before going to Spa for a cure. He died on 2 August. His last murmur was 'Poor Florence, poor Florence, our joint work unfinished'.

Though it is perhaps going too far to say that Miss Nightingale killed Sidney Herbert, there can be no question that her actions, attitude and authority accelerated his death. Only six years before she had been the devoted humane nurse, who would have seen clearly how ill he was, and how unfair to him it would be to drive him on. The change in Miss Nightingale's personality, also expressed by her illness, was manifest in other ways. Though Sidney Herbert was the supreme instrument and victim of her purpose, he was not the only one.

Dr John Sutherland was Sanitary adviser to the Government Board of Health and received £1,500 a year. He met Miss Nightingale at Scutari, was fascinated by her, and thereafter did what she told him. After his appointment to the Sanitary Commission in 1855, he worked without remuneration. Such were the demands Miss Nightingale made that his family life was broken up. She reproved him for his slowness and untidiness. 'As for Sanitary matters—Lord help you I'm only a humbug. I know nothing about them except what I have learned from you. But you would never have found a more practical pupil,' was the only acknowledgement he ever received. And yet Mrs Sutherland adored her and was delighted to run little errands as 'Miss Nightingale's fag'.

Aunt Mai had come to Florence's rescue in Scutari after the departure of the Bracebridges, and again in 1857 to the Burlington when Florence was on her deathbed. Her husband and children became more and more irritated at Aunt Mai's continued absence from home. Uncle Sam refused to visit his wife after the summer of 1859. In the summer of 1860, her second daughter was to be married. Miss Nightingale's deathbed seemed to be a prolonged one, so Aunt Mai decided it was her duty to return home. When Miss Nightingale heard of her decision, she refused to see her or speak to her. Miss Nightingale did not forgive Aunt Mai for nearly twenty years; throughout that time they never met or corresponded. Aunt Mai's place was taken by Florence's old friend and contemporary, Miss Hilary Bonham-Carter.

Arthur Clough's health continued to deteriorate from the devotion of his spare time to performing chores for Miss Nightingale. He was peripheral to her purpose, and to him she was more sympathetic. 'I have always felt that I have been a great drag on Arthur's health and spirits, a much greater one than I should have chosen to be, if I had not promised him to die sooner.' In April 1861, he and his wife went to Greece. In November 1861 he died.

AFTER SIDNEY HERBERT'S DEATH, THE INVALID BECOMES BEDRIDDEN

Miss Nightingale was at Hampstead when she learned of Sidney Herbert's death. She was overwhelmed with anguish and despair. She returned to the Burlington Hotel where she collapsed. 'He takes my life with him,' she told W.E.N. 'My work, the object of my life, the means to do it, all in one depart with him. . . . Now not one man remains (that I can call a man) of all whom I began to work with five years ago. And I alone of all men "most deject and wretched" survive them all. I am sure I meant to have died.' Oddly enough she did not feel remorse, or in any way responsible for his death. But now he was dead he became her 'Master', whose pupil and instrument she had been when he was alive. 'I understood him as no one else,' she wrote. 'How happy widows are,' she wrote to Uncle Sam on 14 August 1861, 'because people don't write them harassing letters in the first week of their widowhood and yet I know of no widow more desolate than I.' She was intensely jealous now, of Lady Herbert, and resentful of the cold obituary notices in the daily press. The extent of her emotional disturbance was displayed in a letter to Sir John McNeill.

Before he was cold in his grave his wife, Mr Gladstone and the War Office have done nothing but harass me. . . . Twice in the first week after his death I was written to for materials for his life. Mr Gladstone was one of these as you will guess.

And he enclosed me a sketch written by *her*. There was not one word of truth in it from beginning to end!!! She represented him as having triumphed (and quoted words of his to this effect) in having effected the reorganisation of the War Office, which he died of regret for not having done. I told Mr Gladstone a little of the real truth and wrote at his request a slight sketch of what he had done. (And the week was not out before *she* wrote to me for another.) . . . This is just what I most dreaded and least asked. In fact I really would hide myself in the East of London not to do it.

However, she cared too deeply for Sidney Herbert's memory and shut herself in the Burlington for two weeks and wrote an account of his work which she had privately printed as 'Private and Confidential. Sidney Herbert—on his Services to the Army'.

After she had finished her memoir she left the Burlington for ever. Its associations, Sidney Herbert, Aunt Mai and Arthur Clough, all now departed from her, were too painful. She returned to Hampstead in despair for her reforms.

Fortunately for her, her seclusion was interrupted by an appeal for help from the Northern United States in the civil war that had broken out in April. She sent out all her memoranda, forms, statistics and evidence before the Sanitary Commission. Her writings were quoted 'largely and incessantly in medical journals as a guide to military management in the Northern States'.

In November 1861 she moved to Sir Harry Verney's house, 32 South Street, which he lent to her. She had again become very ill, but was not long left to herself. The American Civil War seemed likely to involve the United Kingdom against the North. On 3 December, Lord de Grey, the Under-Secretary for War, wrote asking if he could call on her to discuss sanitary arrangements for the troops being sent to Canada, including transport, clothing, feeding and hospitals. She at once responded, working with all her old energy and efficiency. She redrafted the instructions to the officers in charge, and these were accepted. She investigated and planned in detail transport and clothing. Her astonishing capacity for detail was unimpaired.

The Canadian expedition was a success even though war was averted. It was a turning point in her life because it was clear that her unique capability was recognised and would be used. Sidney Herbert's death was not the end of her influence with the War Office. But she was very lonely and most unhappy, and in this mood she wrote a revealing letter to her friend Clarkey in Paris:

. . . You say 'women are more sympathetic than men'. Now if I were to write a book out of my experience, I should begin, Women have no sympathy. Yours is the tradition—mine is the conviction of experience. I have never found one woman who has altered her life by one iota for me or my opinions. Now look at my experience of men.

A Statesman, past middle age, absorbed in politics for a quarter of a century, out of sympathy with me, remodels his whole life and policy—learns a science, the direst, the most technical, the most difficult, that of administration as far as it concerns the lives of men,—not, as I learned it, in the field from the living experience, but by writing dry regulations in a London room, by my sofa, with me.

This is what I call real sympathy.

Another (Alexander whom I made Director General) does very nearly the same thing. He is dead too.

Clough, a poet born if there ever was one, takes to nursing administration in the same way, for me.

I only mention three, whose whole lives were re-modelled by sympathy for me. But I could mention very many others—Farr, McNeill, Tulloch, Storks, Martin, who in a lesser degree have altered their work by my opinions. And, most wonderful of all—a man born without a soul, like Undine—Sutherland. All these elderly men.

Now just look at the degree in which women have sympathy

—as far as my experience is concerned. And my experience of women is almost as large as Europe. And it is so intimate too. I have lived and slept in the same bed with English Countesses and Prussian Bäuerinnen, with a closeness of intimacy no one ever had before. No Roman Catholic Supérieure has ever had the charge of women of the most different creeds that I have had. No woman has excited 'passions' among women more than I have.

Yet I leave no school behind me. My doctrines have taken no hold among women. Not one of my Crimean following learnt anything from me—or gave herself for one moment, after she came home, to carry out the lesson of that war, or of those hospitals. I have lived with a sister thirty years, with an aunt four or five, with a cousin two or three. Not one has altered one hour of her existence for me. Not one has read one of my books so as to be able to save me the trouble of writing or telling it all over again.

. . . A woman once told me my character would be more sympathised with by men than by women. In one sense, I don't choose to have that said. Sidney Herbert and I were together exactly like two men—exactly like him and Gladstone. And as for Clough, oh Jonathan, my brother Jonathan, my love for thee was very great, PASSING THE LOVE OF WOMEN.

Again by Christmas 1861 she was thought to be dangerously ill, more so than at any time since the summer of 1857. However, by the middle of January 1862 she was able to sit up in bed. But this illness marked a further deterioration in her health. She was unable to walk, and had to be carried if she moved from one house to another. She had become bedridden, at the age of forty-two, and did not leave her bed for six years. However, she improved slowly and her father took a furnished house for her in Chesterfield Street, Mayfair. By the spring of 1862 she was sufficiently recovered to begin work again. But she was unhappy and depressed.

As she wrote to her mother:

All the others have children or some high and inspiring interest to live for—while I have lost husband and children and all. And am left to the dreary hopeless struggle. . . . It is this desperate guerilla warfare ending in so little which makes me impatient of life. I, who could once do so much . . . I think what I have felt most during my last 3 months of extreme weakness is the not having one single person to give one inspiring word, or even one correct fact. I am glad to end a day which never can come back, gladder to end a night, gladder still to end a month.

In this revealing passage she clearly shows how, spiritually, Sidney Herbert had become her husband as the Crimean dead were her children.

However, partial success was at hand. Lord de Grey was Under-Secretary at the War Office, and had been immensely impressed by the quality of Miss Nightingale's work for the Canadian Expeditionary Force. Moreover, Lord Palmerston, Prime Minister, was an old and devoted friend. When Hawes died in May 1862, she succeeded in having the office of Permanent Under-Secretary abolished. 'He was', wrote Miss Nightingale, 'a dictator, an autocrat, irresponsible to Parliament, quite unassailable from any quarter, immovable in the middle of a (so-called) Constitutional Government and under a Secretary of State who is responsible to Parliament.' But despite her nominee, Douglas Galton, being made Assistant Under-Secretary, she failed to reorganise the War Office completely. When Sir George Lewis, the Secretary of State, died suddenly in April 1863, she succeeded in getting Lord de Grey appointed as his successor. But she never had with him the intimate relationship that she had had with Sidney Herbert.

Although she was no longer virtually in charge of the War Office, she had achieved a position of extraordinary influence. For the next four years every question affecting the health and sanitary administration of the British Army was referred to this invalid, who never left her home and seldom her bed. She had earned this influence by her passionate devotion, penetrating intellect and unflagging toil. She kept it by the same qualities. Moreover by now she had an immense knowledge of the subject matter and a unique appreciation of how Government and Civil Service worked. She drafted minutes, warrants and regulations, letters, summaries for the Minister's use, and she composed detailed instructions for those who were to implement policy. Her financial genius was equally extraordinary. The system of cost accounting which she devised for the Army Medical Services in 1860–61 was commended by the Select Committee on Estimates in 1947, who learned, to their astonishment, how long ago it had been introduced and by whom. Her contributions were immense. In one year they included: Warrant for Apothecaries, Proposals for Equipment of Military Hospitals, a Scheme for the Organisation of Hospitals for Soldiers' Wives, Proposals for the Revision of Army Rations, Warrant and Instructions for Staff Surgeons, Instructions for Treatment of Yellow Fever, Proposals for Revision of Purveying and Commissariat in the Colonies, Revised Diet Sheets for Troop-Ships, Proposals for appointments at Netley and Chatham, Instructions for Treatment of Cholera.

1861–1868 INDIA

Meanwhile she had a new task. The Royal Sanitary Commission on the Health of the Army in India had been set up in 1859. Sidney Herbert's death had delayed its beginning, so it did not sit till the summer of 1861 in London. Its members were to a large extent nominees of Miss Nightingale and it was on her that the main burden of work fell. She discovered quite early that there were no accurate figures and records on which the work of the Commission could be based. Accordingly she decided to obtain the data for herself. With the help of Sir John McNeill and Sir Charles Trevelyan, at that time Governor of

Madras, she drafted a Circular of Inquiry which was to be sent to every military station in India. She also wrote for copies of all regulations and to military and medical officers serving in India to secure their co-operation. Thus was the present science of epidemiology born, and few disciplines can have had so distinguished a parent. All the reports came to Miss Nightingale, as she lay confined to her bed. She analysed them, assisted by Dr Sutherland and Dr Farr, the latter a statistician. As she moved from house to house the reports went with her. Eventually these reports were gathered into Volume 2 of the Commission's report, nearly 1,000 pages of small print in folio.

The reports provide a detailed picture of military life in India in the years immediately before and after the Mutiny. The first official survey was not undertaken until 1872.

Miss Nightingale had done the bulk of the work but she was not a member of the Commission nor did she qualify as a witness. She was invited to submit remarks which could be incorporated into the Commission's report. These she finished by August 1862 and had a large number of copies printed at her own expense, which she sent to the Queen, Cabinet Ministers and the India Council. The observations therefore preceded the report. 'Miss Nightingale's Paper is a masterpiece in her best style, and will rile the enemy very considerably—all for his good, poor creature', said Dr Farr. 'The picture is terrible but it is all true,' wrote Sir John McNeill on 9 August 1862. 'There is no one statement from beginning to end which I feel disposed to question, and there are many which my own observation and experience enable me to confirm.'

The figures which Miss Nightingale had gathered showed that the death rate of the British Army in India had been 69 per 1000. 'It is at that expense,' wrote Miss Nightingale, 'that we have held dominion there for a century; a company out of every regiment has been sacrificed every twenty months.' The diseases were those which had killed the British Army in the Barrack Hospital at Scutari: the result of overcrowding, lack of drainage and bad water, rendered more lethal in India by

climate and the filth with which the native populations surrounded themselves. The barracks were primitive, with floors
of earth varnished with cow dung. Only two stations supplied
a chemical analysis of the water supply, one of which read like
'an intricate prescription'. At Hyderabad the water visibly
swarmed with animal life. At Bangalore, the tank used for
drinking provided the outlet for the drainage of a bazaar of
125,000 inhabitants. The Commander-in-Chief wrote: 'The
disgustingly filthy nature of the source from which the water
used at Bangalore is taken has been brought to notice scores of
times by me during the last $4\frac{1}{2}$ years but as usual nothing has
been done.' As usual, no provision was made for leisure, except
drink. 'If the facilities for washing were as great as those for
drink, our Indian army would be the cleanest body of men in
the world,' commented Miss Nightingale. Barracks were
crammed. 'At Dum Dum 554 women and 770 children', wrote
Miss Nightingale, 'were crowded together while their hus-
bands were fighting and as many died as in the Cawnpore
massacre in the Mutiny.' The facilities provided for the native
troops were even worse.

These facts quickly faced Miss Nightingale with the general
problem of health in India. 'The salvation of the Indian Army
must be brought about by sanitary measures everywhere,' she
wrote. Miss Nightingale proposed that a Sanitary Commission
should be established at the India Office. In this she failed. The
Sanitary Commission on the Health of the Army in India was a
military commission, and the civil and military administrations
kept themselves aloof. Nevertheless, she had great hopes of the
Commission for Lord de Grey was now Secretary of State for
War. Poor Miss Nightingale. Unknown to her, the Clerk of
the Commission prepared a précis of the evidence which omit-
ted the facts, her abstract of the station reports and her observations. The précis was to be the only edition on sale to the public
and to be the edition presented to the Houses of Parliament.
Only 1,100 copies of the original report had been printed and
were reserved for the Government. The type had already been

broken up. There was nothing she could do and she had to see what could be salvaged. The 1,000 reserved copies could be had on application by Members of Parliament so she wrote to those whom she knew to apply for the Blue Book. Then she published her observations. Finally, she persuaded the War Office of the India Office to allow her to rewrite the précis of evidence. She had to pay for it herself. Nothing, was done because of opposition from officials in India, until Lord Elgin, the Viceroy, died in November 1863 and was succeeded by Sir John Lawrence.

Sir John Lawrence had distinguished himself as Governor of the Punjab during the Indian Mutiny. He had called on her when she was in the middle of her work on station reports in 1861. Now he made haste to call on Miss Nightingale so that he could be instructed on Indian sanitary questions. He stayed with her for several hours, after which he declared himself heart and soul for sanitary reforms. 'Sir John Lawrence so far from considering our Report exaggerated, considers it under the mark,' she wrote in December 1863. Sanitary suggestions were to be issued for the Government of India to work on. These she wrote in 1864, assisted by Dr Sutherland and Dr Farr, and Sir Robert Rawlinson, civil engineer. It was the first sanitary code for India. Again, intention was not followed by action. The India Office pigeon-holed the suggestions.

Meanwhile, Miss Nightingale's circumstances were, on the face of it, unenviable. She was still so weak that she could not move without assistance. Moreover, between 1862 and 1865 she was constantly changing house from 9 Chesterfield Street, 32 South Street, Dover Street, Cleveland Row, Hampstead, Highgate. Finally her father bought 35 South Street in 1865, which became her last home. She had no one to supervise her household and her standards were exacting. She complained that she was lonely but she made herself deliberately so. Her family, of course, were forbidden, but even her personal friends could not see her without an appointment. Hilary Bonham-Carter was sent away in 1862 despite Clarkey's protest. 'My dearest,' she wrote on 5 February 1862, 'if she is as useful to you as a limb, why should you amputate her? . . . the thing she likes best in the world is being with you and being useful to you. . . . I agree with you, she ought to do for herself, but I am not sure her nature can bear it. I give it to you as a problem, think on it.'

On 18 October Lord Palmerston died. On that date she wrote:

He may be passing away even at this moment. He will be a great loss to us. Tho' he made a joke when asked to do the right thing, he always did it. No one else will be able to carry the things thro' the Cabinet as he did. I shall lose a powerful protector. . . . He was so much more in earnest than he appeared. He did not do himself justice.

Despite her loneliness, she would not even see her friends. 'Clarkey Mohl darling,' she wrote on 23 June 1865, 'how I should like to be able to see you, but it is quite impossible. I am sure no one ever gave up so much to live who longed so much to die as I do. It is the only credit I claim. I will live if I can, I shall be so glad if I can't.' The Queen of Holland was also refused. Garibaldi, exceptionally, was allowed an interview, but she was disappointed. 'Alas, alas, what a pity that utter impracticability,' she wrote to Harriet Martineau* on 28 April. He was noble and heroic but he was vague. He had, she wrote, no 'administrative capacity'.

She had, however, acquired the perfect friend in Benjamin Jowett. This was a friendship of intellects which made no demands because it was almost entirely conducted by correspondence.

Her first winter in her own house, that of 1865, was a miserable one. She wrote to Clarkey in March 1865: 'I just keep my place on at the War Office by doing all their dirty work for them, i.e. what they are too cowardly to do for themselves—*les lâches*.' She had been bedridden for four years and began to

---

* Martineau, Harriet (1802–1876), Leader writer of *Daily News* and *Edinburgh Review*, reformer; suffered much from illness.

have severe pain in the back. Massage gave no relief. 'Nothing did me any good,' she wrote to M. Mohl in July 1866, 'but a curious little new fangled operation of putting opium under the skin which relieves one for twenty-four hours—but does not improve the vivacity or serenity of one's intellect.' Her friendship was offered to her cats, of which she had several and about which she used to write long letters to her friends. She worked with a cat curled around her neck. Her daily companion was Dr Sutherland, who had become her slave and who became increasingly irritating to her. 'I know he is your pet aversion as he is mine,' she wrote to Clarkey in 1862. 'I find—I don't know whether you find—it more and more difficult to rouse Dr Sutherland to do the work we have to do,' she wrote to Douglas Galton in 1866. 'He has always some pond to dig in his garden. Confound that Norwood.' But though he irritated her she always saw him however ill she might be, and he acted as host in her house. In the autumn of 1865 she heard that Dr Sutherland was likely to be invited to go to Algiers, Malta and Gibraltar to investigate recent cholera epidemics. She was furious. 'For God's sake,' she wrote to Douglas Galton on 15 December 1865, 'if you can, prevent Dr Sutherland going, he is so childish that if he heard of this Gibraltar and Malta business he would instantly declare there was nothing to keep him in England.' She had pledged her word to have the Indian reports and abstracts ready before Parliament met after the Christmas vacation—'a thing I should never have done if I thought Dr Sutherland was to be sent abroad'. He was offered the appointment and he went. She was very angry, writing to Dr Farr:

Dr Sutherland has been sent to Algiers, and I have all his business besides mine to do. If it could be done I should not mind. I had just as soon wear out in two months as in two years, so the work be done. But it can't. It is just like two men going into business with a million each. The one suddenly withdraws. The other may wear himself to the bone but he can't meet the engagements which he made with two.

However, at the beginning of 1866 Sir John Lawrence had sent a dispatch to the Secretary for India requesting a reconstruction of the sanitary organisation. Alas, the dispatch was lost and not discovered till 5 May. Miss Nightingale was ill and without Dr Sutherland, but by 7 May she had written a draft scheme for the Secretary for India, Lord de Grey. The Government, however, was tottering and the Secretary harassed by party business. It was not till 11 June that Miss Nightingale received instructions to proceed further. He asked her to complete the scheme and add a survey of the sanitary question. By superhuman efforts she completed this formidable task by 19 June. Alas, this was a day too late. The government had been defeated the day before. 'I am furious to that degree,' she wrote to Douglas Galton on 23 June, 'at having lost Lord de Grey's five months at the India Office, that I am fit to blow you all to pieces with an infernal machine of my own invention.'

The Tories were now in power and Miss Nightingale felt herself excluded from government circles. Parliament rose and, at Jowett's suggestion, Miss Nightingale decided to visit her parents. She had not been home for nine years. Her mother was seventy-eight and nearly blind. Her father had had to go north to Lea Hurst, and Parthe was immersed in her own life as mistress of Claydon.

Miss Nightingale travelled to Embley in an invalid carriage and six rooms were given up to her. She worked all the time and saw no one except, occasionally, her mother. Miss Nightingale was not easy. She was exacting in her requirements and to argue with her was forbidden.

When she returned to London, Indian affairs were at a low ebb for Sir John Lawrence's proposals were far from sensible. Following a grandiose scheme, not Miss Nightingale's, for introducing female nursing on a large scale into Indian hospitals, Sir Stafford Northcote, the new Secretary of State for India, wrote suggesting he should call on her. Jowett wrote to her: 'I am delighted to hear you are casting your toils about Sir

Stafford Northcote. May I talk to you as I would to one of our undergraduates? Take care not to exaggerate to him.' After Sir Stafford had gone, Miss Nightingale wrote to Dr Sutherland: 'Well—I've won this. We are to have a department in the I.O. for Sanitary business. I don't know if he saw how afraid I was of him. For he kept his eyes tight shut all the time. And I kept mine wide open. . . . I liked Sir Stafford Northcote.' The establishment of a public health service for India now seemed at hand. 'We will make 35 South Street the India Office till this is done,' wrote Sir Bartle Frere.*

She worked as hard as she had ever done. On 23 October Northcote came to see her again, as a result of which Sir Stafford agreed to members of the Indian Sanitary Committee and consented to establish its authority as supreme in India. He also asked her to prepare a history of the whole sanitary question in India from 1859 to 1867. By the beginning of December she had completed the instructions for the Sanitary Committee, had written the history and had added a memorandum of suggestions and advice. She had also drafted an important dispatch concerning the progress that had been made consequent to the *Suggestions in regard to Sanitary Works required for the Improvement of Indian Stations* which had been sent to guide the Indian authorities as long ago as 1864. The reports received were printed as a Blue Book in 1868 as the India Office Sanitary Annual. This was the beginning of a yearly publication. By the summer of 1868 she had achieved something like her goal, but she had paid a heavy price. The months shut up in South Street, working day and night, had not improved her health. In December 1867 she collapsed completely and fled to Malvern with a little cat. She was not long there before she was called back urgently for work not concerned with India but with England.

* Frere, Sir Henry Bartle Edward, Bt. (1815–84), Member of Viceroy's Council, 1859; Governor of Bombay 1862–67; Governor of the Cape and High Commissioner of South Africa, 1877.

POOR LAW REFORM

In 1861 Miss Nightingale had been approached by William Rathbone of Liverpool who had founded district nursing and who now wanted to find the right sort of girls to do it. With her advice he founded a training school at the Royal Infirmary in Liverpool. His philanthropy took him from the homes of the poor to the workhouse infirmaries in which many were ill and died. In 1864 he began to try to reform nursing in workhouses. That year a pauper died in the Holborn Workhouse and was found at inquest to have died from neglect. Miss Nightingale used the opportunity to write to the President of the Poor Law Board. The President, Charles Villiers, who was a friend of Lord Palmerston, replied at once, called, and became a firm friend. The object was workhouse reform. Ammunition was needed and in 1865 a Form of Inquiry drawn up by Miss Nightingale was circulated to every workhouse infirmary and sick ward in the Metropolitan district.

In March 1865 a contingent of Miss Nightingale's nurses with a Matron, Miss Agnes Jones, arrived at the Liverpool Workhouse Infirmary. They had an agonising experience. Conditions were appalling. Filth, immorality and drunkenness were common both to the inmates and those who were supposed to be looking after them. As Miss Nightingale told Miss Jones: 'It is like Scutari over again.' Supported by Miss Nightingale, Miss Agnes Jones persevered and soon the experiment was a huge success. Not only were the poor sick better looked after, but the cost of doing so was reduced.

Miss Nightingale now decided that an Act of Parliament was necessary. The answers to the Forms of Inquiry revealed facts so shameful that they could not be ignored. Her scheme for reform proposed separate institutions for the sick, the insane, the incurable, and children, under a central administration and supported by a General Rate. In the spring of 1866, Charles Villiers was pressing for such a Bill when the Government fell. 'It was a cruel disappointment to me', wrote Miss Nightingale to M. Mohl on 12 July 1866, 'to see the Bill go just as I had it in my grasp. . . . Alas! alas! alas!' Villiers' successor, Gathorne Hardy, was not very friendly to Miss Nightingale. However, he introduced the Bill, the Metropolitan Poor Act, which became law in March 1867.

The winter of 1867 was a hard one. Unemployment was rife and in Liverpool an epidemic of typhus broke out. Agnes Jones got it and on 19 February she died. The loss to Miss Nightingale was catastrophic as there was no one who could replace her. 'I don't think,' she wrote to Clarkey in April 1868, 'anything in the course of my long life ever struck me so much as the deadlock we have been placed in by the death of one pupil, combined you know, with the enormous Jaw, the infinite female ink which England pours forth on "Woman's work".'

'The more chattering and noise there is about Woman's Mission the less or efficient women can we find,' she wrote to Sir John McNeill on 7 February 1865. 'It makes me mad to hear people talk about unemployed women. If they are unemployed it is because they won't work. The highest salaries given to women at all we can secure to women trained by us. But we can't find the women. They won't come.'

Meanwhile Miss Nightingale had been engaged in another venture. Part of the money raised by the Nightingale Fund had been used to establish a training school for midwives in Kings College Hospital. The school flourished until puerperal sepsis broke out in the wards following the delivery of a woman suffering from erysipelas. The school was closed. An investigation followed and revealed startling gaps in the statistics of mortality in childbirth. Miss Nightingale wrote:

There appears to have been no uniform system of record of deaths, or of the causes of death, in many institutions, and no common agreement as to the period after delivery during which deaths should be counted as due to the puerperal condition . . . the first step is to inquire, what is the real normal death rate of lying-in women? Compare the rate with the rates in establishments into which parturition cases are received in numbers. Clarify the causes of death and see if any particular cause predominates in lying-in institutions; and if so, why so? And, since the attendance on lying-in women is the widest practice in the world, these attendants should be trained; . . . decide this great question as to whether a training school for midwifery nurses can safely be conducted in any building receiving a number of parturition cases.

Despite her preoccupation with sanitary reform in India, she determined that a mass of further facts must be collected, and she began to correspond with doctors, matrons, sanitary experts and engineers. At the end of three years she had accumulated a mass of information, but by then her energy had gone. Dr Sutherland had to put the book into shape. *Introductory Notes on Lying-In Institutions*, published in 1871, advocated the use of small separate rooms to prevent the high rate of mortality, a conclusion reached independently by Sir James Simpson.* The lower mortality in cases delivered at home was due to the fact that 'however grand, or however humble, a home may be in which the birth of a child takes place, there is only one delivery in the home at one time. . . . When Waterford Institution had 8 beds in 1 room the mortality was 8 per 1,000. When the wards were moved and the number of beds reduced to 4, the mortality fell to 3·4 per 1000.'

* Simpson, Sir James Young, Bt. (1811–70), Professor of Midwifery at Edinburgh; pioneer of use of chloroform in childbirth.

Chapter 8

FLORENCE NIGHTINGALE
The Extinction of the Flame

In March 1868 Mr Gladstone became Prime Minister. His interests were far different from those of Miss Nightingale, now aged forty-eight. 'The administrative state of things here is to me unimaginable,' she wrote to M. Mohl on 10 June 1869. 'The War Office is drifting back to what it was before the Crimean War. Pauperism which concerns hundreds of thousands is just left alone. . . . One must be as miserably behind the scenes as I am to know how miserably our affairs go on.' 'What would Jesus have done', she wrote in a private note, 'if He had had to work through Pontius Pilate?'

However, in India she still had enormous influence. Her admirer, Sir John Lawrence, was succeeded by Lord Mayo, who spent an afternoon with her. 'He came to me to be coached, and with Sir Bartle Frere I gave him his Indian education.' Jowett suggested that her title should be 'Governess of the Governor of India', but Miss Nightingale preferred 'Maid of all (Dirty) Work'. A year later, the Commander-in-Chief, Lord Napier, called on her and fell under her spell. Her message was not merely sanitary reform but a new economic policy. Until people were fed they would not be fit for education. Lord Napier and she devised a complete scheme of Indian Army reform, and he asked her to write to the Viceroy: 'a letter from you would have great weight as it was you who raised public opinion in England on these subjects.' Though John Strachey*

* Strachey, Sir John (1823–1907), Anglo-Indian administrator; President of permanent sanitary commission, 1864; Chief Commissioner of Oudh, 1886.

criticised her, he was honest enough to say: 'Of the sanitary improvements in India three-fourths are due to Miss Nightingale.' However, she was not always right. She had never been to India and when she wrote a memorandum to the Government advising that windows of barracks should be kept open through the hot weather, Sir John Lawrence had to tell her that nothing on earth would induce him to issue such instructions. Meanwhile, the engineers were building barracks completely oblivious of Miss Nightingale's views. Cholera broke out and in 1870 *The Times* vociferated against the extravagance of building palaces in which soldiers died.

Miss Nightingale was losing ground on all sides, yet she hardly resisted. In the summer of 1868 she went to Lea Hurst, where she had long talks with her father on metaphysics, and whither Jowett went for a week. Jowett urged her to write and she began a treatise on the reform of the Poor Law. Her extraordinary loss of energy now became apparent. She found composition intolerable. The treatise was shortened to an article. It was corrected by Sir Harry Verney and partly by Dr Sutherland, who put it into shape and sent it to Fraser's Magazine as a note on pauperism. That summer she also asked Dr Sutherland to expand her notes into 'Notes on Lying-In Institutions'. She never touched them again.

In 1870 the Franco-Prussian War broke out and the British Red Cross Aid Society was founded. Miss Nightingale was pressed to take control but she declined. Her friends and colleagues were on the executive committee and when in 1872 Dunant founded the International Committee of the Red Cross, he said: 'Though I am known as the founder of the Red Cross and the originator of the Convention of Geneva, it is to an Englishwoman that all the honour of that Convention is due. What inspired me . . . was the work of Miss Florence Nightingale in the Crimea.' In 1872 she wrote: '1872. This year I go out of office.' Lord Mayo was assassinated and his successor, Lord Northbrook, did not consult her before he sailed.

She decided that she must leave the world and she determined to apply to St Thomas's to enter as an ordinary patient. She mentioned this to Jowett who, in 1872, wrote dissuading her. That year she decided to return to her family home. Her father was seventy-seven and her mother eighty-three, and their property was not efficiently managed. She at once became a woman of affairs. The last housekeeper had died and the household discipline had disintegrated. Miss Nightingale had to cope. 'I am so stifled by dirty anxious cares and sordid defensive business,' she wrote in a private note of August 1872. 'Like the maid of all work who has to wipe her dirty hands on her dirtier apron before she can touch clean people.' 'Oh to be turned back to this petty stagnant stifling life at Embley,' she wrote later that summer, 'I should hate myself (I do hate myself) but I should LOATHE myself, oh my God, if I could like it, find "rest" in it. Fortunately there is no rest in it, but ever increasing anxieties. *Il faut que la victime soit mise en pièces.* Oh my God!'

Jowett again came to the rescue. He suggested she should write some philosophical essays on the laws of the moral world. Two were published in 1873—'A Note of Interrogation' and 'A Sub-Note of Interrogation: What will our Religion be in 1999?' Jowett also asked her to help him in revising his translations of Plato's Dialogues, and remarked: 'You are the best critic I ever had.' He asked her to make a selection of Bible stories. In reply she wrote: 'The story of Achilles and his horses is far more fit for children than that of Balaam and his ass, which is only fit to be told to asses. The stories of Samson and of Jephthat are only fit to be told to bull dogs; and the story of Bathsheba to be told to Bathshebas. Yet we give all these stories to children as "Holy Writ".' She summarised the book of Samuel and the books of Kings as 'Witches. Harlots. Talking Asses. Asses Talking. Young Gentlemen caught by the Hair. Savage Tricks. Priests' Tales.' She began to work on a book 'Notes from Devotional Authors of the Middle Ages. Collected, Chosen and freely translated by Florence Nightingale.'

However, she still kept her finger on the pulse of the Nightingale Training School. In the spring of 1873 she could stand
Embley no longer. She returned to London and at once threw
herself into the reconstruction of the Nightingale School, setting
out clearly everything that she thought was necessary for a
nurse. She had had to bring Fanny to London, but alas Fanny's
maid and Florence's maid quarrelled and Fanny had to return
to Embley. Miss Nightingale had to return too and the dismal
round began again. In January 1874 her father died and Florence
took Fanny to Lea Hurst. Fanny was almost blind and almost
demented. In 1874 Florence wrote in a private note, watching
the shadow cast by the night-light on the wall: 'Am I she who
once stood on that Crimean height? "The Lady with a Lamp
shall stand." The lamp shows me only my utter shipwreck.' Her
friends were dying one by one, but Miss Nightingale had to
remain at home. In June 1878 she wrote to Lord Napier* that
she was 'ground to powder in the country by family affairs.
I have not had one day's rest since my father's death 4½ years
ago. . . . There is no one to do anything for the place or for
the people.' Her only relief was the Nightingale School which
she continued to control by correspondence. When Clarkey
reproached her, she wrote in 1879:

> Why do you abuse me for being here? Do you think I am
> here for my own pleasure? Do you think any part of my life
> is as I please? Do you know what have been the hardest
> years of my life? Not the Crimean War. Not the 5 years with
> Sidney Herbert at the War Office when I sometimes worked
> 22 hours a day. But the last 5 years and three quarters since
> my father's death.

At length, in 1880, Fanny died at the age of ninety-two.

Fanny's death freed Miss Nightingale at last. She became
gentler, and almost tolerant. After Uncle Sam died in 1881, she
became reconciled to Aunt Mai and they began to write to one

* Napier, Robert Cornell, First Baron Napier of Magdala (1810–90), Field
Marshal; Commander in Chief, India, 1870.

another affectionately. She became friendly with Parthe for the first time and began to visit Claydon, where a room was set aside for her. The change in her attitude is displayed in a letter to Clarkey: 'I cannot remember the time when I have not longed for death. After Sidney Herbert's death and Clough's death in 1861, 20 years ago, for years and years I used to watch for death as no sick man ever watched for the morning. It is strange that now I am bereft of all, I crave for it less. I want to do a little work, a little better, before I die.' Although her capacity for work was now only a fraction of what it had been, her opportunities were still immense. She still wielded enormous influence in India where her old friend, Lord de Grey, now the Marquis of Ripon, was appointed Viceroy in 1880. He was a reformer much to her taste. One of the reforms that he backed was the Ilbert Bill, which would give Indian magistrates power to try and sentence Europeans. This aroused immense opposition, even hysteria, amongst the Europeans in India and certain sections at home. Miss Nightingale threw her whole personality into the fight for reform, interviewing officials, Members of Parliament, journalists and those setting out to govern India. The campaign was not entirely successful. Lord Ripon resigned in 1885. The Marquis of Dufferin succeeded him and called on Miss Nightingale to receive from her his Indian education. His term of office ended in 1891. On his way home he wrote to Miss Nightingale: 'Among the first persons whose hands I hope to come and kiss will be yours.' He was succeeded by the Marquis of Lansdowne, a close friend of Jowett, who also came to call on her and subsequently corresponded regularly.

In 1891 she began her final crusade for India, proposing a method of taxation which would provide a pure water supply and drainage. There was an enormous correspondence terminating in the Government's answer in 1894 that they could not accept her suggestion but would press the claim of sanitation upon local governments and upon administrations as opportunity offered.

She became friendly with Gordon, whose religious altruism and missionary zeal for under-privileged people had so much in common with hers.

Miss Nightingale's health steadily improved. She went out for drives in the park when the weather was fine. She visited Claydon. In 1882 she made her first personal visit to the Nightingale School of Nursing, and in November of that year she went with Sir Harry Verney to Victoria Station to see the return of the guards from the first Egyptian Campaign. A few days later she attended a review, and on 4 December was present at the opening of the Law Courts, where Queen Victoria spoke to her and expressed her pleasure that Miss Nightingale looked so well. Her appearance had changed and at seventy-five she had become a rather stout but very dignified old lady with a large, good-humoured face. Parthe became crippled in 1883 and Miss Nightingale became an essential part of the Claydon household. In 1890 Parthe died. Thereafter Miss Nightingale took charge of Sir Harry. She was often at Claydon and when she went to London she wrote to him daily. When they were both in London he called on her every morning. Her health was so far improved that she was able occasionally to take a small stroll walking on his arm. He died in 1894 and afterwards her visits to Claydon became infrequent.

Nursing continued to flourish and large numbers of important hospitals, including St Mary's Paddington, the Westminster Hospital, Edinburgh Royal Infirmary, Leeds Infirmary, Liverpool Infirmary, and the Royal Victoria Hospital, Netley, had Nightingale-trained Matrons. In 1887 Queen Victoria decided to devote most of the money which had been presented to her by the women of England as a Jubilee gift to the cause of nursing the sick poor in their own homes by means of trained nurses, for which Miss Nightingale had done so much. Alas, Miss Nightingale had a setback. She had for thirty years raised 'nursing from the sink' by training of character. 'You cannot select the good from the inferior by any test or system of examination,' she wrote in 1890. '. . . Most of all and first of all must the moral qualifications be made to stand pre-eminent in estimation.' The British Nurses' Association put forward a scheme to qualify nurses by examination. Miss Nightingale opposed it. In 1889 the British Nurses' Association published its policy, including an application for a Royal Charter and the formation of a Register. Princess Christian accepted its presidency. For the next four years the battle was on. After much debate and controversy, the Association petitioned the Queen through Princess Christian for a Royal Charter. The petition was referred to a special committee of the Privy Council and was heard in 1892. They got their Charter but not a register. At least Miss Nightingale had not lost her last great battle.

1887 was also Miss Nightingale's jubilee, for it was in 1837 that the voices had first called her and she had completed her fifty years of service. She wrote Aunt Mai:

Dearest Aunt Mai—thinking of you always, grieved for your sufferings, hoping you have still to enjoy. In this month 34 years ago you lodged me in Harley Street (Aug. 12) and in this month 31 years ago you returned me to England from Scutari (Aug. 7). And in this month 30 years ago the first Royal Commission was finished (Aug. 7). And since then 30 years of work often cut to pieces but never destroyed. God bless you! In this month 26 years ago Sidney Herbert died, after five years of work for us (Aug. 2). And in this month 24 years ago the work of the second Royal Commission (India) was finished. And in this month, this year, my powers seem all to have failed and old age set in.

Her friends died one by one. In 1889 Aunt Mai, in 1891 Dr Sutherland, and in 1893 Jowett.

Jowett's relationship with Miss Nightingale had been an extraordinary one. They had corresponded regularly and at great length. He had influenced her not only in decisions but in interest and in directing her activities. She had helped him with his Dialogues of Plato. She also drew up a special form

of Daily Service for Balliol Chapel but the project was dis-
allowed by the Bishop of Oxford. Eventually she asked him for
a singular favour—to come and administer to her the Holy
Sacrament. He complied. Afterwards he regarded the occasion
as a solemn event in his life, but her pleasure was not unmixed.
She remarked one day: 'He comes to me, and he talks to me as
though I were someone else.' His last letter to her said: 'Fare
you well . . . How large a part has your life been of my
life'.

In 1894 Sir Harry Verney died at the age of ninety-three, and
six months later Mr Shore Nightingale.* These were great
griefs to her. The old lady had changed a great deal since her
productive years. 'There is so much to live for,' she wrote on
12 May 1895, 'I have lost much in failures and disappointments,
as well as in grief, but do you know, life is more precious to me
now in my old age.' She continued for a while to visit Claydon
but after 1896 she never left South Street and thereafter spent
the whole of her life in her bedroom.

The old invalid was now more than ever a legend. She continued to be consulted by the War Office and to receive all
papers on Indian sanitary matters. In 1897, the Queen's Jubilee
was celebrated, amongst other things, by a Victorian era exhibi-
tion. This included a section representing the progress of trained
nursing, planned around Miss Nightingale. One of the organisers
was an exceptionally pretty and charming woman, Lady
Wantage. She succeeded in borrowing Miss Nightingale's bust
by Steell, and the Crimean carriage, which had been discovered
in pieces in an Embley farmhouse. It later went to the Nightingale Training School. The relics were treated with extraordinary respect. Flowers were laid daily in front of the bust
and old soldiers had been seen to come forward and kiss the
carriage. Miss Nightingale was disgusted. She wrote to Shore
Nightingale's son:

* Aunt Mai's son. Heir to W.E.N.'s estate.

Now I must ask you about my bust. (Here I stop to utter a great many bad words not fit to put on paper. I also utter a pious wish that the bust may be smashed.) I should not have remembered it but that I am told that somebody came every day to bedeck it with fresh flowers. I utter a pious wish that that person may be—saved. . . . What is to be done about the bust?

In 1884 her sight began to trouble her. After that it gradually failed until in 1901 she became blind. At the same time her mind began to fail. For some years she managed to keep up appearances. Before an important visitor arrived she would be coached about him. Lord Kitchener called in 1903; he remarked how astonishingly Miss Nightingale in her old age followed what was going on. At length in 1906 the India Office had to be told that it was useless to send papers on sanitary matters to Miss Nightingale for she no longer had the power to under-stand them. In 1907 she was awarded the Order of Merit by Edward VII. No ceremony was possible. By Royal Command the Order was brought to her home. Sir Douglas Dawson, after a short speech, handed the insignia to Miss Nightingale. Lying there in bed she dimly recognised what had happened. 'Too kind, too kind,' she murmured. The next year she received the free-dom of the City of London. The Roll of Honour was brought to her bedside and her hand was guided to write 'F.N.' but it was clear she did not understand or know what she was signing. In May 1910 was the Jubilee of the foundation of the Nightin-gale Training School. To mark the occasion a meeting was held in Carnegie Hall in New York, where Mr Choate delivered a eulogy on Miss Nightingale. By that time there were over 1,000 training schools for nurses in the United States.

Miss Nightingale was now conscious only at intervals and on 13 August 1910 she fell asleep never to wake again. Her will was immense, dividing her possessions in meticulous detail. In it she expressed the wish that 'no memorial whatever should mark the place where lies my Mortal Coil'. If this were impossible she wanted her body 'to be carried to the nearest convenient burial ground accompanied by not more than two persons without trappings'. She also directed that her body should be given 'for dissection or post-mortem examination for the purposes of Medical Science'. This was not done, but in deference to her wishes a national funeral and burial in Westminster Abbey was declined. Her coffin was carried by six sergeants to the family grave at East Wellow. A line on the family tombstone reads: 'F.N. Born 1820. Died 1910'.

Chapter 9

MISS NIGHTINGALE'S ILLNESS

The popular view of Miss Nightingale's illness was expressed by Barbara Harmelink.[8]

> After the war was over, Florence was never the same again. The two years of overwork soon turned her into a permanent invalid. For nearly all the rest of her ninety years she lived in bed, working with her pen, and giving orders to her small group of devoted fellow workers.

In his great biography of 1913, Cook[1] wrote:

> The history of her case points, I am told, to dilatation of the heart and neurasthenia. The former of these states, though often distressing in its symptoms, yields, I understand, to drugs and rest; and for the atonic condition of the nervous system, which is called neurasthenia, and which is often the product of excessive stress upon the functions of the mind, complete rest is also often a remedy.

And this was probably the diagnosis of the doctors. Florence chose Malvern for the same reason as Darwin, because of the reputed efficacy of its water cure for such complaints as neurasthenia.

Fortunately medicine has advanced a great deal since those early days. Overwork was certainly not the cause of her illness. Nor does neurasthenia have any precise meaning. Reviewed in the light of our present day understanding, Miss Nightingale's case is not only a beautiful example of a psychoneurosis with a purpose, it is also one of intense human interest.

Acute dilatation of the heart is a rare condition which develops during attacks of rapid heart action due to paroxysmal tachycardia. This Miss Nightingale did not have since it never lasts very long. A rapid heart action was, as I have related in Chapter 2, erroneously regarded as a sign of organic heart disease. I have related how this erroneous belief, and the fear it engendered in doctor and patient, was a common cause of a cardiac neurosis (Da Costa's syndrome*). We have also seen that rest in bed is the most effective method to ensure the persistence of the malady. This is precisely what happened to Miss Nightingale at Malvern in 1857 when her doctor told her she was not to get up until her pulse had become normal, so she never did. Da Costa's syndrome was not described till the American Civil War and was virtually unknown in Britain until the 1914–18 war. It was recognised as a psychoneurosis in 1941.

Neurasthenia was thus described in the textbook I used as a student:[9]

A condition of weakness or exhaustion of the nervous system, giving rise to various forms of mental and bodily inefficiency. The term covers an ill-defined, motley group of symptoms, which may be either general and the expression of derangement of the entire system, or local, limited to certain organs; hence the terms cerebral, spinal, cardiac, and gastric neurasthenia.

The name neurasthenia has now disappeared from textbooks of medicine. It is recognised as being one of the manifestations of a psychoneurosis.

A psychoneurosis would thus represent the translation into modern terms of the diagnosis made at the time by Florence Nightingale's doctors. It would be hard to find a more classical case. Attacks of breathlessness, palpitation, giddiness, induced by unwanted events or events that cause apprehension, are typical, and this is what Miss Nightingale displayed. Her illness

* See Chapter 2.

prevented her from seeing unwanted visitors, and her mother and sister in particular, who would have wasted so much of her time. But her illness allowed her to do a prodigious amount of work from her invalid couch, and to tyrannise those with whom she worked and who became, in effect, her devoted slaves: Sidney Herbert, Arthur Clough, Dr Sutherland, Aunt Mai. It also allowed her to live till she was ninety, for it had no organic basis. The function or purpose of the illness was perhaps even more clearly apparent in Miss Nightingale than in Mr Darwin.

The cause of Miss Nightingale's illness was the unresolved conflict between what she wanted to do, namely to help the less fortunate, and the circumstances preventing her from doing so, chiefly her mother and sister. So when young she was ill frequently, though intermittently, and particularly when thwarted by her family. From the moment she took charge of No. 1 Harley Street, until the end of the Crimean War, her illnesses were purely organic, and her physical and mental resistance was truly remarkable. She was doing what she wanted to do, and that consumed her whole being. She began to be ill after her return, when those who had the power were indifferent or opposed to her wishes. And she became an invalid when nothing else sufficed to protect her against the irrelevant and time squandering intrusions of her mother and sister. When her passion for reform was spent, she began to get up and go out. Both the cause and the purpose of her illness had passed, though the habit lingered.

The illnesses were very similar in their nature and function in Mr Darwin and Miss Nightingale, though one was a man, the other a woman. In each case the illness was protective. But in Mr Darwin's case his family was the first line of defence, the illness the tactical reserve. In Miss Nightingale's case the family was the danger, her illness was the front line and the reserve. It was her all. Apart from the purpose of their illnesses, there are also striking similarities between the two eminent patients. Each was financially independent. Each had a willing band of servitors; in Mr Darwin's case his family; in Miss Nightingale's her admirers and friends. Each had a consuming mission.

The history of Miss Nightingale's illness may be conveniently divided into five periods. In each her mission was in a different phase of development; and the forces that threatened its success were equally different.

The first phase ended in Harley Street. In this phase Miss Nightingale was spoken to for the first time by God. She knew what she did not want to do. She did not want to shine in society. And that was the sole ambition of her mother and elder sister. What she wanted to do, nay what it was her duty to do, gradually became clear. It was to be a nurse. How degrading, thought her mother and sister. And so they did everything to frustrate her desire. On each occasion Florence became ill. So she did when the object of her only passionate attachment, Marianne Nicholson, severed their friendship. Moreover, she refused two offers of marriage from most desirable suitors. Her family's fury again made her ill.

Scenes and illness succeeded one another till Miss Nightingale decided to leave home in 1853. She was then thirty-three. Florence's agony of mind found its outlet in daydreams, which she recorded frequently from her early twenties and which she ceased to record when she was occupied and happy.

The second phase of Miss Nightingale's life began on 12 August 1853, when she took up residence at No. 1 Harley Street. It ended on the evening when she entered the door at Lea Hurst on her return from the Crimea. This period is sharply defined, to the day, almost to the minute. In it Miss Nightingale did exactly what she wanted, or, as she might have said, what God had called her to do. And she did it without interference from her family.

During this period she revealed her strength; her strength of character, of intellect and of constitution. Few people, male or female, could have worked so intensely, so long, so efficiently and in the face of such confusion, indifference and implacable opposition as she did in the Crimea. She had earned the right to say 'I have now had all that this climate can give, Crimean fever, Dysentery, Rheumatism and believe myself thoroughly acclimatised and ready to stand out the war with any man.' Despite the long hours of meticulous and devoted work needed for organising and implementing the care of the sick today, tomorrow and next week, she had the time and energy to write long, detailed and immensely lucid letters to Sidney Herbert describing and analysing the defects of the system and out-lining plans to put them right. After she had nearly died from Crimean fever (typhoid or typhus) she refused convalescence abroad, and was back at her work after only a few weeks. Reviewing her astonishing resilience and fortitude during the Crimean campaign, it would be hard to imagine anyone less likely to become a psychological invalid, which she was to become within a few months of her return home.

The third period lasted from her return in 1856 to her collapse on 11 August 1857.

Miss Nightingale returned from the Crimea apparently a changed woman. It was not that she was a national heroine; that disgusted her. It was not that she was thin and pale and worn, and that her hair had not yet grown since it had been shorn as she hovered on the brink of death from Crimean fever. The whole personality seemed to have altered. She had fallen in love, not as a bride with her husband, but as a mother with her children. The children were the soldiers she had nursed; and her children had been murdered. She vibrated with anger and vengeance. But it was creative vengeance; her passion was not for destruction but for reform. As she wrote soon after her return:

We can do no more for those who have suffered and died in their country's service. They need our help no longer; their spirits are with God who gave them. It remains for us to strive that their sufferings may not have been endured in vain —to endeavour so to learn from experience as to lessen such sufferings in the future by forethought and management.

Miss Nightingale became ill within a month of her return.

She was deeply disturbed and bitterly frustrated by the fact that Sidney Herbert and Lord Panmure eluded her, the two instruments who alone could carry out her wishes, and exorcise the spirit that had taken hold of her. She suffered from palpitations, found difficulty in breathing and felt sick at the sight of food. Not unnaturally this illness was attributed to her exertion and privations in the Crimea, and she was urged to rest. She could not and would not, and she was right, for these were the symptoms not of overwork but of anxiety, and she was indeed anxious lest her urgent purpose should fail.

We have seen how Miss Nightingale's skill, tact, and persistence led to the setting up of the Royal Sanitary Commission, how she was prepared ruthlessly to exploit her position as a national heroine unless she got what she wanted, and without delay, and how her prodigious efforts in collecting, sifting and analysing evidence and in draughtsmanship led to the report being finished in a year. All this had to be done, but the natural difficulties were immensely augmented by Fanny and Parthe, who insisted on sharing the apartment in which she lived and worked, not to help, but to obstruct, and share in the reflection of their illustrious daughter and sister. Having driven herself mercilessly without rest it is not surprising that she collapsed in August 1857 when the report was finished. She must have realised that she could never work under such circumstances again. Her illness took her to Malvern. She was so breathless that both her father and Dr Sutherland thought the end was near. The Malvern doctor found her heart was beating rapidly. He told her she must lie down and not get up till her heart had become normal. From that time to the end of her life, another fifty-three years, she lived in bed, on a couch, or in a wheel chair, and this a little more than a year after those astonishing feats of endurance in the Crimea.

The fourth phase, that of the invalid slave driver, lasted from 1857 to 1868.

There can be little doubt that the Malvern doctor's instructions, and Dr Sutherland's fear for her life, frightened Miss

Nightingale, not of death but of death before her task was over. Affairs took on a new urgency. Not only must she do everything to preserve herself, but she must get back to work and make sure that others worked as hard as she did. So Dr Sutherland was made to come to Malvern and work with her while she was ill in bed.

After her return to the Burlington Hotel with Aunt Mai in September 1857, Parthe insisted on joining her. Florence at once became extremely ill. From now on she had an attack whenever her mother, sister or father threatened to come and visit her. In Dr Sutherland's words 'it was excessive hurried breathing with pain in the head and heart'. She had at last found the instrument to protect herself from the irritating trivialities imposed by her family and which interfered so gravely with her work.

Her illness also solved other problems. As she had been ordered to remain lying down till her pulse settled, she was confined to her bedroom and the couch in her sitting-room. She could not go out and visit the people with whom she was working. They had to come to her. Moreover because it was now apparent that an unwelcome visitor would bring on an attack, all visits had to be by appointment and such was her delicate health that some could not be arranged at all. This enabled her to plan her time so that she could use it in the way she desired and in that way only. And so we have the extraordinary incident of one of her oldest friends, Clarkey, being refused admittance as well as the formidable personage of Mr Gladstone. In fact the friendships were from now on largely kept alive by correspondence, much to the gain of posterity.

Her illness proved an invaluable ally in another and most important respect. Her life was thought to hang upon a thread, and she could hope to live only a few months at most. And so all her projects assumed an even greater urgency. She worked with great concentration and efficiency for some sixteen hours a day. She expected her colleagues and helpers to do likewise. And such was the magic of her legend and the power of her personality that they did. Whether or not she hurried Sidney Herbert and Arthur Clough to the grave, it certainly seemed like it.

Not only did she act like a slave driver, her whole personality changed, in that direction. She had been an autocratic exacting leader of women and men in the Crimea, but she had been gentle and compassionate as every soldier knew. How different was the tyrant who sent her faithful Sidney Herbert away to die with such cruel words.

Poor faithful Aunt Mai was excommunicated for twenty years because she had been inconsiderate enough, after three years as Miss Nightingale's slave, or 'Virgin Mother', to accede to her family's request that she should return home to prepare for her daughter's wedding. The recipient of Queen Victoria's brooch seemed to have forgotten its inscription 'Blessed are the Merciful'.

It was thus to the use she made of her psychoneurosis that this unique woman owed her remarkable output of informed, lucid, trenchant, and ruthlessly logical books, reports, papers, memoranda, instructions, recommendations, which resulted in the transformation of the War Office, the British Army, the Indian Army, sanitation, hospitals, nursing, the Poor Law, and the beginning of the scientific discipline of epidemiology and statistics. And all this was done by an invalid, mostly bedridden, in twelve years.

The last phase, that of the extinction of the fire, began about 1868.

As we saw in the last chapter, something of great moment happened to Miss Nightingale between 1866 and 1868. In 1866, though bedridden, she was writing with her accustomed venom and vigour. She not only supplied the ideas, initiative and drive, she also wrote all the memoranda, instructions, drafts, terms of reference, and other documents which were the instruments through which her policy was formulated and put into effect. After 1868, she wrote nothing of major importance that was new. Her writing was largely done for her by Dr

Sutherland. She was busy, she was important, she had immense influence and used it, but her volcanic quality had gone. What had happened? Four explanations may be considered.

The first is that Miss Nightingale, having worked so hard and for so long, had simply exhausted her reserves of energy. Such an event is by no means uncommon in creative workers, artists, scientists, poets and novelists. It is less common in those 'with fire in their belly', that is those who are driven by some passionate desire or impulse, unless that passion has achieved its purpose or been extinguished. Such was Miss Nightingale's intellectual acuity, that I find it difficult to believe that she could have persuaded herself that the progress made between 1856 and 1868 was so spectacular that it made effort on her part unnecessary at anything like its previous intensity.

The second possibility is that this was a consequence of chemistry; that between these dates Miss Nightingale experienced the menopause or change of life, and that her personality changed with it. It is not possible to prove or disprove this hypothesis, which must be regarded as plausible. Nevertheless, it is fair to say that modern medicine is not so prone as was medicine a century ago to assign such great importance to this event. It was too often used as a convenient explanation for effects which have subsequently been shown to have a different cause.

The third possibility is that this change was due to an external event of great impact and lasting importance. Is it possible that after 1868 Miss Nightingale became a habitual taker of opium or morphine, in other words, a morphine addict? No hint of this occurs in any of her letters or in any of the biographical material so far studied, at least to my knowledge. But it is by no means impossible. She had, as we have seen on p. 149, been exposed to morphine and she had enjoyed it. Moreover, the reason for which she received morphine, for undiagnosed and persistent pain, has subsequently proved to be one of the commonest methods of initiation. For the state of mind induced by the injection is so alluring and euphoric, that if the cause is still present when the effects wear off, the case for repetition, and indefinite repetition, is very strong. The number of repetitions required to produce addiction varies greatly from one person to another. One lady doctor of my acquaintance received three injections of morphine for renal colic and told me she would have loved to go on. Another had morphine by mouth twice a day for a month for severe leg pain produced by a prolapsed intervertebral disc. The disc was removed, the pain went, and her desire for morphine was utterly extinguished.

Nowadays, doctors at least know the risk and are forewarned. In Miss Nightingale's day, the risk was far less well known, and hence less appreciated. Amongst the great creative writers here considered, Elizabeth Barrett long was, and Mary Baker Eddy became, partly dependent on it. Two very great doctors of her period became morphine addicts, and yet maintained their eminence and their secret, Sir William Gowers* and W. S. Halsted.† Alethea Hayter has shown how common the morphine habit was in poets and novelists of the nineteenth century.

Perhaps the most likely explanation of the extinction of Miss Nightingale's extraordinary capacity for literary composition is that the conflict which caused her psychoneurosis had become less intense. In one respect it certainly had. In the summer of 1868 she spent three months at Lea Hurst with her family, the first time for twelve years. That autumn she wrote to M. Mohl: 'I am becoming quite a tame beast, fit for a lady to ride or drive, as horse dealers say of their most vicious brutes.' From this time on she continued to meet her mother and sister. The relationship was perhaps not a cordial one but at least she saw them from time to time.

I have mentioned several times in this account that Miss

---

* 'As narrated to the Osler Club of London in 1927 by Dr James Collier, Physician to the National Hospital, Queen Square.'
† Halsted, William Stewart (1852–1922), First Professor of Surgery at Johns Hopkins, 1890. Had previously perfected technique of operating with local or regional anaesthesia by cocaine, a drug to which he became addicted. In the course of his 'cure', morphine was substituted for cocaine.

Nightingale's personality seemed to change after her return from the Crimea. Dr Whitty has suggested to me that it was not her personality that changed, it was the circumstances surrounding that personality. It is commonly believed that the two great motive powers in human behaviour are love and hate, and that these frequently co-exist. Florence's love was the health of common people, as expressed in nursing and the British soldier; her hate was for her mother and sister who prevented or threatened to prevent the fulfilment of her love. Hence that astonishing period of her life beginning when she left home for Harley Street and ending in her return from the Crimea, when her love was virtually unopposed. In this vein, the ending of Florence's extraordinary energy and drive, and the improvement of her illness, may be seen as due to her family having become, in her mother's old age and her sister's marriage, powerless to stand between her and her love, for which in any case, perhaps, passion was nearly spent. Also, in the same vein, the contrast between the merciful nurse in the Crimea and the merciless hounder of Sidney Herbert to his death was not so great as it seemed. For the British soldier personified the object of her (maternal) love, while Sidney Herbert was the broken instrument of her purpose. The more I reflect on it, the more this idea commends itself to me.

The sudden decline in Miss Nightingale's powers occurred about 1868. Its cause has been discussed but not solved. What is clear is that the old passion was spent. From now on she had less need of her illness, and so it improved. The improvement became particularly conspicuous in 1880 when her mother's death removed the last threat to her way of life.

The strange fantasy of her relationship with her co-workers had ended. Sidney Herbert who, in her view, belonged to her more than to his wife, Arthur Clough for whom 'her love exceeded the love of women' were dead; Aunt Mai, the 'Virgin Mother', had gone. A similar fantasy never recurred. The longing for death persisted in her letters for some years. But at length that perished too. In her old age she wanted to hold on to life, which she succeeded in doing for some years more.

She continued to live the life of an invalid till she died. No doubt she had got into the habit, and it was easier that way. Moreover, her illness had served her well and it is hard to part with an old friend. But it also contributed to her legend. The 'Lady of the Lamp' was a more romantic figure in the form of an elderly invalid recluse, whose influence was known to be immense, than it would have been had that person been constantly in evidence.

And her illness continued to serve her cause nearly as faithfully in old age. Though she started nothing new, she never lost her interest in, and good will for, her creations. Perhaps the elderly invalid whom new Viceroys of India came to consult (by appointment of course), and to whom the War Office and India Office sent the relevant papers, exerted more influence than she would have done had she been like everybody else. And the memory of that fury who did all her work from her bed was not easily erased.

Oddly enough, Miss Nightingale's illness has never excited the interest or controversy that Charles Darwin's did. I know of no publications on it, though Zachary Cope recognised it as a psychoneurosis.[2] And yet her illness was much more severe and disabling than Darwin's. Nor do I know of any publications on it by Freud's disciples. The part played by her mother would make it possible to fit the illness into the framework of the Oedipus complex. But unfortunately her father's visits also provoked attacks. Moreover such a hypothesis does not explain, as the one advanced here does, nearly all the features of her illness. Its explanatory value is an important function of a hypothesis. In this respect, the Freudian interpretation is of even less help in Miss Nightingale's case than it was in Mr Darwin's.

Two other peculiarities of Miss Nightingale's character deserve notice. She lived in a world emphatically dominated by the male: her activities seemed again and again to show that she was a better man than their best. Moreover she achieved her ends by making men work for her, by dominating them by force and clarity of her ideas, by her ruthless persistence and efficiency. She gave battle and won. Where they had failed, she strikingly succeeded. Her tendency towards masculinity was displayed in another way: in the David and Jonathan picture that she herself painted of her relationship with Sidney Herbert and Arthur Clough; and in her repeated attachments to attractive young women whose love was repaid with the demands of a slave-driver, tinged with contempt. And her greatest passion seems to have been for Marianne Nicholson.

Had Miss Nightingale been alive today and had she been diagnosed as I have suggested, presumably her doctor would have called in a psychiatrist, either when she was ill in Malvern or soon after her return to London. There would have been long interviews, perhaps deeper therapy, even psychoanalysis. Had this been successful, the conflicts would have been exposed and neatly tucked away so that her illness disappeared. She would have become able to move in society again, like other 'normal' people. She would have undoubtedly found good works to do and done them. But we can be sure that we should not have been given the long succession of new facts, and the reforms based on them, that flowed from the invalid's couch. Which would have given more satisfaction to Miss Nightingale and which gave most to the world?

Of one thing I am quite sure, I should not have liked to be the doctor who tried to explain to Miss Nightingale the nature of her illness.*

* See p. 128 for her reply to Dr Sutherland's attempt to advise her.

Chapter 10

A NEW THEME

Many creative artists, painters and musicians have gone through a period of great turmoil and torment of mind before producing a masterpiece. The Agony in the Garden of Gethsemane was a necessary prelude to Christ's sacrifice on Calvary. Such disturbances of the mind may be regarded as part of the act of creation, in that this turmoil provides the drive or the directive, or both, for what happens subsequently.

When I was young, I had three vicarious experiences of this kind. All were minor, and it would perhaps be stretching a point to call them illnesses. One of my friends at Cambridge was exceptionally well favoured. He was a brilliant scholar, an excellent games player, good looking, and generally liked by seniors and contemporaries. In his second year he changed utterly; he became withdrawn; he no longer laughed; his work and games suffered. He was not, seemingly, physically ill; he was disturbed. In his third year he became his old, gay, charming and very active self. But he was now a sincere convert to Communism. This was my first and vicarious experience of religious conversion. To him, I have no doubt, it meant a great liberation of soul. And it was in the withdrawn, depressive phase that the conversion happened.

I was a more distant witness of a similar process in J. B. S. Haldane. He consulted me professionally about his heart. His case at that time was not unlike that of Darwin and Florence Nightingale. I explained the origin of his symptoms to him, and the view that I took of them and him. I did not see him again for some years, when I met him socially. I asked him about his health. He said, 'I have had no further trouble since I provisionally accepted the Marxist hypothesis.'

My third experience was with my old chief, Sir Thomas

Lewis, to whom I personally owe an enormous debt. When Lewis was working out a problem he was almost maniacal. Until the experiments were finished and the results obtained and written up to the point of reaching at least a tentative conclusion, Lewis was happy, tireless, and brooking no opposition. But when that phase was over, and whilst he was groping for a new problem, he was a different man, depressed, sulky, and irritable. He found fault with everything and everybody until a chance observation or a chance remark sparked off a new idea or a new experiment, and then he was back to his happy, productive phase. I had little doubt at the time, and subsequently have not had occasion to change my views, that the withdrawn, unhappy, phase was just as important to Lewis's scientific creativity as the active phase. For it was only in the aimless phase that Lewis was at all accessible to new ideas; in the active phase he had neither the time nor the patience.

But the best-known example of a seemingly disturbed mind leading to great events is the romantic, if somewhat shadowy, figure of Joan of Arc.

The story of Jeanne d'Arc is well known. She was born in 1412, the youngest of five children of a well-to-do peasant Domrémy, on the borders of Champagne and Lorraine. She received no formal education, could neither read nor write, and was employed partly in the house and partly as a shepherdess. She was intensely pious and deeply disturbed by the ill-success of France, then engaged in the Hundred Years War with England. When she was thirteen she heard a supernatural voice accompanied by a bright light from the direction of the church; the voice bade her to be of good conduct. The girl was frightened until she realised that the voice came from Heaven. From then on, the visions became more frequent, definite and urgent. St Michael, dressed as a knight, and attended by St Margaret and St Catherine, bade her to go to France where she would deliver Orleans. This she set out to do. She eventually succeeded in securing an audience with the Dauphin, whom she picked out at once, though he was clad so as to be indistinguishable from the rest. She declared that she had a divine mission, that she would proclaim him the true king and heir of France, and that she would lead his armies to eject the English from France. She succeeded in relieving the siege of Orleans, which was regarded as a miracle and proof of her divine mission. She had the courage and resolution to lead the Dauphin and his small army through enemy-held territory to Rheims, where he was crowned as Charles VII, King of France. Alas, Charles lacked resolution and was badly advised. The Maid was wounded in a sortie, captured by the Burgundians, sold to the English, tried as a witch, convicted, and burnt at the stake in the market place at Rouen in 1431, protesting her innocence and the veracity of her voices.

My difficulty with Jeanne d'Arc is one of interpretation. Attitudes of mind were so different in her age to ours. Nowadays the hearing of voices and the seeing of visions as definite as were those seen by the Maid are regarded as evidence of some mental disorder, in fact, of a psychosis. I remember vividly when, as a student, this was explained to me, and illustrative patients demonstrated, I wondered how long the Old Testament Prophets and indeed Christ himself would have survived outside a mental institution in the present age. Miss Nightingale, whose sanity was beyond doubt, held that God had spoken to her four times in her life (see p. 100).

Jeanne was undoubtedly inspired and her inspiration was infectious enough to galvanise an irresolute monarch and dispirited troops. And no doubt her inspiration came to her suddenly (as it did to Darwin, see p. 62) and in a series of revelations. Perhaps these were a little embroidered in the mind of a pious, fanatically nationalist, and ill-educated adolescent. The problem is one about which psychiatrists, historians, theologians and philosophers will be able to argue to the end of time. All I can do is to pose it.

John and Isobel-Ann Butterfield have analysed her case as

thoroughly as medieval records allow, and suggest that Joan was suffering from a tumour, probably a tuberculoma, of the temporo-sphenoidal region of the brain.[1] 'Hearing voices' and 'seeing faces' are sometimes the only features of such a disease.

These sketches serve as an introduction to the more substantial characters shortly to be described. All of them display the same type of relationship. Each subject was afflicted with a psychoneurosis, the attempted self-cure of which produced the ideas and the energy to establish those ideas that made him or her famous. This process was given the name mental catharsis by Joseph Breuer,* to explain what a young woman with a hysterical paralysis had discovered in herself. When she talked freely about her affliction and how it began, she was temporarily cured. In using this term, Breuer tried to bring concepts of mental disease into line with concepts then common about the nature and cure of physical disease. Much of physical disease was then thought to be due to poisoning of the blood by means of waste substances that accumulated in the bowel. Accordingly, most diseases were treated by ritual purging or catharsis. The practice was still current when I was a young doctor forty-five years ago, and, indeed, lingers today. What Breuer meant by his term mental catharsis was a process by which the mind was purged of what was disturbing it. Nowadays we believe that psychoneurosis is, in general, the result of a conflict between a wish and its fulfilment. The more intense the desire, and the more completely it is frustrated, the more severe the psychoneurosis. If by some process the forces opposing the desire can be removed, or materially reduced, then the psychoneurosis may be cured.

There seems to be an important difference between the process as it is generated within the patient's own mind, and as it is induced from without. In every case known to me where a great creative work has resulted, the solution to the conflict has originated in the subject's own mind. The method of bringing peace of mind from without through the confessional has long

* See p. 209.

been used by the Roman Catholic Church. A similar method, using a different technique, underlies contemporary psychotherapy. Neither of these externally induced methods of clearing the mind results in an act of creation. This is not surprising. As any eager, curious child or adolescent knows, there is all the difference in the world between discovering something for oneself and being shown it. In one the mind is active, in the other, passive. Exceptional works require exceptional mental activity. This can only arise from within the mind. It can so arise in the course of resolving a conflict. Where this happens a vast flow of psychic energy previously pent up may be released and find its direction. This seems to be what happened in the subjects who follow. The role of psychological illness in the creative process is quite different in these subjects from what it was in Charles Darwin and Florence Nightingale. Of the two, I suspect that the role we are now considering is the more important.

Chapter 11

MARY BAKER EDDY

My second example of a psychological illness as an essential part of the creative process is Mary Baker Eddy. The case is clear cut, but unfortunately Mrs Eddy in her later years was given to over-dramatising her own role in the course of events. Thus Mrs Eddy's own reminiscences[1-6] differ seriously from scholarly accounts based on contemporary evidence.[7-11]

Mary Morse Baker was born in 1821 at Bow near Concord in New Hampshire. She was the youngest of six children of Mark Baker and his wife Abigail Barnard Ambrose. Both her parents claimed descent from English settlers in Massachusetts in the seventeenth century. Her father's farm was about 500 acres, but was even then becoming unproductive. His sons refused to work on it and so he gave it up when Mary was fifteen and moved to Sanbornton Bridge (now Tilton), a small town near-by. Mark was fairly well-to-do, and was known as 'the squire'. Mary was small and delicate, but rather pretty, with very striking blue eyes. She was often ill, suffering, amongst other things, from seizures which were judged to be hysterical by the local physician.[7] Because of her health she was an irregular attender at school, though she read a good deal, especially her Bible. She studied some Greek, Latin, and possibly Hebrew, with her brother, who graduated in Law from Dartmouth College, where he was Phi Beta Kappa. He seemed destined for a distinguished career in politics at the time of his early death. She also wrote poems, several of which were published in the local paper. From an early age she was in fierce conflict with her father, a stern and uncompromising Calvinist, who enjoyed predicting hell-fire and eternal damnation. When thwarted Mary would go into a tantrum. At the age of twelve, she tells us, she declared war on the paternal doctrine of predestination.

At the age of seventeen, she expressed reservations on Calvin's doctrine, which almost led to her exclusion from the Tilton Congregational Church. When Mary was growing up, religious training and exercises were as much a part of the regimen as eating and drinking. New Hampshire, and its neighbour Vermont, saw the birth of several new and peculiar sects. Within a few miles of her home, colonies of Shakers practised their strange cult. Joseph Smith was born fifty miles away, and received the tablets from which he translated the Book of Mormon in the neighbouring upper New York State. Spiritualism and mesmerism were widely discussed and the Bakers' family doctor tried to treat Mary's probably hysterical seizures by suggestion, without much success.

At the age of twenty-two, Mary married George Washington Glover, a friend of her elder brother. He had settled as a builder in Charleston, South Carolina. He owned slaves and Mary was then, and remained afterwards, a fierce abolitionist. Within the year Glover died of yellow fever, and Mary moved back to her father's house to give birth to her only child, named George Washington Glover after his father. Following the birth she was very ill and the child was sent to a wet nurse. Her husband's death, her arduous journey from Carolina to New Hampshire, the difficulties of childbirth, aided no doubt by her father's cool reception, led to an illness from which she was slow to recover. Baby George was cared for by the hired girl, Mahala Sanborn, daughter of the local blacksmith. To make a living, Mary had tried teaching, but without success, and she became destitute, entirely dependent on her father and a married sister. When Mary's son was four years old, her mother died and her father married again. It was decided that Mary's son would have to be sent away. Mary moved to her sister's house where she quickly became an invalid, suffering from a 'spinal weakness which caused spasmodic seizures followed by prostration which amounted to a complete nervous collapse'. To calm her, her father would rock her in his arms like a baby, while her sister had her rocked by a farm hand in a large cradle.

Relief came after nine years of this unhappy widowhood when, aged thirty-two, she married Dr Daniel Patterson, an itinerant dentist and homeopathist. He was a big, handsome, vulgar man, lavish in his attention to women and with a taste for ostentation which led him to carry his silk hat and kid gloves into remote country villages. They lived for a time in North Groton, where little George Washington Glover was established with his old nurse, but the reunion was not to his mother's taste, and she and her husband moved to Rumney, another small New Hampshire village. The son removed with his foster parents to Minnesota. She did not see her son again till he was thirty-four years old. They were poor and Dr Patterson was often absent. She was usually ill. After her husband had been injudicious enough to fall into the hands of the Confederates when visiting the battlefield of Bull Run, and to spend two years in a southern gaol, Mary moved back to her sister's house as a helpless invalid. She had to be carried up and down stairs.

She determined to consult Dr Phineas Parkhurst Quimby of Portland, Maine, who had achieved fame by some remarkable cures. Quimby had started life as a clock mender but had learned the technique of hypnotism from Charles Poyen, a Frenchman who visited Belfast, Maine. Quimby had been led to abandon mesmerism by a remarkable experience. He employed a youth named Lucius Burkmar. When thrown into a trance he responded to Quimby's slightest suggestions and even, Quimby believed, to his unvoiced thoughts. Quimby believed himself to be suffering from kidney trouble. Lucius looked into him and saw a piece three inches long separated from one of his kidneys, to which it was connected only by a slender thread. Quimby asked him if there was any chance of recovery. 'Yes,' said Lucius, 'I can put the piece on so that it will grow and you will get well.' He then put his hand on the doctor and said he had united the pieces, and from that day Quimby had no more trouble. Quimby was dissatisfied with the explanation. 'The absurdity of his remedies,' he wrote, 'made me doubt the fact that my kidneys were diseased. . . . I concluded . . . that when he said he could cure me he drew on his own mind; and the idea was so absurd that the disease vanished by the absurdity of the cure.'[9] So he abandoned mesmerism and devoted himself entirely to mental healing. He would sit down opposite the patient, put his hands on the patient's head, and explain the mental character of the disease. He said: 'The explanation is the cure'; thus arriving at a similar conclusion to Freud, though by very different means.

In order to satisfy the curiosity of his patients, Quimby began to write out his ideas in two manuscript volumes, 'Christ or Science' and 'Questions and Answers'.

Bates and Dittemore give this account of Quimby's ideas:

The guiding thread of Quimby's speculations was his endeavour to surmount the obstacles incident to his initial belief that all disease is mental. One obvious objection to such a view arises from the sufferings of children who yet have no notion of the nature of their illness. Quimby met this difficulty by the hypothesis of an unconscious mind which assimilates the suggestions of others without lifting them into consciousness. He was here upon the track of one of the most fruitful conceptions of modern psychology, but, characteristically, he did not follow it beyond his immediate need, which was merely to establish the power of mental suggestion, conscious and unconscious, and to differentiate between good and bad suggestions. Hence he did not follow up the distinction between the conscious and the unconscious, but turned to another line of approach. In this he distinguished between 'mind', embracing unconscious thought, normal physical sensations, and the ideas arising from these, and 'intelligence', embracing higher powers of insight and intuitition. The former, he held, belonged to 'the natural man', the latter to 'the spiritual man'. The natural man, deceived by his physical senses, holds all manner of erroneous 'beliefs', 'opinions', or 'knowledge' (Quimby not differentiating among the three), including the belief in physical disease. The spiritual man, with spiritual sense active in telepathy and clairvoyance, attains to the divine principle of Wisdom and knows that there is no such thing as physical disease. This knowledge of the essentially spiritual nature of man and reality Quimby called 'Truth' or 'Science' or 'Christian Science'.[9]

Reports of Quimby's remarkable cures and his equally remarkable ideas were published from time to time in the New England papers and during 1860-1 references to them were frequent. The lonely Mrs Patterson, avid reader as she was, undoubtedly came across them. In September 1860 the *Portland Evening Courier* reported the cure of a case remarkably like hers, of a woman ill with spinal disease who had not taken a step for five years but who walked four miles within two weeks of her first visit to Quimby. In February 1862 the *Portland Advertiser* carried an article by Quimby in which he said:

I deny disease as a truth, but admit it as a deception, started like all other stories without any foundation and handed down from generation to generation till the people believe it. My way of curing convinces him (the patient) that he has been deceived; and if I succeed I cure him.

In May 1862 Mrs Patterson wrote to Quimby asking him to come to Rumney to see her. She stated that she had been ill for six years 'with spinal inflammation and its train of sufferings—gastric and bilious' and she had confidence in his philosophy and that she feared she would die unless he could save her. He could not leave his huge practice, so eventually she made the journey and on 10 October 1862 she arrived in Portland so feeble that she had to be helped up the steps to Quimby's office in the International Hotel.

Quimby sat down beside her to get into the sympathetic and clairvoyant relation with her nature which he called rapport. Gazing fixedly into her eyes he told her, as he had told others, that she was held in bondage by the opinions of her family and physicians, and that her animal spirit was reflecting its grief upon her body and calling it spinal disease. After wetting his hands he rubbed her head, declaring that in this manner he imparted healthy electricity. He suggested that 'she let go the burden of pain just as she would have done had morphine been administered'. The relief was no doubt tremendous. 'She was set free from the excruciating pain of years. Quimby himself was amazed at her sudden healing; no less was he amazed at the interpretation she immediately placed upon it, that it had been accomplished by Quimby's mediatorship between herself and God.'[4]

Quimby effected a remarkable cure. Moreover he recruited an ardent disciple. She stayed three weeks, during which time she hardly left his side. He answered her questions and allowed her free access to his manuscripts. On 7 November the *Portland Courier* contained a long commentary on her case in which she said:

Three weeks since I quitted my nurse and sick room en route for Portland. The belief of my recovery had died out of the hearts of those who were most anxious for it. With this mental and physical depression I first visited P. P. Quimby; and in less than one week from that time I ascended by a stairway of one hundred and eighty two steps to the dome of the City Hall and am improving ad infinitum. To the most subtle reasoning such a proof coupled too as it is with numberless similar ones demonstrates his power to heal. Now for a brief analysis of his power.

Is it spiritualism? Listen to the words of wisdom, 'Believe in God; believe also in me; or believe me for the very work's sake.' Now, then, his works are but the result of superior wisdom, which can demonstrate a science not understood; hence it were a doubtful proceeding not to believe him for the work's sake. Well, then, he denies that his power to heal the sick is borrowed from the spirits of this or another world; and let us take the Scriptures for proof. 'A kingdom divided against itself cannot stand.' Now, then, can he receive the friendly aid of the disenthralled spirit, while he rejects the faith of the solemn mystic who crosses the threshold of the dark unknown to conjure up from the vasty deep the awestruck spirit of some invisible squaw ?*

Again, is it by animal magnetism that he heals the sick ? Let us examine. I have employed electro-magnetism and animal magnetism, and for a brief interval have felt relief, from the equilibrium which I fancied was restored to an exhausted system or by a diffusion of concentrated action. But in no instance did I get rid of a return of all my ailments, because I had not been helped out of the error in which opinions involved us. My operator believed in disease, independent of the mind; hence I could not be wiser than my master. But now I can see dimly at first, and only as trees walking, the great principle which underlies Dr Quimby's faith and works; and just in proportion to my right perception of truth is my recovery. The truth which he opposes to the error of giving intelligence to matter and placing pain where it never placed itself, if received understandingly, changes the currents of the system to their normal action; and the mechanism of the body goes on undisturbed. That this is a science capable of demonstration, becomes clear to the minds of those patients who reason upon the process of their cure. The truth which he establishes in the patient cures him (although he may be wholly unconscious thereof); and the body, which is full of light, is no longer in disease. At present I am too much in error to elucidate the truth, and can touch only the keynote for the master hand to wake the harmony. May it be in essays, instead of notes! say I. After all, this is a very spiritual doctrine; but the eternal years of God are with it, and it must stand firm as the rock of ages. And to many a poor sufferer may it be found, as by me, 'the shadow of a great rock in a weary land'.[9]

* Referring to the 'little Indian guide' who even yet seems useful in spiritualistic seances.

As was her wont she also wrote a poem.

She returned to her sister Abigail at Sanbornton Bridge a healthy woman. She continued to correspond with Quimby and sought his help when she felt one of her old spells coming on. She visited Portland again in 1864 and on this occasion stayed two months, spending every afternoon in his office and later writing down what she had learned during the day. She took away a copy of 'Questions and Answers'. She went to visit another patient at Warren, Maine, and began to try out her own powers as a faith healer, and to lecture publicly on the Quimby art.

Quimby died in 1866 and she wrote this poem:

Lines on the Death of Dr P. P. Quimby, Who Healed with Truth that Christ Taught in Contradistinction of all Isms.

> Did sackcloth clothe the sun and day grow night,
> All matter mourn the hour with dewy eyes,
> When Truth, receding from our mortal sight,
> Had paid to error her last sacrifice?
>
> Can we forget the power that gave us life?
> Shall we forget the wisdom of its way?
> Then ask me not amid this mortal strife—
> This keenest pang of animated clay—
>
> To mourn him less; to mourn him more were just
> If to his memory 'twere a tribute given
> For every solemn, sacred, earnest trust
> Delivered to us ere he rose to heaven.
>
> Heaven but the happiness of that calm soul
> Growing in stature to the throne of God;
> Rest should reward him who hath made us whole,
> Seeking, though tremblers, where his footsteps trod.

Lynn, 22 January 1866   MARY M. PATTERSON[9]

Nothing could be more characteristic of Mrs Eddy's later

ingratitude and utter disregard for truth than the statements she made during and after the controversy as to her debt to Quimby. She wrote:

About the year 1862, while the author of this work was at Dr Vail's Hydropathic Institute in New Hampshire, this occurred: A patient considered incurable left that institution, and in a few weeks returned apparently well, having been healed, as he informed the patients, by one Mr P. P. Quimby, of Portland, Maine.

After much consultation among ourselves, and a struggle with pride, the author, in company with several other patients, left the water-cure, *en route* for the aforesaid doctor in Portland. He proved to be a magnetic practitioner. His treatment seemed at first to relieve her, but signally failed in healing her case.

Having practised homœopathy, it never occurred to the author to learn his practice, but she did ask him how manipulation could benefit the sick. He answered kindly and squarely, in substance, 'Because it conveys *electricity* to them.' That was the sum of what he taught her of his medical profession. . . .

After treating his patients Mr Quimby would retire to an anteroom and write at his desk. I had a curiosity to know if he had indited anything pathological relative to his patients, and asked if I could see his pennings on my case. He immediately presented them. I read the copy in his presence and returned it to him. The composition was commonplace . . . it was not at all metaphysical or scientific. . . . He was neither a scholar nor a metaphysician. I never heard him say that matter was not as real as Mind, or that electricity was not as potential or remedial, or allude to God as the divine Principle of all healing. He certainly had advanced views of his own, but they commingled error with truth, and were not Science. . . .

It was after Mr Quimby's death that I discovered, in 1866, the momentous facts relating to Mind and its superiority over matter, and named my discovery Christian Science.[3]

Her husband reappeared while Quimby was effecting her cure, and she joined him. Eventually he set up as a dentist in Lynn, Massachusetts. On 3 February 1866, the Lynn *Reporter* contained this:

Mrs Mary Patterson of Swampscott fell upon the ice near the corner of Market and Oxford streets on Thursday evening and was severely injured. She was taken up in an insensible condition, and carried into the residence of S. M. Bubbier, Esq., nearby, where she was kindly cared for during the night. Dr Cushing, who was called, found her injuries to be internal and of a severe nature, inducing spasms and internal suffering. She was removed to her home in Swampscott yesterday afternoon, though in a very critical condition.

Her physician believed her to be suffering from concussion, and possibly a spinal dislocation. He administered morphine and had her taken by sleigh to her home. On the third day she sent those who were in her room away and opened her Bible. Her eyes fell on the account of the healing of a palsied man by Christ.* She wrote:

It was to me a revelation of Truth. The last chord of Truth, healing as of old. I caught this consciously from the Divine Harmony. The miracles recorded in the Bible which had before seemed to me supernatural, grew divinely natural and apprehensible. Adoringly I discerned the principle of His holy heroism and Christian example on the cross when he refused to drink the vinegar and the gall, a preparation of poppy or aconite, to allay the tortures of the crucifixion.[13]

In this exalted state she rose from her bed, dressed, and walked into the parlour where a clergyman and a few friends had gathered, thinking it might be for the last words on earth of the sufferer, who they believed was dying. Mary Baker had

* Matthew IX, 1–8.

5 The first known daguerreotype of Mary Baker Eddy, formerly in the possession of her friend, Belle Peabody Brown

(b) Freud, 1906, aged fifty

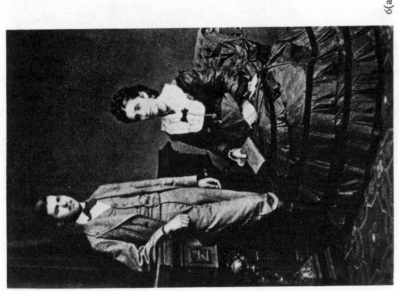

6(a) Freud, aged sixteen, with his mother

more than experienced a cure. She had received a revelation for which she had been preparing herself. She herself wrote:[9]

In the year 1866 I discovered the Christ Science, or divine laws of Life, and named it Christian Science. God had been graciously fitting me, during many years, for the reception of a final revelation of the absolute divine 'Principle of scientific being and healing'. When apparently near the confines of mortal existence, standing already within the shadow of the death valley, I learned these truths in divine Science: that all real being is in God, the divine Mind, and that Life, Truth, and Love are all-powerful and ever-present; that the opposite of Truth,—called error, sin, sickness, disease, death,—is the false testimony of false material sense—of life in matter; that this false sense evolves, in belief, a subjective state of mortal mind which this same so-called mind names *matter*, thereby shutting out the true sense of Spirit.*[1]

Soon after this episode, the dentist eloped with the daughter of a wealthy citizen, who had employed his services professionally. He never came back and gradually sank in social status. Seven years later Mrs Eddy was able to secure a divorce for desertion. She resumed her former name of Mrs Glover. Having separated from her husband, lost her father, and quarrelled with her sister, she was, at the age of forty-five, in desperate straits with no means of earning a livelihood. Referring to these years she later wrote: 'I then withdrew from society about three years—to ponder my mission, to search the Scriptures, to

* Such was Mary's version of the origin of Christian Science. However, she always had a tendency to 'gild the lily' and in later life, when this was written, her accounts differed seriously from the facts. According to Dr Cushing, who attended her, and other evidence collected by Milmine, Dakin, and Bates and Dittermore, the course of events was much more prosaic. However, if we remove the melodrama, Mary's account may not be wholly wrong. But certainly the idea had been implanted by Quimby and had been growing in her mind steadily as she wrote and finally completed the first edition of *Science and Health*.

find the Science of Mind.' She sought a livelihood from teaching and practising what she called a new system of healing, based largely on Quimby's methods, her clientele being mostly among spiritualists.

In 1870 she set up practice in Lynn, Massachusetts, with a young man who described himself as Dr Kennedy. He soon had a profitable practice while she taught and wrote. Within two and a half years, when they separated, she was able to buy 8 Broad Street, Lynn, later a shrine for her followers. Her first students paid a hundred dollars for their lessons. Subsequently the fee was raised to three hundred dollars for twelve lessons. This fee, she afterwards said, greatly troubled her, but 'a strange providence' finally led her to accept it. Her manuscripts, which she gave to her students, no longer bore Quimby's name, but her own. Slowly in the top floor of her house she composed her book *Science and Health*, which was published in 1875. Only a thousand copies were printed and these were paid for in advance by two of her students. The impact of this book has been truly remarkable considering how poorly educated a person was its author. Her thesis was briefly this.

Eternal mind is the source of all being. There is no matter. What the five senses report are only beliefs of mortal mind. Disease is caused by mind alone. Science is the wisdom of the Eternal Mind revealed through Jesus Christ who taught the power of Mind to overcome the illusions of sin, sickness and death. Hence the appropriateness of calling metaphysical science 'Christian Science'.

That *Science and Health* owed something to Quimby cannot be doubted. But there can be no doubt that it was Mary Baker's forceful mind to which the concept in its entirety was due. The glowing assurance that mind working in harmony with the Eternal could triumph over bodily infirmities often brought comfort where logic would have failed. In later years she and her followers laid special emphasis on the unreality of evil holding that sin was primarily wrong thinking. It thus made a strong appeal to those who believe in eternal goodness. This has without doubt been a factor in its remarkable success in attracting adherents.

The force of Mrs Eddy's personality was displayed by the apparent ease with which she recruited servitors. A substitute for Kennedy was found in Daniel H. Spofford, one of her students and an ardent admirer who became her first sales manager. And then on New Years Day 1877 she surprised everyone by marrying Asa Gilbert Eddy, agent for a sewing machine manufacturer and many years her junior. She was then fifty-six. On the wedding certificate both their ages were given as forty. He was an insignificant little man, in poor health, whom Mary had cured and converted. Within a year Spofford was exiled in disgrace, the Christian Scientists' association having notified him that he had been expelled for immorality. What the author of *Science and Health* meant by immorality was malicious animal magnetism, a process akin to mesmerism by which evil-minded persons could produce misfortune or disease.* A paranoid fear of this was to pursue her all her life. To protect her from this, in later life members of her household were ordered to concentrate their minds on warding off the evil which she vaguely feared or specifically mentioned.[10]

Eddy was useful in several ways. He was a prop against malicious animal magnetism. But he also helped his wife to tackle the question of copyright of *Science and Health*. He saw to it that the second and third editions were properly launched; that the authoress obtained her royalties; that she was protected

* It was the fashion in the late nineteenth century to explain the unknown by the known. It was known that magnets were surrounded by lines of force demonstrable by iron filings and other means. It was presumed that hypnotism or mesmerism was an analogous process, so it was called animal magnetism. Mrs Eddy supposed that the forces could be exerted over long distances. Her religion was based on the power of mind over matter. She benefited mankind through the agency of the instructions given in Christian Science. She supposed that her enemies tried to harm her through the forces projected from their own minds. This was the meaning of malicious animal magnetism.

from piracy, and that the sacred text was preserved from adulteration. Finally, he was a Boston man with a circle of acquaintances through which Mrs Eddy was asked to lecture in the metropolis. She dressed well (in black) and her clear musical voice and the general appeal of her subject brought large audiences.

In 1876 the informal group of her students, who called themselves Christian Scientists, formed the Christian Scientists' Association and in 1879 gained a charter as The Church of Christ Scientist. The membership was small for many years and so weakened by dissensions that the Eddys decided to move from Lynn to Boston. She had previously secured a charter for the Massachusetts Metaphysical College, and this moved with them to Columbus Avenue, Boston, in 1882. Mrs Eddy was its regular instructor.

However, the affairs of the new religion and its foundress did not progress without interruptions. Mary became increasingly paranoid. She was also very ambitious and extremely shrewd. No rivals could be tolerated to share her intellectual, material and religious property, or her ascendency. As each appeared he was cast out from the church by being accused of malicious animal magnetism (M.A.M.). Mesmerism and head rubbing, which had first formed part of Quimby's practice, were examples, but no proof was needed. Kennedy was the first to be so treated, Spofford followed, and so on until at the end of her life it was her most devoted and loyal disciple, Augusta Stetson, who had founded the New York branch and had the temerity to propose building a bigger church than the mother church in Boston. There were innumerable law suits, six in 1878 alone. Even little Dr Eddy was gaoled for allegedly contriving the murder of Spofford, but was judged 'not guilty'.

When she found that the original Christian Science Church was getting out of hand for lack of her personal supervision, she closed it, dissolved the congregation, and wound up its affairs. Her decision was unquestioned. 'No sooner were my views made known than the proper measures were adopted to carry them out, the votes passing without a dissenting voice.' The Metaphysical College was also brought to an abrupt end. The Reverend Mother, 'Professor of Obstetrics, Metaphysics and Christian Science', was no longer equal to the exertion of teaching. Without her, a centre of orthodoxy might develop into a cradle of heresies. The Reverend Mother informed the world that she dreaded the 'unprecedented popularity' of her college, that there was a danger of its being 'placed on earthly pinnacles', and that the time had come 'wherein the great need is for more of the spirit instead of the letter, and *Science and Health* is adapted to work this result'. She observed:

A Primary Class student richly imbued with the spirit of Christ, is a better healer and teacher than a Normal Class student who partakes less of God's love. After having received instruction in a Primary Class from me, or a loyal student, and afterwards studied thoroughly *Science and Health*, a student can enter upon the gospel work of teaching Christian Science, and so fulfil the command of Christ. But before entering this field of labour he must have studied the latest editions of my works, be a good Bible scholar and a consecrated Christian.[2]

The latest editions of her works then cost three dollars each.

Soon after their removal to Boston, Asa Eddy's health began to fail. Mary was certain he was a victim of malicious magnetism. His condition became so serious that Mary actually called in a physician, Dr R. Noyes, a graduate of Dartmouth Medical School, who diagnosed organic disease of the heart, a diagnosis confirmed by necropsy after his death in June 1882. Despite the evidence to the contrary, Mary made known her belief that her husband had died of 'mesmeric poisoning', mentally administered by one of her former students, a malpractitioner who had been heard to say that 'he would follow us to the grave'.

After Asa Eddy's death, her family affairs were, to say the least, unusual. Her son, George Washington Glover, had vanished into the Middle West, where he had been at one time encouraged to believe that his mother was dead. Soon after Asa's death, she began to employ Calvin A. Frye, a young machinist from Lawrence, Massachusetts, who had been her student and was now a loyal Christian Scientist. From 1882 until her death, he served as steward, secretary, book-keeper, and footman. Then came in 1888 Dr Ebenezer Johnson Foster, a homœopathic physician of Waterbury, Vermont, who had been a student at the Metaphysical College. In November of that year he was formally adopted as a son, taking the name of Ebenezer J. Foster Eddy. Frye and Foster Eddy accompanied her when she moved to Concord. Foster Eddy was dismissed in 1906, but Frye remained with her till the end. It is to his diary that we owe details of her later life and illnesses.

In 1883 the *Journal of Christian Science* began publication with Mary B. Glover Eddy as editor and chief contributor. *Science and Health* appeared in edition after edition. The sixteenth was prepared by Rev. James Henry Wiggins, a former Unitarian minister, who improved its literary style conspicuously. The royalties, never less than a dollar a volume, amounted to $19,000 by 1895 and $50,000 a year by 1900. In 1888 Mrs Eddy moved into 385 Commonwealth Avenue, Boston, which cost $40,000. In that year too Mrs Eddy received an extraordinary welcome at the third annual convention of Christian Scientists in Chicago, when the whole audience rose to greet her, and after her lecture scores of believers pressed forward to touch the hem of her garment. However, she had become tired of students and next spring moved to Concord, New Hampshire. 'Our dear Mother in God,' wrote the *Journal*, 'withdraws herself from our midst and goes up into the Mount for higher communings.'* But she maintained her decisive influence on affairs. First she acquired the ground in Boston and set up the organisation which built and managed The First Church of Christ Scientist, of which Mrs Eddy was 'Pastor Emeritus'. Despite the fact that she visited Boston only four times in the succeeding nineteen years, she never lost her

* Concord is approximately 400 ft above sea-level.

firm grip on affairs, ruthlessly suppressing rivals or doubters. Her son, adopted son and nephew tried to acquire control of her fortune by bringing a legal action to prove she was of unsound mind. They were defeated. The new religion prospered. When she died, six hundred and eighty churches acknowledged her as their spiritual head. Her last great act was the founding of the *Christian Science Monitor* in 1908, so that the movement should have its own newspaper.

Despite her worldly success (her estate amounted to two and a half million dollars), Mother Eddy was, in her latter years, a frail, elderly, lonely woman, pursued by delusions of persecution, forever talking about malicious animal magnetism. Her strange seizures at night, for which a morphine tablet or a hypodermic injection was administered, became more frequent. From these attacks she would rise with amazing energy, her mind much more alert. It was in this fashion that some of her more successful business coups were made. Malicious rumours spread about her, and so in January 1908 she moved to Chestnut Hill, Boston, where in December 1910 she died. In her last years she suffered from a painful disease, probably kidney stones, for which she required increasing hypodermic injections of morphine. In the 1905 edition of *Science and Health* appeared for the first time the statement that whenever pain too violent for mental treatment occurs, a Scientist may call a surgeon to administer a hypodermic injection.*

After the death in 1910 of its foundress, the future of Christian Science depended on the machinery that she had designed and set up. The Church Manual, which she had initiated and which she had repeatedly revised and expanded, laid down the laws by which the affairs of the Church were to be conducted. The Board of Christian Science Trustees, which she had established and over which she presided, was the ultimate power. It is a

---

* 'If from an injury or from any cause a Christian Scientist were seized with pain so violent that he could not treat himself mentally and the Scientist had failed to relieve him, the sufferer would call a surgeon who would give a hypodermic injection.' 1906 edition, p. 464.

testimony to her extraordinary ability that the Christian Science Church continued to flourish ever more vigorously after her guiding hand was no more.

So far as illness is concerned, Mary Baker Eddy's life falls into three periods. In the first period, which began in her childhood and ended with her self-cure after her fall at Lynn, she was usually ill and often incapacitated. In the second period, which lasted for another thirty years, she was remarkably active and creative, though subject to strange, nocturnal attacks, and was increasingly suspicious of those who might challenge her supremacy, gradually becoming distinctly paranoid. In the third period, that of her old age, she suffered from the afflictions so prevalent at that phase of life, a painful disease, loneliness, and fear. This third period, when her productive life was nearing its end, does not concern us; though during it she did found the *Christian Science Monitor*.

In her youth we know that she was sufficiently unwell to be unable to attend school at all regularly, and that she suffered from seizures. At such an age the commonest cause of seizures is epilepsy. The second commonest cause is hysteria. The differentiation between these two is not difficult if the physician is able to witness the attacks, and to find out under what circumstances they occur. Neither piece of evidence is available to us. Nevertheless, they were to her family physician, Dr Ladd, who could always be relied on to bring Mary out of an attack. His diagnosis was hysteria mingled with bad temper. Mary seems to have been well enough to accompany Glover to South Carolina after her first marriage, and to live with Patterson during his rare intervals at home. But after Glover died, and particularly after the death of her mother, she was dependent on her father and sister, and she became once again a chronic invalid. The seizures recurred, and to calm her, she had to be rocked like a child. She was unable to fend for herself. After Patterson's several desertions, she became dependent on her sister and became so weak that she had to be carried up and down stairs.

This illness was terminated dramatically by Quimby's faith healing. She was again temporarily incapacitated after her fall on the ice at Lynn. After her own self cure these illnesses vanished, and this remarkable woman revealed her own extraordinary intellectual capacity, and her physical and intellectual stamina.

The manner of its cure stamps this illness as hysterical. There is no other cause of seizures and paralysis that can be cured so dramatically in this way. On William of Occam's principle of the paucity of hypotheses, we may judge that hysteria was the cause also of her childhood seizures.

Nowadays hysterical symptoms are seen as responses to distressful situations. They are commonest in 'a person predisposed by an attention-seeking, emotionally unstable, and egocentric personality'.[14] Their purpose is to draw attention to the patient, who thus becomes the centre of attention in contrast to the ill-treatment or neglect that she feels she receives during her ordinary life. In Mrs Eddy's case the distressful situations are painfully clear. In her youth, this sensitive, intelligent girl rebelled against her authoritarian father and his Calvinist doctrine of punishment by hell-fire. Hysteria and other forms of psychoneurosis are by no means an uncommon manifestation of a revolt against distasteful parental authority. In womanhood her first husband's death and her second husband's desertion thrust her on the unwilling charity of her father and sister and robbed her of her independence. Again this must have been a highly distressing experience to this naturally proud young woman. Fortunately she had the enterprise and energy to seek out the faith-healer, Quimby. Like her father, she was fundamentally deeply religious, though the tenets of their religion were opposite, and so she saw her remarkable cure as by the hand of God. The way was opened for the subsequent self-cure and the birth of Christian Science.

To interpret her psychoneurosis in terms of the idiom used elsewhere in this book presents no difficulty. It was due to the unresolved conflict between the personality that she would have wished to project to the world, and the actuality, as revealed by the opposition of her father, her poverty, and her later dependence on the unwilling charity of father and sister. What she wanted to be is clearly revealed by her subsequent behaviour and course. She wanted to be, and she became, the most celebrated, most powerful, and one of the richest women of her day. In 1898, the *Christian Science Journal* (of which she was editor) wrote: 'Hungry are the throng to hear the Bible read in connection with the text-book of Christian Science, Science and Health with Key to the Scriptures by Mary Baker Eddy. These are our only preachers. They are the word of God.'[15]

What Quimby's cure began, and what her own self-cure completed, was to show her the way in which the conflict could be resolved by making the actuality conform to the ideal. This interpretation accounts for the extraordinary energy and creativity displayed by this hitherto obscure middle-aged invalid. The continued success of all her ventures, and the increasing renown, prestige, power, and wealth which these ventures brought should have gratified the most voracious ego. I have no doubt that her idea of Christian Science, of the power of the mind to produce health, right behaviour and happiness, though taken from Quimby, was sincerely and honestly developed by her until it became known. And there is no doubt that her works have brought health and happiness to millions and have done something towards reaching that seemingly inaccessible goal, world peace. But I am profoundly shocked by her mental dishonesty as revealed by the Quimby affair and many others, by her utter selfishness, and her ruthless discard of those who had befriended and helped her, when they had ceased to serve her purpose or had come to menace her sovereignty. Mark Baker is said to have remarked: 'Mary acts like an old ewe that won't own its own lamb,' and it is difficult to conceive of a mother who exhibited less loving kindness to her only son, though characteristically she wrote a poem about 'Mother's darling' when he was sent away. And her husband,

Daniel Patterson, died in the poorhouse and was buried in the potter's field in 1896, when his former wife was worth a quarter of a million dollars.

To superficial inspection it seemed as though Mrs Eddy's cure had been complete. But she continued to get strange attacks, in which she cried out during the night and for which in her later years she was sometimes given morphine to quieten her. The description of these attacks[7-10] does not resemble those of epilepsy. Rather they seem to have been episodes of uncontrollable terror, such as are seen in children and in adults who have lived through a shattering experience. And in fact she became increasingly paranoid till she died, her fear being that her former assistants to whom, indeed, she had acted basely were trying to injure her through malicious animal magnetism. Nevertheless, such was her capacity for work and for detailed work during the daylight hours that her achievements were stupendous. The retirement to Concord, New Hampshire at the age of sixty-eight was undoubtedly a stroke of genius for she was able to effect her purpose without getting embroiled in day to day business. But it exposed her to loneliness, the outstanding hazard of old age. The paranoia worsened, the nocturnal attacks became more troublesome, painful colic occurred, and the doctors treated this rich old woman with morphine, on which, like other characters in this book, she may have become dependent. And the text of *Science and Health* was duly amended.

If my interpretation of Mrs Eddy's illness, of the cause of that illness, and the full import of its cure, are correct, then the doctrine of Christian Science should bear witness. For if Christian Science was indeed an example of what Breuer would have called mental catharsis,* its content should reflect her rejection of those attitudes which had caused so much distress to its author, namely the Puritan Calvinistic doctrines of her father, and the misfortunes to which she, as a daughter, sister, wife, and mother, had been exposed. As evidence I cannot do

* See p. 181.

better than quote H. A. L. Fisher,* who wrote of *Science and Health*:[12]

It was a welcome contrast to the melancholy and forbidding tradition of Puritan austerity to learn that happiness was the key to health, and that health was the first article in the code of duty. . . . It is not improbable that some part of the vogue of this unusual book may be due to the fact that it may be regarded in certain aspects as a feminist manifesto. 'We have not so much authority in Divine science,' observes the authoress, 'for considering God masculine as for considering Him feminine.' If 'Jesus of Nazareth was the most scientific man that ever trod the globe', Mrs Eddy was the most scientific woman. In language characterised by earnestness and vigour the case is put for a revision of the traditional view of the relations of the sexes. The rights of women are placed upon an equality with those of men. The unfair discrimination between the sexes, which was then a mark of the legal system both in the United States and in Great Britain, is very justly attacked. 'If a dissolute husband deserts his wife, certainly the wronged, and perchance impoverished, woman should be allowed to collect her own wages, enter into business agreements, hold real estate, deposit funds, and own her children free from interference.' On this side of her apostolate, as also in her denunciation of alcohol, Mrs Eddy was in advance of her times.

Fisher also remarks:

Why, of all the many modes of mind-cure which had a vogue in the United States, did Christian Science alone achieve the dignity of an established and popular religion? The name counted for much. In two words it combined the deepest

---

* Fisher, H. A. L. (1865–1940), historian, statesman, and Warden of New College, Oxford, 1925–40; Member of Parliament 1916–26; President of the Board of Education 1916–22; Author of Education Act of 1918.

spiritual interests of the American people, Christianity and science. The doctrine of Mrs Eddy was certainly not Christian in the accepted sense of that word; still less was it scientific; but the title was a stroke of genius. That it was first employed by Quimby in a casual, unsystematic way does not detract from the credit of his pupil. Mrs Eddy was the first to see the supreme value of those two words 'Christian Science' as the trademark of her great exclusive venture. With fine business instinct she seized upon that happy title and made it her own. In the United States, where the psychology of advertisement is a serious subject of academic study, there is no bolder or more persuasive commercial label in any line of goods.

In many ways, Mrs Eddy is the most remarkable character that I have studied in this book. She founded a religious movement which has developed and prospered until it is now a major world force. Its success was entirely due to Mrs Eddy. It was based on a dogma, *Science and Health*, which she wrote and continued to revise and edit until her death. It was her magnetic personality that attracted students and disciples and devotees. It was she who acquired the property on which the First Church of Christ Scientist was established and expanded. It was she who formulated and initiated the system of government of the church. It was she who founded and edited the religious journal. It was she who established, at the age of eighty-seven, a daily newspaper, the *Christian Science Monitor*, which is today profoundly respected, by me amongst others, for its informed and wise opinion on world affairs. These are astonishing achievements for a single person. They are almost unbelievable in a hitherto obscure invalid of forty-five years, deserted by her husband and slighted by her close relatives. These great achievements were made possible by her illness and the use she made of it.

Chapter 12

SIGMUND FREUD

In the realm of mental illness, no name is better known than Sigmund Freud. Freud developed a method of exploring the unconscious mind, the technique of psychoanalysis by free association. As a consequence of his discoveries with the method, he put forward a number of new and startling ideas: that sexual feelings existed from early infantile life and did not suddenly appear in adolescence; that the repression of thought and memory was an active process with a purpose and not simply a passive forgetting; that fantasy life was not just idle day dreaming but had a symbolic meaning, often of a sexual nature; and particularly that the origin of psychological illness lay in traumatic experiences in childhood, again usually sexual. Oddly enough, Freud himself seems to have been suffering from a psychoneurosis when he did his most important work. His own interpretation of the cause of his own illness led him to 'know' the cause in others and to tolerate no deviation from his dogma.

Sigmund Freud was the first-born of Jacob Freud and his second wife, Amalie (née Nathansohn) in Freiberg, Moravia in 1856. He was already an uncle at birth, for his half brother, Emmanuel, had begun a family. Jacob Freud was a wool merchant, and both he and his wife were Jews from Galicia. His business took him and his family to Leipzig and then to Vienna where Sigmund was educated and worked till he was rescued from the Nazis by Ernest Jones in 1938 and brought to England. He died here of cancer of the palate a year later. Sigmund's mother was only twenty-one when he was born; she had subsequently five daughters and two other sons. She was slender, beautiful and witty.

Sigmund had a brilliant career at the Gymnasium at Vienna,

being particularly good at languages. His father had been brought up an orthodox Jew, and the family was a patriarchal one, with a thorough knowledge of the Old Testament. Freud's choice of medicine as a profession was due to his admiration for Darwin's theories, and the impression made on him by a beautiful reading of Goethe's essay on Nature in his last year at school. He never felt particularly drawn to medicine as an absorbing pursuit, and throughout his life preserved his interest in, and love for, philosophy, history and the world's greatest literature. Outstanding was the beauty of his own German prose, which had the Viennese lucidity and lightness of touch, which that from the North so often lacked.

Freud was seventeen when he began to study medicine at the University, and twenty-five when he graduated M.D. in 1881. He took so long because he had become interested in zoology and marine biology and spent extra years working on the histology of the nervous system in Brücke's Physiological Institute.[5]

He had no leaning towards medical practice and so became a demonstrator in physiology, continuing his studies in neuro-histology. However, as Brücke pointed out, such was the short-age of senior posts that Freud had no hope of a livelihood. So he went to the hospital and served in a variety of departments, becoming a Privat-Dozent (lecturer) in Neuropathology in 1885. Later that year he won a postgraduate award with which he betook himself to Charcot,* then at the height of his fame, though perhaps not of his powers, at the Salpêtrière in Paris. Freud spent four months with Charcot. At that time Charcot was interested particularly in hysteria, which he managed to aggravate, with his histrionic gifts, by his demonstrations of these unfortunate patients, mostly young women. Charcot and Freud became personal friends and Freud translated Charcot's lectures into German. Freud returned to Vienna where he began private practice in April 1886. In September of that year he

---

* Charcot, J. M. (1825–1893), probably the greatest neurologist of his day. His name is still given to at least three diseases.

married Martha Bernays, to whom he had been betrothed for a stormy four years, for Martha had a possessive mother who did not take eagerly to her prospective son-in-law.

One of the difficulties that had delayed marriage was poverty, which indeed afflicted the young pair for several years. Freud realised he must succeed in private practice and therefore must make a name for himself. This his painstaking and highly competent essays in neuroanatomy seemed unlikely to do. In 1884 he obtained, with Martha's money, a supply of cocaine, the little known alkaloid from the coca leaf, to study its physiological action. He gave himself a twentieth of a gramme; it turned the bad mood he was in to cheerfulness and gave him the feeling of having dined well 'so that there is nothing at all one need bother about', but without having robbed him of energy. He gave it to his friend Fleischl, who had become a morphine addict because of severe nerve pain, in the hope of weaning him. Fleischl quickly took to the new drug, and became an addict to both. Freud tried to relieve trigeminal neuralgia by injecting it around the nerve, but was unsuccessful. In his monograph, a scholarly work giving a comprehensive account of the history of the drug, he praised its action in relieving exhaustion and depression and producing exhilaration and euphoria without any tendency to habit formation. He noted its capacity to anaesthetise skin and mucous membranes and thought it might prove useful in relieving the pain of infections. But he did not pursue this. And so its usefulness as a local anaesthetic passed him by. His friend Koller introduced it to ophthalmology, and Halsted of New York used it for local and regional anaesthesia, becoming addicted to it in the process.

Freud went on working with cocaine hoping to cure diabetes with it. He also tried to investigate its effect on muscular performance, and on reaction time. The results were published in the *Wiener Medizinische Wochenschrift* in 1885. It is the only experimental study Freud ever published and, as Ernest Jones remarks, 'its rather dilettante presentation shows that this was not his real field'.*¹ In this respect Freud reminds me of John Locke. For Locke was a physician and friend of Robert Boyle. Boyle entrusted Locke with instruments to make observations in a mine. But Locke could not make the instruments work. Freud and Locke were thus alike in being unsuited to new discovery in sciences depending on accuracy of observation and measurement. Their forte was in the imaginative use of their minds, Locke in philosophy, Freud in psychiatry.

Freud hoped to win international fame as an advocate and pioneer in the use of this magical drug. But alas, by 1886 its capacity to produce an addiction, even more demanding than morphine, was becoming known. Freud was attacked by many. Erlenmeyer termed cocaine 'the third scourge of humanity'.

At thirty-six, Freud was a competent but relatively undistinguished Viennese neurologist. As Ernest Jones said: 'Freud had proved himself as a good clinician, a highly skilful histologist, and a thinker. His attempts in experimental physiology were conspicuous failures.' Then an event occurred which transformed his life. As usual it was due to chance, and the chance came through Joseph Breuer.

Joseph Breuer was a precocious Viennese Jew, born in 1842, who was so young when he entered the university that at first he was not allowed to study medicine; he attended lectures on history, philosophy and economics. At seventeen he began his medical training proper, but did not become interested until he started to study physiology under Brücke, the inspiring professor in the University of Vienna. Breuer qualified as a doctor at twenty-five, becoming assistant to Oppolzer, and received from Tuerck, a laryngologist, the idea that breathing was a self-regulatory activity. He took this idea to Hering, then Professor in the military medical school in Vienna, Joseph's

---

* Freud himself recognised his defects. He wrote: 'I have very restricted capacities or talents. None at all for the natural sciences; nothing for mathematics; nothing for anything quantitative.'

Academy. Together they discovered the reflex, bearing their joint names, which regulates breathing through stimulation of nerve endings in the alveoli by inflation and deflation of the lungs. This was the first demonstration of a self-regulatory mechanism, which has now become so important in our knowledge of how the body regulates itself. There seems no doubt that Breuer did most of the experiments and Hering gave him full credit for the work, a splendid example of how the elder should treat the younger. When they made their discovery Hering was thirty-four and Breuer twenty-six.

Oppolzer's successor did not like Breuer, who went into private practice as a physician, in which he was most successful. The burden of his work left him enough energy and curiosity to work at night, in a room at his flat, on the mechanism of the semi-circular canals of the ear. He showed that their function was to recognise rotational movement. He also worked out the anatomy and function of the otoliths.* Breuer retired at seventy, but lived till he was eighty-three.

Breuer's neurological practice, like Freud's, was dominated by people with functional nervous disease. Between 1880 and 1882 he treated a remarkable case. A girl in her twenties had been bedridden for several months with a long array of symptoms. Both legs and the right arm were paralysed, sight and hearing were impaired, the neck was painfully contracted and there was a persistent cough, occasional nausea and recurrent difficulty with speech. In addition she had periodically a mental state, which Breuer termed 'obscure', in which she mumbled to herself. Breuer had the unusual initiative and perception to take notes of her words. Later, after inducing hypnosis, he gave them back to her and she revealed to him the fantasies that had occupied her dreamy states. She awakened much improved. He subsequently discovered that if the patient could recall fully the circumstances under which the symptoms had begun and express freely the accompanying emotion, the symptom would

---

* The semicircular canals and the otoliths are part of the internal ear. The otolith is suspended in the otocyst; it is a device to recognise gravity.

disappear for good. This process he named 'mental catharsis'.*
He discovered that all the symptoms had arisen as a series of
separate events when she was nursing her father through a
painful, protracted and mortal illness. For example, her father
had awakened from a nap and asked the time; she found difficulty in seeing the clock through her tears and was terrified lest
her father would notice her distress. When she recalled the
incident and her accompanying emotion, her vision was restored. Each of her symptoms had to be pursued through a
labyrinth of fantasies until the origin was uncovered.

Breuer became so obsessed with this case that at home he
could talk of nothing else. His wife was convinced he was in
love. Breuer realised what had happened and told the patient
she would have to stop seeing him. That evening, Breuer was
called back to find her in the throes of a hysterical childbirth
from which Breuer was able to relieve her by hypnosis. He fled
and left Vienna never to see the patient again. The patient,
Bertha Pappenheim, had a very checkered career, in which she
was a morphine addict for a time, and became Germany's first
social worker who, amongst other exploits, rescued children
whose parents had died in pogroms.

Freud had known Breuer since he entered the Physiological
Institute and he learned of this case in 1882. After his return
from Paris, Freud was deeply engaged in translating Charcot's
works, including those on hysteria which Charcot regarded as
due to auto-suggestion. Freud therefore tried to induce Breuer's
mental catharsis by hypnosis and had some measure of success.
One of his patients fell in love with him. Freud told Breuer,
who was so relieved, he was able to tell Freud the whole story
about Bertha, and thus to close an episode which had made the
case so painful that Breuer had repressed it. And so Freud
was able to persuade Breuer to join him in a publication '*Studien
über Hysterie*' in 1893. One of the cases described was Elizabeth
R. who proved refractory to hypnotism. Freud nevertheless
determined to proceed. He remembered a remark of Bernheim's

* See p. 181.

that things remembered in hypnosis were forgotten after-wards. He therefore devised and used for the first time in this case, a new technique of mental concentration without hypnosis designed to elicit the memories which had been forgotten and which, when brought into consciousness, brought about a cure by mental catharsis.

1892 is thus the turning point in Freud's life for in this way was born the technique of psychoanalysis.

This new technique had another advantage. Hypnosis did not always establish the intimate relation between physician and patient that was the key to the confession. With the patient lying comfortably relaxed on a couch, as for the induction of hypnosis, he or she was encouraged to say whatever came into his head and to go on from there; he must say everything whether indecent, revolting, shameful or criminal. To assist in this the psychiatrist sat out of the patient's range of vision. The technique was called 'free association'. It is the unique contribution of Freud to the advancement of medicine and medical science and it is still the basis of psychoanalysis.[4]

Freud realised that his new technique gave him the opportunity for the first time to explore the unconscious mind. He soon discovered that certain patients come to a point where every kind of device is employed as an excuse for not 'telling every-thing'. This he termed 'resistance', and the memories which were temporarily inaccessible 'repressed'. Most of these repressions were of a sexual nature; their release was imperative for cure. Extensive experience led to a startling discovery. The associations led the patient into his past until

experiences were finally reached which belonged to his infancy and concerned his sexual life; and this was so even when an ordinary emotion, not of a sexual kind, had led to the outbreak of the disease. Without taking into account these sexual traumas of childhood, it was impossible to explain the symptoms, comprehend their determination, or prevent their return. After this, the unique significance of sexual experiences in the aetiology of the psychoneuroses seemed incontestably established.[4]

One of the commonest emotions to be repressed in this way was sexual attraction to the parent of the opposite sex. The incest motive and the Oedipus* complex thus became dominant ideas in Freud's concept of the cause of neurosis.

Freud discovered many other properties of the unconscious: the frequency of fantasy in otherwise apparently sober-minded individuals particularly in childhood, the apparent remembrance of a desired, but forbidden event as though it had actually happened; the importance of the self or 'ego' and its libidinous component, the 'id'; the importance of dreams as manifestations of suppressed wishes, and the extraordinary resources of the unconscious mind in transferring objects to less recognisable forms. All cylindrical objects are substitutes for the phallus, and all receptacles such as pockets for its female counterpart.

To me, one of Freud's most charming and scholarly essays was on 'slips of the tongue'.[3] To the rest of mankind these were due to chance and of neither interest nor importance. But Freud believed that every action of the mind was the result of a causal sequence, and that in this case the slip expressed a suppressed wish, in the same way as missing, or being late for an appointment did. He pointed out that in *The Merchant of Venice*, when Portia had completely lost her heart to Bassanio but had necessarily to conceal the fact, Shakespeare makes her tongue slip as follows:

> One half of me is yours, the other half yours,
> Mine own, I would say.

I have not described all Freud's discoveries or ideas. But it is at once evident that they were of the stuff that makes instant

---

* Oedipus was the son of Laius and Jocasta of Thebes. Ignorant of his parentage, he killed his father and married his mother. In consequence of this incestuous alliance, Thebes was visited by a plague. The oracle exposed Oedipus, who put out his own eyes. Sophocles wrote his play *Oedipus Tyrannus* about it.

rejection by most people inevitable. It was all quite novel. As Wilfred Trotter remarked, there is no more powerful antigen known to man than a new idea. And the new ideas were quite shocking. Infantile sexuality, anal eroticism, the frequency of suppressed desire for incest, the idea that nearly all neurosis is due to a suppressed desire for incestuous sexual intercourse— really, these were ideas 'that no decent man or woman, let alone a student at St Thomas's Hospital, would ever entertain', as one of my teachers* might have said. So it was inevitable that Freud's ideas and his disciples should be shunned and persecuted.

Freud, however, was a man already established in neurological circles in Vienna, well liked for his wit, charm and integrity, and respected for the width and accuracy of his scholarship. Besides, he had a flourishing practice. So he preserved his position and continued to develop his ideas. Freud also slowly began to gather around him a group of younger men, receptive to new ideas, and all thrilled with the new adventure of the mind.

So far, all has happened as might be expected to happen to any pioneer in medical science. What is most extraordinary and almost unique is the degree to which these young men subsequently broke away from Freud and were ostracised by their former master.

It is, of course, not uncommon for some junior disciples to revolt against their Master and attempt to found a rival school. But in Freud's case this seemed to occur again and again. The novelty, and the nature of the ideas, and the brilliance and drive of the disciples may have played some part, but Freud's own personality and neurosis must also have been involved. A hint of this same reaction against independence appears at times in Florence Nightingale, and was of course conspicuous in Mrs Eddy.

Adler was one of the earliest and the first of the distinguished ones to leave the circle. His own psychoanalytic experiences

* Sir Henry Tidy, whom Lord Moran called the 'Queen Mary of Medicine'.

had led him to a different concept of the origin of neuroses. Instead of sexual fantasies and derivatives of the sexual life of childhood, he noticed everywhere the subtle effects of the striving to dominate, degrade and triumph over others. The neurotic subject, striving for superiority and being frustrated, resorted to headaches, fatigues, and even paralysis, which compelled his friends and relatives to wait on him. Why? Because he had an 'inferiority complex' for which his illness was a 'compensation'. Adler's concepts and his terminology have since become respectable and have passed into psychiatric, and indeed into everyday, thought. But they represented a deviation from the teaching of Freud. So there were arguments and quarrels, and Adler went off to establish a rival school. After the Nazi regime began he emigrated to the United States. In 1937 he was invited to lecture in Aberdeen where he died suddenly of a cerebral haemorrhage. The University held a memorial service for him with all the notables and academics in their full panoply. Freud remarked: 'For a Jew-boy out of a Vienna suburb, a death in Aberdeen is an unheard of career in itself and a proof of how far he got. The world really rewarded him richly for contradicting psychoanalysis'.

For Freud, the bitterest pill was Jung. Freud was quite delighted when C. G. Jung of Zurich called on him and later joined his circle and the Psychoanalytic Association. Whereas all Freud's previous disciples had been rather small Jews, Jung was a large Gentile of unquestioned Germanic ancestry. Freud was attracted to him physically and by his mind. He saw in Jung his successor, the man who would lead psychoanalysis on from strength to strength. In April 1909, Freud formally adopted him as his eldest son and annointed him as 'successor and crown prince—*in partibus infidelium*'. Freud pointed out in a letter to Jung that on the same day that Freud had adopted him, Jung had divested him of his paternal dignity. It was a significant statement, for a breach rapidly developed and became insurmountable.

Jung was *au fond* a gullible Teutonic romantic. He believed in poltergeists, and the occult and the inheritance of tribal memories and customs. One day when Jung came to visit Freud and to argue with him about the occult, Jung abruptly felt as though his diaphragm was red hot. Suddenly there was a loud report from the wall. Jung remarked, 'There, that is an example of so-called catalytic exteriorisation phenomenon.' 'Oh come,' said Freud, 'that is sheer nonsense.' 'It is not,' Jung replied. 'You are mistaken Herr Professor and to prove my point I now predict that in a moment there will be another loud report.' The second loud noise duly followed as the ancient timbers continued to contract.

In 1908, Freud and Jung were invited to give courses of lectures at Clark University, Worcester, Mass. Freud entertained Jung and another of his disciples to lunch. Jung turned the conversation to the peat bogs of Northern Germany where mummified corpses had been found. Freud burst out several times, 'Why are you so concerned with these corpses?' According to Jung, Freud was inordinately vexed by the whole thing and during one such conversation he suddenly fainted. 'When he came round he said he was convinced that I had a death wish towards him. I was more than surprised by this interpretation. I was alarmed by the intensity of his fantasies—so strong that they obviously caused him to faint.'[6]

On the transatlantic voyage the two men analysed one another's dreams. Jung said he could do much better with Freud's if he knew more details of Freud's private life. 'Freud's response to these words was a curious look—a look of the utmost suspicion. Then he said, "But I cannot risk my authority".' Jung added, 'At that moment he lost it altogether. The sentence burned itself into my memory.'[6]

The rift became inevitable when Jung published his paper on 'Symbols of the Libido' in the *Jahrbuch der Psychoanalyse* in 1911. As he later wrote,

To me incest signifies a personal complication only in the rarest cases. Usually incest has a highly religious aspect, for which reason the incest theme plays a decisive part in almost all cosmogonies and in numerous myths. But Freud clung to the literal interpretation of it and could not grasp the spiritual significance of incest as a symbol.

Jung had been President of the International Psycho-analytic Association for some years. In November 1912 he met Freud to arrange an exchange in editorship of Journals. The meeting ended satisfactorily at just after 11 a.m. and Freud and Jung set out for a long walk. Freud let off steam and did not spare Jung a good fatherly lecture. Lunch followed. Freud turned to Jung and another Swiss psychiatrist and asked them why they had not acknowledged him in their papers as the originator of psychoanalysis. Jung replied that this was so well known that to mention it was unnecessary. Freud slid to the floor in a dead faint. The powerful Jung picked him up and carried him to a couch where Freud recovered consciousness, saying 'How sweet it must be to die.' In a letter to Jones, Freud recalled that he had a similar attack in the same hotel some ten years previously when he had had a disturbing episode with an ear, nose and throat surgeon, Fliess, to whom Freud was emotionally attached and with whom he quarrelled because Fliess accused him of stealing his idea of everyone being part male and part female. Freud wrote about these two episodes, 'There is some piece of unruly homosexual feeling at the root of the matter'.

The end came after the last Congress of the International Psychoanalytic Association in Munich in September 1913, when Jung was re-elected President, despite a schism between the Zurich and other members. Freud planned to disband the Association, deprive Jung of his editorship and reform the group without the Swiss. However, his colleagues persuaded him that the rules did not permit such a course. After Freud had published a bitter polemical essay, Jung at last resigned. Freud was delighted. 'So at last we are rid of them,' he wrote to Abraham, 'the brutal, sanctimonious Jung and his disciples.'

In his reminiscences, written at the age of eighty, Jung wrote, 'After the break with Freud all my friends and acquaintances dropped away. My book was declared to be rubbish; I was a mystic and that settled the matter.'[6]

In order to prevent the break-up of the movement, Jones proposed the formation of an international committee of men who had been analysed by Freud and who would promise not to depart from the strict limits of psychoanalytic theory without previously discussing it with the others. The Committee was Freud, Ferenczi, Sachs, Rank, Abraham, Eitingon and Jones. Freud was delighted; he insisted that it be a *secret committee* and gave each member an antique Greek intaglio which each mounted in a ring. Alas, Rank and Ferenczi were to prove unfaithful and to break away.

Inside the committee there were endless bickerings and tensions. In fact Jones regarded Abraham as the only completely normal member. The rest were suffering from neuroses of various kinds. Ferenczi and Rank conceived a great antipathy to Jones, and Freud tended to side with them. Then Rank learned that Freud had cancer and thus in the future would not provide a source of income by referring patients. Rank and Ferenczi wrote a book *The Developmental Aims of Psychoanalysis* which set out the propensity of patients to live out their unconscious impulses in actions. Since this implied that discussion of the contemporary situation might well be sufficient without probing deeply into childhood, several members of the Committee saw this as heresy.

Then Rank produced a work of his own, *The Trauma of Birth*. Rank maintained that psychoanalytic treatment should set out to repeat the birth experience in the transference situation and if a rebirth could be achieved the patient would be freed from the *angst*, the hidden terrors which had haunted him or her ever since the inexorable machinery had expelled him from the placid comfort of the womb into the hurly-burly of life outside. It was wrong to stop at the Oedipus complex; to go even further back was essential. This again was heresy.

Abraham saw the situation plainly and said so to Freud. Eventually, ten days before the Salzburg conference of 1924, the Committee was formally dissolved.[2]

Rank finally committed the sin of openly advocating a short course of psychoanalysis lasting only a few months instead of the long drawn out exercise prescribed by Freud. When Freud was finally convinced of the heresy, Rank too was discarded. According to Jones, Rank was not just a neurotic, he was a psychotic with a manic depressive psychosis.

Ferenczi's deviation took the form of caressing and kissing his patients and encouraging them to reciprocate. Freud was horrified. He felt that one must draw the line, 'otherwise we shall have accepted the whole repertoire of *demi-vièrgerie* and petting parties'. Freud became more irritated with Ferenczi and finally persuaded his colleagues not to elect him President of the Psychoanalytic Association, but to elect Jones instead. Ferenczi in fact had pernicious anaemia of which he died in 1933.

Jones and Abraham remained steadfast friends and disciples of Freud. Abraham's chief contribution, according to Freud, was the concept of anal eroticism, the idea that a child is proud of its faeces for they are the child's first independent creation. He died at the age of forty-eight of bronchiectasis. Jones rescued Freud from the Nazis at some risk to himself and brought him back to England in 1938. Freud was by then a frail old man with advanced cancer of the palate.

In April 1923 Freud had a local excision of a cancer of the roof of his mouth, recently discovered, and attributed to his heavy smoking of cigars. Unfortunately the trouble spread, and in October he had a radical operation in which the upper jaw on one side and a mass of tissue was removed. From then on he had to wear a prosthesis, a large substitute for the upper jaw. This had to be taken out, cleaned and replaced. The cancer recurred in 1936, leading to another operation in September 1938 in London. But the cancer recurred, spreading to his face and accompanied by much pain and a horrible stench. All this Freud bore with exemplary courage and fortitude. He took aspirin but did not receive morphia until a few days before his death on 23 September 1939.

Freud's last work was an extraordinary testament to his learning, inventiveness and courage. *Moses and Monotheism* was mostly written in 1934 but not published until August 1938. He was then eighty-two. Freud suggested that Moses was not a Jew at all, but a highly born and very intelligent Egyptian, and that was why he bore an Egyptian and not a Jewish name. The princess who brought him up was probably his mother. He accepted the monotheistic proclamations of the then Pharaoh Akhenaten. After Akhenaten's death, there was a counter-revolution. And so Moses chose to leave Egypt in company with a people of his own choosing who would accept his teaching. He brought ritual circumcision from the Egyptians to the Jews. The religion of Aton, with its ideals of truth and justice, replaced the blood-thirsty, aggressive tribal god of the earlier Old Testament. This bold exercise in the interpretation of the Old Testament was naturally received with righteous indignation from Jews and scholars, but it won praise from scientists such as Einstein and imaginative writers like H. G. Wells.

FREUD'S PSYCHONEUROSIS

While I read Freud's works over the past forty-five years, it had never occurred to me that he was a neurotic. And yet this was Jones's view, a view that commands the respect due to a distinguished psychiatrist who knew Freud intimately and wrote his definitive life. Jones wrote:[1]

However unpalatable the idea may be to hero-worshippers, the truth has to be stated that Freud did not always possess the serenity and inner sureness so characteristic of him in the years when he was well known. The point has to be put more forcibly. There is ample evidence that for ten years or so— roughly comprising the nineties—he suffered from a very considerable psychoneurosis. An admirer might be tempted to paint this in the darkest colours so as to emphasise by way of relief Freud's achievement of self-mastery by the help of the unique instrument he himself forged. But there is no need to exaggerate; the greatness of the achievement stands by itself. After all, in the worst times Freud never ceased to function. He continued with his daily work and with his scientific investigations, his care and love for his wife and children remained unimpaired, and in all probability he gave little sign of neurotic manifestations to his surroundings (with the sole exception of Fliess). Nevertheless, his sufferings were at times very intense, and for those ten years there could have been only occasional intervals when life seemed much worth living. He paid very heavily for the gifts he bestowed on the world, and the world was not very generous in its rewards.

Yet it was just in the years when the neurosis was at its height, 1897–1900, that Freud did his most original work. There is an unmistakable connection between these two facts. The neurotic symptoms must have been one of the ways in which the unconscious material was indirectly trying to emerge, and without that pressure it is doubtful if Freud would have made the progress he did. It is a costly way of reaching that hidden realm, but it is still the only way.

That Freud dimly perceived this connection even at the time is shown by several allusions to his mode of working. He did not work well when he felt fit and happy, nor when he was too depressed and inhibited; he needed something in between. He expressed this neatly in a letter of 16 April 1896: 'I have come back with a lordly feeling of independence and feel too well; since returning I have been very lazy, because the *moderate misery necessary for intensive work refuses to appear.*'

Freud of course recognised the existence of his neurosis, and several times in the correspondence uses that word to describe his condition. There seems to have been no 'conversion' physical symptoms, and he would later doubtless have classified it as an anxiety-hysteria. It consisted essentially in extreme changes of mood, and the only respects in which

the anxiety got localised were occasional attacks of dread of
dying (*Todesangst*) and anxiety about travelling by rail
(*Reisefieber*). . . .

The alternations of mood were between periods of elation,
excitement and self-confidence on the one hand and periods
of severe depression, doubt and inhibition on the other. In
the depressed moods he could neither write nor concentrate
his thoughts (except during his professional work). He would
spend leisure hours of extreme boredom, turning from one
thing to another, cutting open books, looking at maps of
ancient Pompeii, playing patience or chess, but being unable
to continue at anything for long—a state of restless paralysis.
Sometimes there were spells where consciousness would be
greatly narrowed: states, difficult to describe, with a veil that
produced almost a twilight condition of mind (6 December
1897).

The relationship between Freud's ill-health and creativity
expressed itself in another way.

He was a chronic sufferer from an obscure abdominal com-
plaint. It was in this part of his person where production
seemed to manifest itself to begin with. Increased discomfort,
with various other symptoms of general malaise, always preceded Freud's best work. When, as happened sometimes,
he was in a state of perfect health and in a euphoric mood
there was no question of writing anything. 'I have long known
that I can't be industrious when I am in good health; on the contrary, I need a degree of discomfort which I want to get rid of.'

In 1897 began the Herculean task of analysing himself in an
attempt to cure his neurosis. It is not surprising that Freud's
views on the nature of neurosis and the importance of the sexual
trauma in infancy, the incest wish and the Oedipus complex
were based on the subject with whom he was most familiar and
could most trust—himself. Freud wrote to Fliess on 15 October

1897: 'I was crying my heart out because my mother was nowhere to be found. . . . When I found my mother was not there . . . I cried still more!' In a letter of 3 October, he recalled spending a night with his mother, seeing her naked and having sexual wishes about her. In a later letter he spoke of his infatuation with his mother; he had a dream about her that he traced back to an obscure and evidently sexual craving. He wrote in 1926:

> The existence of unconscious psychical processes, the theory of resistance and repression, the appreciation of the part played by sexuality and the Oedipus complex are the main contents of psycho-analysis and the basis of its theory. Whoever does not accept them should not be counted among the psycho-analysts.

By 1899 Freud was convinced that his self analysis had done him a great deal of good; he was more serene and benign. But he told Jones that he never gave it up, devoting half an hour a day to the process—not unlike a religious devotion.

Jones attributes Freud's illness to his relations with Fliess and Breuer. Fliess was a Jewish ear, nose and throat specialist practising in Berlin and having a Viennese wife. He met Freud through Breuer. The two men were mutually attracted. Fliess had an agile mind, a great facility with numbers, of which twenty-three and twenty-eight came to have a special significance for him in unlocking the secrets of the universe. He developed a number of all-embracing concepts, which apparently delighted Freud but which are so speculative and founded on so little evidence that they would have been anathema to any scientist. Freud and Fliess met as often as they could for 'Congresses' and corresponded profusely; fortunately Freud's letters to Fliess were preserved. These letters make it plain how dependent Freud had become on Fliess. The association was so close that Frau Fliess became jealous and indeed preserved Freud's letters to her husband in the hope of harming him. Freud wrote to Fliess on 7 July 1897, the month he began his own analysis.

What has been going on inside me I still do not know. Something from the deepest depths of my neurosis has been obstructing any progress in the understanding of neuroses, and you were somehow involved in it all. For the paralysis of writing seems to me to have been designed to hinder the intercourse of our correspondence. I have no guarantee for this idea; it is a matter of feeling—of an exceedingly obscure nature.

The correspondence with Fliess also contains the evidence for Freud's antagonism to Breuer at that period. Freud had persuaded Breuer with great difficulty to join him in publishing on the psychology of hysteria, a subject which the profession and the public regarded as not quite reputable. 'Rightly or wrongly, Freud thought that Breuer never forgave him for having drawn him, or pushed him, into this unpleasant association. At all events he felt that Breuer's behaviour towards him in the following years had become very disagreeable.'[1]

Freud conceived a violent antipathy to him which he later recognised as in the nature of a transference from earlier figures in his life—ultimately his father. For Breuer had always stood in father relationship to Freud, had helped, encouraged and supported him, and even lent him money. And yet at this time he was failing in his role of father figure by repudiating Freud's researches and rejecting his conclusions. 'So hatred was directed against Breuer, and love towards Fliess—both in an excessive degree out of proportion to the merits or demerits of the persons themselves.'[1]

Freud's recovery followed soon after his quarrel with Fliess in 1900.

Karl Popper has pointed out that a scientific theory must be capable of refutation.[7] Such was not Freud's view of his hypotheses; they had to be accepted; any attempt at refutation was, of course, to question the very fundamentals of the creed. Freud really believed he was a great scientist and was deeply disappointed when he did not receive a Nobel Prize. Before psychoanalysis, his scientific record was mediocre. Psycho-analysis was a brilliant new method. Some of the credit, though not the most, must go to Breuer. But the empire that Freud built on this method was not a science, it was a religion. We have seen how Jung was selected as 'successor Crown Prince', and eventually regarded as crazy and cast into outer darkness because he deviated from the orthodoxy ordained by Freud. Adler had the same fate and, though deeply respected by other psychiatrists, died rejected and despised by Freud. Then there was the secret committee sworn to defend the letter of the law and joined by the rings conferred on them by the Founder. That broke up and two of the six openly disagreed with Freud. They were cast out and the Committee disbanded.

This extraordinary relationship between Freud and his younger followers is unlike any situation with which I am acquainted in science. It belongs more to religion and the implicit acceptance of and obedience to revealed truth. In fact, Freud's relationship with his disciples was not unlike that of Mrs Eddy with hers. We may see this as a manifestation of Freud's neurosis, as undoubtedly were his fainting attacks at decisive moments in his extraordinary relationship with Jung, in which Freud thought there must be a homosexual basis. The situation was undoubtedly partly due to two other factors. Freud was a Jew, and though he had abandoned religion as such, he retained the Jewish attitude towards the family and the authority of the father. Secondly, his views were persecuted and that no doubt hardened his inflexibility. Nevertheless, his complete lack of insight into the essentially unscientific nature of his own attitude and the oddness of his behaviour to his young is truly remarkable. For all his writings reveal a sensi-bility, a true accuracy of mind, a rare perceptiveness and a surprisingly catholic interest in the products of the human mind which delight the reader. It is for this as well as his courage in venturing for the first time into the world of the subconscious that I for one shall always deeply respect him.

Chapter 13

MARCEL PROUST

Proust's reputation, and it is very high,[2-4] rests on a single novel, albeit a very long one, *À la recherche du temps perdu*. He began to write it in 1909. He was still working on it when he died at the age of 51 in September 1922. By that time it had reached a million and a quarter words in eight parts. It is beautifully written and beautifully translated into English by Scott Moncrieff.[1] Its subject is Proust.

Its first part, *Du côté de chez Swann* (1913), begins with Proust going to bed in his aunt's house in Combray (Illiers). His childhood memories come flooding back, the shape of the ceiling, the medieval knight riding to Genevieve's castle, that his magic lantern would project on the wall.

> My sole consolation when I went upstairs for the night was that Mamma would come in and kiss me after I was in bed. But this good night lasted for so short a time: she went down again so soon that the moment in which I heard her climb the stairs, and then caught the sound of her garden dress of blue muslin, from which hung little tassels of plaited straw, rustling along the double-doored corridor, was for me a moment of the keenest sorrow. So much did I love that good night that I reached the stage of hoping that it would come as late as possible, so as to prolong the time of respite during which Mamma would not yet have appeared. Sometimes when, after kissing me, she opened the door to go, I longed to call her back, to say to her 'Kiss me just once again,' . . .[1]

But, alas, there came the night of the dinner party. The little boy was sent off to bed and as he was about to kiss his mother, the dinner bell rang. 'And so I must set forth without viaticum; must climb each step of the staircase "against my heart", as the saying is, climbing in opposition to my heart's desire, which was to return to my mother, since she had not, by her kiss, given my heart leave to accompany me forth.' Then came the agony of waiting, exacerbated by his mother's failure to answer the note he had sent her imploring her to come. At last his parents came to bed and surprisingly enough it was his father who discerned his son's unhappiness and insisted that his mother sleep in the same room.

Proust's inspiration for his great work came at the beginning of 1909—he was then thirty-eight and already an invalid. He returned late at night, chilled, to his home and was given a cup of tea and some dry toast by his servant Céline.[4] The smell of the unfamiliar drink, and the lamp-light of his room suddenly brought back vividly the memory of the garden of his great uncle Louis Weil at Auteuil, and the savour of the madeleine, soaked in tea, which his aunt would give him. It was this vivid and unexpected opening of the gates of memory that inspired Proust to begin a work based on what had hitherto been unconscious memory. As he wrote:

And so it is with our own past. It is a labour in vain to attempt to recapture it: all the efforts of our intellect must prove futile. The past is hidden somewhere outside the realm, beyond the reach of intellect, in some material object (in the sensation which that material object will give us) which we do not suspect. And so for that object, it depends on chance whether we come upon it or not before we ourselves must die.

The incident is recalled in his shaking out the dried lime blossoms for his aunt Léonie's tissane. 'Presently my aunt was able to dip in the boiling infusion in which she would relish the savour of dead or faded blossom, a little madeleine, of which she would hold out a piece to me when it was sufficiently soft.'

The remainder of this vast novel is the reconstruction through memory and imagination of Proust's adolescent and adult experiences partly through Swann and partly through the Narrator, the dramatis personae having been synthesised from Proust's friends and acquaintances. The subsequent parts were *À l'ombre des jeunes filles en fleurs* (1918), awarded the Prix Goncourt in 1919; *Le Côté de Guermantes I* (1920); *Le Côté de Guermantes II*; *Sodome et Gomorrhe I* (1921); *Sodome et Gomorrhe II* (1922); *La Prisonnière* (1923); *Albertine disparue* (1925); *Le Temps retrouvé* (1927). Much of the subsequent story was related to Balbec, an imaginary town near the mouth of the Seine and the neighbouring coast centred on the seaside resort of Cabourg in which Proust for years spent his summer holidays.

À LA RECHERCHE DU TEMPS PERDU

Proust's recollections of childhood, with which the work opens, are most vividly and beautifully presented: his relatives and their relationship to the village, Françoise the maid and her cruelty with the kitchen maid, the two walks, the Guermantes way and Méséglise way.

The 'Méséglise way' with its lilacs, its hawthorns, its cornflowers, its poppies, its apple-trees, the 'Guermantes way' with its river full of tadpoles, its water-lilies, and its buttercups have constituted for me for all time the picture of the land in which I fain would pass my life, in which my only requirements are that I may go out fishing, drift idly in a boat, see the ruins of a gothic fortress in the grass, and find hidden among the cornfields—as Saint-André-des-Champs lay hidden—an old church, monumental, rustic, and yellow like a mill-stone; and the cornflowers, the hawthorns, the apple-trees which I may happen, when I go walking, to encounter in the fields, because they are situated at the same depth, on the level of my past life, at once establish contact with my heart. And yet, because there is an element of individuality in places, when I am seized with a desire to see again the 'Guermantes way', it would not be satisfied were I led to the banks of a river in which were lilies as fair, or even fairer than those in the Vivonne, any more than on my return home in the evening, at the hour when there awakened in me that anguish which, later on in life, transfers itself to the passion of love, and may even become its inseparable companion, I should have wished for any strange mother to come in and say good night to me, though she were far more beautiful and more intelligent than my own. No: just as the one thing necessary to send me to sleep contented (in that untroubled peace which no mistress, in later years, has ever been able to give me, since one has doubts of them at the moment when one believes in them, and never can possess their hearts as I used to receive, in her kiss, the heart of my mother, complete, without scruple or reservation, unburdened by any liability save to myself) was that it should be my mother who came, that she should incline towards me that face on which there was, beneath her eye, something that was, it appears, a blemish, and which I loved as much as all the rest—so what I want to see again is the 'Guermantes way' as I knew it, with the farm that stood a little apart from the two neighbouring farms, pressed so close together, at the entrance to the oak avenue; those meadows upon whose surface, when it is polished by the sun to the mirroring radiance of a lake, are outlined the leaves of the apple-trees; that whole landscape whose individuality sometimes, at night, in my dreams, binds me with a power that is almost fantastic, of which I can discover no trace when I awake.[1]

The book has three main themes, Time and Memory; Love and Jealousy; and Society. Proust's own perception and experiences are the core of the book, though somewhat disguised. For example, there are three main love affairs, Swann's for Odette, Marcel's for Albertine, and Baron Charlus' for the violinist Morel. The first went back to a boy and girl affair of the teens with Marie de Bénardaky, who becomes Gilberte,

Swann and Odette's daughter. When in 1887 Proust ceased to see Marie, he wished to commit suicide by jumping from the window of 9 Boulevard Malesherbes. His first attempt at falling in love with a woman other than his mother had failed. Subsequently there were no further serious affairs with the other sex, though there may have been transient ones, as with people like Louisa de Mornand. The second great love affair was with his servant and chauffeur Agostinelli, who became Albertine in the book. Agostinelli eventually escaped from Proust's service and was drowned while training to fly. Proust continued to have his amorous adventures with a series of good-looking young men-servants. Sodom and Gomorrha, and the third love-theme of Charlus for Morel are thus expressions of Proust's deep seated preference for sexual relations with his own sex, a not uncommon consequence of a love affair between mother and son.

Apart from its beauty, the great merit of *À la recherche du temps perdu* is as a chronicle and commentary of the times. But it is strictly circumscribed. There are beautiful descriptions of apple blossom, the sea, churches, and social intercourse in an affluent society, of love, jealousy, indifference and hate. But the social circle whose manners he depicts, and from which his characters are drawn, is a narrow one. In this Proust is much inferior to his intellectual master, Balzac, whom he surpasses in his sensibility. But the book was Proust, and Proust's life had been a protected one, protected first by his mother and later by his wealth and his illness.

The beginning of *Swann's Way* strikes in me a most responsive chord. The smell of wet bracken or the song of a skylark brings back as though it were yesterday the many happy summer holidays I spent on my grandfather's farm in the parish of Elsdon, Northumberland. Although it is fifty years ago, the view down the valley towards Rothbury, the burns in which I used to fish, and the people who lived in the farmhouse, and who came and went, come back easily and always with delight. And a certain chime of a church clock evokes Rothbury, with my aunt's garden with an ice-house at the bottom sloping down to that most gorgeous of small rivers, the Coquet, sparkling over its red, green and purple porphyry pebbles and holding the most beautiful golden trout.

Why then did Proust write a masterpiece while I have not? A difference of talent no doubt. Moreover Proust was rich and never had to earn his living. While Proust was able to devote his whole talent to creating his book, I was leading an extremely busy life of practice, teaching, research and public affairs. But there is another great difference. While I was devoted to my mother, as he was to his, and while I had more need of her, since my father died when I was three, my '*Recherche du temps perdu*' would not have lingered on or indeed referred to any incident when my mother withheld the good night kiss. If she did so, I have no memory of it whatsoever.

Proust was, in fact, in love with his mother and she with him. She combined, as it were, the functions of mother and wife. He was dependent on her for every small detail of planning and execution. Proust is an interesting example of a not uncommon and, as yet, ill-studied group of men who have achieved great distinction, and who have had a unique relationship with their mothers, who often survive into old age. In Proust's case, as in others personally known to me, the relationship becomes crystallised at an early period of the son's life. Such men have never married, and they seem in some way to have been protected and supported by this relationship; the strength they have derived from it is part of the secret of their success.

Marcel Proust was born in 1871, the son of a successful and distinguished physician and Professor of the Faculty of Medicine at Paris, Adrien Proust, and his wife Jeanne, the daughter of a rich Jewish stockbroker, Nathé Weil. His father was an expert on public health and developed the concept of the *cordon sanitaire* to stop the spread of epidemics like cholera. Their Paris home was a large flat at 9 Boulevard Malesherbes. But it was his maternal grandfather's garden at Auteuil, and his aunt's house at Illiers, which provided him with his most vivid experiences and memories and therefore the material for *À la recherche du temps perdu*. Combray is Illiers.

Proust had a brother Robert, two years his junior. Robert followed his father in becoming a distinguished medical man. Oddly enough, Robert seems to have played very little part in Marcel's life. His name is seldom mentioned in his letters to his mother or father, and he does not appear in the novel. This is all the more odd since Marcel lived so much in his family, and particularly in the ambience of his mother and grandmother.

Marcel began to suffer from asthma at nine. The attacks did not seem to interfere with his childish games and adventures, chiefly with little girls, in the Champs Elysées, close to his home. These are charmingly and nostalgically described in *Swann's Way*. He went to school at the Lycée Condorcet, where he had a distinguished if not outstanding career as a scholar. At eighteen he volunteered for the Army to take advantage of the reduction to one year of service for volunteers. He was seventy-third out of seventy-four in his instructional platoon and got through his year without serious illness.

In 1890, after release from the army, Proust entered the Faculté de Droit of the Sorbonne. He also joined the École des Sciences Politiques, so that he could decide later whether to follow a career in Law or Diplomacy. In the event he did neither, for he wanted to be a writer: his parents were rich, he had begun to enjoy the salons of the Faubourg Saint-Germain. His asthmatic attacks helped him to indulge himself. In 1895, at the insistence of his father, who wished his sons to have careers, Marcel passed the examination of *licence ès lettres*; and began his tragi-comic career as honorary librarian of the Mazarine Library in the Institut de France. In this post, he applied for and received repeated long leaves for reasons of health. By 1900 he had not set foot in the library for four years and was ordered to return to work. In default of this he was deemed to have resigned.

Although *Les Plaisirs et les jours* was published in 1896 and he was writing small pieces and reviews, Proust's real occupation in his twenties was social advancement. He was rich, witty, learned and charming, and he missed no opportunity of impressing his personality on literary and artistic lions and society hostesses. Their personalities adorn his novels. In 1895 he began his first novel, *Jean Santeuil*, which was not published till after his death, but which foreshadowed *À la recherche*. He was not at all satisfied with it. Fortunately, he discovered Ruskin, and with the help of an English girl, Marie Nordlinger, began to translate him into French. Ruskin's aesthetic sensibility, his love of beauty, his passion for gothic architecture and his fastidious choice of language profoundly influenced Proust.

In 1896, Lorrain published a review of *Les Plaisirs et les jours*, which hinted that Proust had homosexual relations with Lucien Daudet. Proust challenged Lorrain, and a duel was fought on 7 February, both parties firing into the air. Proust on a later occasion was to challenge to a duel a skilled swordsman who courteously declined. He was not devoid of courage.

The two dominant factors in Proust's life were his illness and his relations with his mother. Each year hay fever began about the middle of April and continued till the autumn. Asthma became more and more frequent. Eventually, it prevented his going again to Illiers and led him to take his holidays either in the Alps or on the Normandy coast. Difficult breathing induced insomnia and both were treated with drugs. In 1902, demoralised by indigestion and insomnia, he visited the great Dr Vaquez, who advised a regime of bed, trional and cold tubs, and abstention from alcohol and morphine. Because his asthma tended to be worse by day, he developed the habit in his late twenties of sleeping from 8 a.m. to 3 p.m. and of working during the night. Frequently he would dine alone in the Ritz at 4 a.m.

As is frequently the case when mother and son fall in love with each other, the relationship becomes frozen at an early stage. Mme Proust always seemed to think of her son as a little boy. She wrote this letter to him when he was nineteen and serving in the army.

One month's already gone, darling. There are only eleven slices of the cake left for you to eat, and of these, one or two will be consumed on leave. I have thought of a way in which you may make the time seem shorter. Put aside eleven slabs of chocolate (you know how fond you are of chocolate), and make up your mind to eat one on the last day of every month. You will be surprised to find how quickly they vanish—and, with them, the months of your exile. . . .[2]

When Proust was thirteen he gave this answer to a stock questionnaire:

'What do you regard as the lowest depth of misery?'
'To be separated from Mamma.'

He wrote to her and she to him daily when he served in the army, and at brief intervals when he was on holiday or having a cure. Even when at home he would frequently leave her a note telling her how well or ill he was or asking that something should or should not be done. Some extracts from his letters illustrate this extraordinary relationship.[3]

Fontainebleau, Thursday, 11 p.m. (22
October 1896)

Ma chère petite Maman, I write to you in a state of deep dejection. In the first place this money that's lost (and as I suspect stolen, for I've since remembered that it wasn't in the pocket with a hole), after annoying me at first now takes on fantastic proportions. This evening it cut across my stomach-pains and the concert etc. and pursued me like a crime, a crime against you almost. Now I understand people who kill themselves for nothing at all. More than thirty francs! And while we're on the subject, the most urgent thing to send me is money (please send me a lot too much, and I still tremble to think it mayn't be enough), because without it I couldn't come back if I decided to. I think that my feeling so unwell, of which I spoke to you this morning on the telephone, comes partly from my stomach, I mean from the accumulation of the iodine I've been taking, and perhaps from eating inattentively. I'm going to be careful about it. . . .

Evian-les-Bains, In bed at one o clock in the afternoon, Thursday (?28 September 1899)

I've just heard the hotel will be closing any day now. So I need you to tell me in your *very next* letter what you want me to do, whether I ought to come straight home, or whether (supposing I can find a companion) I should return by way of the Italian lakes and Venice (please find out from Reynaldo where Coco is), or whether (but I should disapprove of this) I ought to move to the hotel at Thonon.

Friday evening (15 August 1902)

Vaquez recommended me not to let myself be carried away by morphine (he's no need to be afraid!) or alcohol, which he considers just as detrimental in all its forms. He says he wonders why invalids aren't content with their illnesses, but insist on creating new ones by making themselves unhappy for people who aren't worth the trouble. I couldn't help admiring this philosopher, though in my opinion he was baffled. If you were to make a thousand vows of deadly secrecy, I'd tell you something really exciting. But can I have absolute confidence, *more than I had in the matter of the alarm clock?* I'm a thousand times less sad. I still don't miss you. Mille tendres baisers, Marcel.

Monday evening, after dinner, 9 p.m. In the dining-room, 45 Rue de Courcelles (18 August 1902)

Your absence, although coming at such a disastrous period of my life, is beginning to bear fruit (please don't take that susceptibly like Mme Roussel!). For instance, yesterday

evening and this evening I've left off my 2nd pair of underpants,
and last night and again just now I've left off my 2nd Pyrenean
sweater in bed, which was infinitely more difficult. As I took
cold just now I don't know whether I shall be able to repeat
that tonight, . . .

(1902)

Ma petite Maman, As I'm unable to speak to you, I'm writing
to tell you that I simply can't understand your behaviour. You
know, or you must guess, that I've spent every night since I
came back in weeping, and not without good cause; and all
day long you say things to me like: 'I couldn't sleep last night
because the servants didn't go to bed till eleven o'clock.' I
only wish it was nothing worse than that that keeps *me* from
sleeping! Today, when I had a choking fit and needed the
things for a fumigation, I was so misguided as to ring for
Marie who'd just told me she'd finished her lunch, and you
immediately punished me for it, as soon as I'd taken my trional,
by seeing to it that there was a noise of hammering and shout-
ing all day. Thanks to you I was in such a state of nerves, that
when poor Fénelon came with Lauris, just for a few words he
said (very disagreeable ones, I must say) I went for him with
my fists (Fénelon, not Lauris), and without knowing what I
was doing I took the new hat he'd just bought, stamped on it,
tore it to pieces and ripped out the lining. As you might think
that I'm exaggerating I enclose a piece of the lining so that
you can see it's true.

(About December 1903)

Ma chère petite Maman, I'm writing you this little note, while
it's impossible for me to get to sleep, to tell you I'm thinking of
you. I should like, and I'm so absolutely determined, to be
able to get up at the same time as you, and drink my morning
coffee by your side. To feel that our sleeping and waking
hours are portioned out over one and the same expanse of
time will be my delight. With this end in view I went to bed

at 1.30, but had to get up again, and then I couldn't find my safety-pin—the one I used to fasten and tighten the waist of my drawers. So it was good-bye to my night's sleep. I tried to find another in your dressing-room, etc. etc., but the only thing I succeeded in catching in those perambulations was a violent cold (I'm only joking when I say 'violent')—and no sign of a safety-pin. I got into bed again but rest was impossible.

(23 September 1904)

Ma chère petite Maman, what were you thinking of, when you knew I was determined to come to Dieppe (and I'd be there already if I wasn't unwell, which I couldn't have foreseen), to choose a hotel where they can't warm the rooms (in which I shouldn't be able to go to bed without a fire) except with hot-air vents (which I couldn't bear for a single hour without having a choking-fit). It makes it impossible for me to come and join you, unless just to spend the afternoon with you and return to Paris in the evening. I had half a mind just now to send you some flannel nightgowns, which I hear you thought for a moment of taking with you. But I quite realize you're 'old enough to do what you like', and you'd have asked for them if you wanted them. . . . As you suspected, I haven't had my hair cut, but I can only repeat that I rushed through all my day-time business the very minute I got out of bed, for fear of making my already late hours still later owing to the bad night (but *without* asthma) I'd had.

(Undateable)

Ma chère petite Maman, Please don't fail to have someone in this evening. Although I'm a thousand times less in pain, I'm naturally spending a far worse day than yesterday, as so far it's been impossible to rest lying down, even without going to sleep, and I'm fumigating all the time. As a precautionary measure you might get some heroin on the offchance, although I'm absolutely determined not to take any. But one

can't tell what might happen with these attacks, that are so
unlike what I've been used to. So it would be much better to
be prepared than to have to wake a chemist up tonight. I feel
better at the moment. I hope this rain will put me in better
condition. Please get the heroin in any case, just for safety's
sake.

Mme Proust died on 25 September 1905. As she died she said
to Marcel: 'My dear boy musn't be afraid; his Mama won't
leave him.'

After his mother's death Proust retired from the world and
to his bedroom where he wept copiously. In December he
entered the sanatorium of Dr Solliers at Billancourt, where he
hoped to reform his habits. But Proust was tougher than the
doctor, and after six weeks during which he had regained his
old habits, he finally escaped from the demands of health. He
moved from his parent's large house in 45 Rue de Courcelles to
a smaller apartment in the Weil building at 102 Boulevard
Haussmann. His hours became more and more fixedly nocturnal and he gradually withdrew, over the years, from his social
engagements. He became more and more overtly homosexual.

In 1909 he had that remarkable experience which recalled
the madeleine which his aunt had given him and opened his
mind to '*temps perdu*'. Writing at night in his bedroom which
he had lined with cork to reduce dust and noise, he constructed
the immense work which seemed to grow of its own accord
rather than from any initial plan. About 1911 he thought himself in sight of the end and sought a publisher. He then con-
templated three volumes, *Du côté de chez Swann* or perhaps *Le
Temps perdu*, *Le Côté de Guermantes* and *Le Temps retrouvé*. He
wrote to Louis de Robert:

I have been working, as you may know, ever since I began to
be ill, at a long book which I call a novel because it lacks that
quality of the casual which is the mark of a volume of Memoirs
(it is casual only in so far as it presents the casual nature of

life), the design of which is strongly marked though not easy to grasp because of its complexity. I am quite incapable of telling you what *kind* of novel it is. Some sections of it have a country setting, others varying social backgrounds: some parts are quite family affairs, many are terribly indecent. . . . The novel is so long (though to my mind, very concise) that it will run to three volumes of four hundred pages each, or, what would be better, two, one of seven hundred, the other of five.

A publisher was found with difficulty and 'Swann' was published in 1913. Proust went on writing and the work had swelled to eight parts when he died in 1922. Even the proofs were greatly added to. His illness gave him seclusion, and a sense of urgency lest he should die before the work was finished. But as he got older, his illness, and the drugs he took, made work more and more of an effort. By 1916 he was unfit for any other way of life than insomnia, fumigation (as he called the powders he used to burn for his asthma) and confinement to bed for six and a half days every week. He used opium and heroin intermittently, but chiefly the powerful and long-acting hypnotics, trional and veronal. In 1919 came the final calamity. After his mother's death he had moved to 102 Boulevard Haussmann, a family house of the Weils, and therefore redolent with associations particularly of his mother and grandmother. Then this was sold by his aunt to a banker. Proust had to move to 8 Rue Laurent-Pichat; with great thrift he sold the cork lining of his bedroom to a wine-merchant. In March he developed a speech defect, partly, according to his doctor, because his anxiety had induced him to take an overdose of veronal. In September 1919 he staggered and fell in his bedroom. In October he accidentally poisoned himself with an overdose of veronal, dial and opium. In 1922 he overdosed himself with adrenaline which he took by injection partly to counteract the effects of veronal. From time to time he had attacks of giddiness, of weakness, and of speech difficulty. These he attributed to uraemia, but they were more probably due to the large doses of drugs that he was taking. In September 1922 he had several attacks of giddiness; his speech and memory were affected. When he ventured to the Ritz for dinner at 4 a.m. he instantly improved and attributed the attacks to carbon monoxide poisoning from cracks in his chimney. So a fire in the grate was prohibited. He continued to be deeply engaged in rewriting the beginning of *La Prisonnière*. In October he attended a soirée on a foggy evening, caught a cold which quickly developed into bronchitis. Proust continued to write; on 24 October he had finished *La Prisonnière* and now turned to revise *Albertine disparue*. On 8 November he developed bronchopneumonia. On 18 November he died; his last word was 'Mother'.

From a medical point of view, Proust's case is by no means simple. He undoubtedly had an organic disease, bronchial asthma, and he was an eccentric. But these alone are not enough to account for his behaviour and the extent to which illness dominated the latter part of his life. I cannot escape the conviction that in that period, at least, a psychoneurosis was the dominant cause of his ill-health and the ensuing pattern of his behaviour.

Proust's long and complicated illness began with asthma. His first attack, vividly described by his brother, occurred when Marcel was aged nine, and they were returning from a walk in the Bois de Boulogne. The attack was quite typical. Asthma is due to hypersensitivity to an inhaled foreign protein. The reaction of the body induces contraction of the bronchi. Hay fever, from which Proust also suffered, is a closely related disease. Although asthma is thus an example of a disease due to a specific peculiarity of the body, it very frequently becomes greatly influenced by the patient's mind. In this it probably resembles the Pavlov conditioned reflex. Pavlov's pupils showed that if a dog is given injections of apomorphine, which cause it to vomit, at the same time as another, unrelated,

7 Proust

8(a) Elizabeth Barrett, with Flush, from an unpublished water-colour by her brother Alfred, dated 27 September 1843

(b) Elizabeth Barrett Browning—Rome, February 1859—engraving by T. O. Barlow from a photograph by Macaire Havre

stimulus, then after a sufficient number of exposures, this other stimulus alone suffices to produce vomiting. In Proust's case, it was said that even looking through his window at chestnut trees in flower would provoke an attack. In him, his asthma assumed another function which steadily increased in import-ance. His illness restored to him his mother's affection.

Before his mother's death, Proust had accommodated him-self to his asthma. He was indeed an eccentric, as he showed by his behaviour in the only appointment he ever held in his life, that of honorary Librarian to the Mazarine Library. When he was thirty-two he was best man at his brother Robert's wed-ding. He wore three overcoats and numerous mufflers; his chest was padded and his collar lined with swathes of cotton wool. Thus dressed he was too bulky to move along the pews and had to stand in the aisle during the service. He announced that he could not dress otherwise; that he had been ill for months and would be ill again that evening. He clearly took his illness very seriously and it came to absorb him, as we can see from his letters to his mother. It was after his mother's death that Proust's illness assumed increasingly the characteristics of a psychoneurosis. We have seen how he broke down completely when she died, how he entered a sanatorium where he hoped that medical treatment would enable him to reform his habits and how that failed. He surrendered more and more to his ill-ness. He ceased to frequent salons, concerts, theatres, and he gave up the gay social life which had been the most cherished part of his earlier life. More and more of his life was spent alone in his bedroom. His habits became more and more nocturnal. He became increasingly a slave to his drugs: iodides and stramonium to relieve the attacks, and opium, dial, veronal and trional to induce sleep, and caffeine and adrenaline to wake him. These drugs, to which he had become addicted, helped to terminate his life. And alone in his bedroom, at night, the memories would come flooding back and the words kept flow-ing from his pen with immense advantage to posterity.

Henri Mondor wrote this of Proust:

The year 1905, the watershed and turning point in that exceptional life, is in fact the time when the worldly Marcel Proust was to give way to Marcel Proust the recluse, and when the dilettante was eclipsed by the writer. The giddy round of an extremely brilliant social life had to be replaced by solitude, silence and the obscurity of the sick-room; he had to bid farewell for ever to the meadows, gardens, pleasures of the table and entertainments, even to the air outside with its all too potent aromas. With the death of his mother, that crucial event in the writer's life, the year 1905 also marks the point at which Marcel Proust changed from the overgrown child into the lonely orphan; at the same time, perhaps, it gave him the greater urgency and freedom to express himself in his work with all the necessary facts.[5]

Why was it that his mother's death had such a profound effect upon the habits, behaviour and attitude of Proust? Was it simply grief at the loss of someone he loved more than he had ever loved, or would ever love again? The effect on her son was far too profound for that. Moreover, there is clear evidence that there was more to it. In 1907, not long after his mother's death, Proust was shocked to read in his *Figaro*, that his friend, Henri van Blarenberghe, had stabbed his mother to death and then killed himself. Marcel was asked by the editor to write an article on it for *Figaro*. He began at 3 a.m. and wrote till he was stopped by writer's cramp at 8 a.m. His article was entitled 'The Filial Feelings of a Matricide'. He set out to prove that van Blarenberghe had only done suddenly and by violence what other men do gradually and by degrees, and that all men kill their mothers. While he and his mother had loved one another, their love had been a mockery, because he had never forgiven that fatal omission of the goodnight kiss:

Every day, for nearly thirty years, when he displayed his asthma, extorted her service, received her visits at his idle bedside, or left her to go with his friends, he had been exacting retribution. He saw that as surely as Henri had killed his mother, so too had he.[4]

Painter quoted Proust's article thus:

The fact is that we age and kill the heart that loves us by the anxiety we cause, by the uneasy tenderness we inspire and keep in a state of unceasing alarm. If we could see in a beloved body the slow work of destruction carried out by this anguished affection, the ravaged eyes, the hair which stayed indomitably black now defeated like the rest and turning white, the hardened arteries and obstructed kidneys, the courage vanquished by life, the slow, heavy step, the spirit that knows there is nothing left but despair, though once it rebounded tirelessly with unconquerable hopes, the inborn and seemingly immortal gaiety dried up for ever.

Painter went on that Proust concluded that if, in a moment of lucid sanity like van Blarenberghe's when he saw his mother bleeding to death, we could see all these things, then we too would shoot ourselves like him. Proust wrote:

In most men this agonising vision fades all too soon in the returning dawn of joy in life. But what joy, what reason for living, what life can bear to look it in the face? Which is true, it or joy? Which is the Truth?

Painter concluded:

The night on which he wrote '*Filial Feelings of a Matricide*' was a turning-point in Proust's life. For the first time he acknowledged his guilt, and was therefore able to forgive his mother; he had gone back beyond the evening at Auteuil when Time Lost began, into the world outside Time where his novel awaited him. He began to descend from the mountains of his mother's death, the watershed of his life, to make the long journey towards revelation and extinction. Which would come first? In the words of his question, which was the truth, it or joy?[4]

After his mother died, Proust's intellectual and emotional situation was peculiarly difficult. He had been her little boy, metaphorically tied to her apron strings. Now he was alone and defenceless, and riddled with the fear and the guilt that he was responsible for her death. It is not surprising that his illness grew worse, severe enough to make him a hermit. His illness thus brought him solitude and he found his solace by escaping from the world of the present, from which his mother had gone, into the world of the past, where his mother still lived and he was free of guilt. So began *À la recherche du temps perdu*, which he recognised as the work of his hitherto unconscious memory. It grew and grew as his memories and the fantasies based on them flooded into his mind and on to his writing paper. As the good physician knows, and the Roman Catholic Church has established in the Confessional over the centuries, the doubter and the sinner may gain something like peace of mind by recalling his past and sharing his fears, his doubts, and his desires, with others.

If this interpretation of Proust's illness is correct, then *À la recherche du temps perdu* falls into line with *Science and Health* as an example of mental catharsis. It represented Proust's escape from his grief and guilt occasioned by his mother's death into a world, part real and part imaginary, which existed largely before that tragic event took place. Unlike *Science and Health*, it did not cure the psychoneurosis, though no doubt it made its cause easier to bear. And unlike the author of *Science and Health*, Proust was still creating his great work when he died.

Chapter 14
ELIZABETH BARRETT
BROWNING

Many of my literary friends suggested that Elizabeth Barrett Browning was a splendid example of my thesis. So I examined her case eagerly. I found that she was not in the same category as my earlier examples. She was creative and she was apparently mentally ill. But there seemed to be no relationship between the two. Elizabeth Barrett is an example of a third category, in which psychoneurosis and creativity are independent of one another. As Alethea Hayter[1] has pointed out, Elizabeth was in many ways a professional writer. She wrote poetry from the age of six until she died, and its flow throughout was independent of her various illnesses. It must not be supposed, however, that she was in any way uninspired. Chesterton[2] said of her: 'With her reappeared in poetry a certain element which had not been present in it since the last days of Elizabethan literature, the fusion of the most elementary human passion with something which can only be described as wit. . . .'

One might have guessed that the category to which she belongs would exist, which makes its discovery all the more pleasing. Another difference between her case and the others is that her illness was at first physical, and the mental illness that succeeded it was almost entirely imposed from without, by her doctors, aided by the personality of her father. In the other instances, psychoneurosis arose within the patient's own mind, though in the cases of Charles Darwin and Florence Nightingale, the doctors helped the symptoms to persist.

Elizabeth Barrett Browning was a partial invalid from the age of fifteen and a complete invalid from the age of thirty-two to the age of forty, when Robert Browning persuaded her to elope with him, and to lead a vigorous life, despite the fact that she had become a morphine addict.[3] She died aged fifty-three. She wrote poetry before she became ill, during her illness, and after she recovered from it. Her poetry written in all three periods was very highly esteemed during her lifetime, much more so than her husband's. Now the position is reversed. From the point of view of my thesis I am not aware that it has ever been suggested by any of the high-priests of literary criticism that the poetry of one period is superior to that of another, particularly if one considers her youth when she first became ill.[4]

Elizabeth Barrett was born in 1806, the eldest of the twelve children of Edward Barrett Moulton Barrett and his wife, born Mary Graham Clarke. Edward had been born Moulton and had added the surname Barrett after inheriting wealth, property and slaves in Jamaica. He bought an estate in Herefordshire where he built a house in the Turkish style, called Hope End. Here Elizabeth spent her remarkable and happy childhood. The Barrett children were a numerous and lively lot and they had many friends who joined them in sport and play. Elizabeth was the liveliest as well as the eldest and so became the leader. Her constant companion and greatest friend was her eldest brother, Edward, 'Bro'. She recorded in her Autobiography written at fourteen: 'At four I mounted Pegasus . . . At eleven I wished to be considered an authoress. At twelve I enjoyed a literary life in all its pleasures. Metaphysics were my highest delight and having read a page of Locke my mind not only felt edified but exalted.'[5] This infant prodigy was not in fact an insufferable little prig, but a very gay, very active and extremely intelligent little girl.

When she was six she presented her father with some lines on 'Virtue', as a consequence of which he dubbed her 'the poet laureate of Hope End'. She continued to write both verse and prose and at fourteen her father had privately printed for her *The Battle of Marathon*, her first published poem, begun when she was eleven years of age. It was not a great poem and

Elizabeth described it later as 'Pope's Homer done over again, or rather undone'.

When she was fifteen she had her first serious illness variously attributed to a fall or to a strain when she was saddling her pony —she was very small. Disease of the spine was suspected. She became an invalid for the first time. Her illness may or may not have been exacerbated by Bro's being sent to Charterhouse while she, being a girl, had to make do with education at home. How long she was in bed I have been unable to ascertain, but she never resumed her former activities and no longer rode her pony. But this gave her all the more time for books. She could translate Greek, Latin and Italian; she had learned German and enough Hebrew to read her Old Testament through in the original. She continued to write verse. When she was nineteen, *The Rose and the Zephyr* was printed in the *Literary Gazette*, as were her *Irregular Stanzas* a year later. Her second volume of verse *An Essay on Mind* was published in 1826 when she was twenty years old.

Edward Moulton Barrett lost his wife in 1827 and then most of his West Indian fortune. He had to sell his Herefordshire estate in 1832. During the later years Elizabeth became very friendly with a learned neighbour, Hugh Boyd, who was blind. His classical learning matched hers and their friendship undoubtedly helped her genius to develop.

From Herefordshire the Barretts moved to Sidmouth where they lived for three years. In 1833 the Bill abolishing slavery was passed. Her father saw further ruin to his Jamaican fortune but Elizabeth was delighted. In 1835 they moved to 74 (now 95) Gloucester Place in London. Since her mother's death and the move from Hope End, the family had been more and more dominated by her father and had lived increasingly a life of their own with relatively few visitors. Of these the most important was John Kenyon, a cousin of Edward Moulton Barrett, a fellow undergraduate at Trinity, Cambridge, and, like him, inheritor of a West Indies fortune. It was John Kenyon who introduced Elizabeth to Miss Mitford and who was to bring

Mr Browning. For Kenyon was the friend and patron of poets and writers.

The move to London depressed Elizabeth who had now become habituated to her couch. In 1837 she wrote to Miss Mitford,* with whom she corresponded copiously and delightfully for the next nine years:[6]

. . . And it would be so wise if you would learn to be a *lollard* like me, and establish yourself on a sofa instead of on a chair, study the art, not a very difficult one, of writing in a recumbent position. I can write as well or as badly when I lie down, as at a desk. I used once to suffer from a feebleness in the spine; and even now it is exceedingly fatiguing to me, to sit bolt upright without the mediation of the back of a chair, for any length of time. But with *your* tendency, I am quite sure that a recumbent—not a merely leaning position—would be essentially useful to you. It would lessen both the actual fatigue, and the evils consequent upon sedentary habits. This is very learned is it not?—I think I deserve a diploma.

1838 saw the move to 50 Wimpole Street and the publication of *The Seraphim and other Poems* by Elizabeth Barrett Barrett, the first poems under her own name, which firmly established her reputation.

Elizabeth's illness began late in 1837. On 29 November 1837 she wrote to Miss Mitford:

I caught a cold nearly two months ago which turned into a cough and has kept me to the house ever since and in a very weak state—and Dr Chambers whom I was kindly persecuted into seeing yesterday (I have an abhorence of '*medical advice*', but my sisters were obdurate) says that I must not think of stirring into the air for weeks to come. He assures me that there is no *desease*—only an excitability, and irritability of

* Mitford, Mary Russell (1787–1853), novelist and dramatist; author of *Our Village*.

chest, which require precaution. And nothing is much more disagreeable than *precaution.*

She continued to be troubled but in June 1838, when they had moved to Wimpole Street, was able to report that Dr Chambers (Physician Extraordinary to the Queen) thought she had not lost ground. In July she reported: 'I was given into the safe keeping of Digitalis yesterday, for my *pulse* which keeps pace with the Wild Huntsman—and it is tamer today; and Dr Chambers goes on to think me in a better state upon the whole.' Her doctors thought a winter in London would be fatal and so she was sent to Torquay whence in September she wrote:

Dr Barry seems to be quite sure that the respiration is clearer on the affected side—and the spitting of blood is very little, —almost (?) less than it has been at all since the first appearance of that unpleasant symptom. At the same time the last ten days have been dreary, uncomfortable ones to me, haunted throughout by weakness, an oppressive *sense* of weakness, and a lowness of spirits from which I am generally free. Such lowness of spirits, that I could have cried all day if there were no *exertion* in crying—and feel the consciousness of there being no cause for gloom, just as a new mortification instead of as a comfort, the whole time! This was the result of taking digitalis for three weeks instead of one—and now I am reviving, and rising again to the 'high estate' of common sense and cheerfulness.

A prolonged cough accompanied by the spitting of blood is strongly suggestive of pulmonary tuberculosis, which in those days was a common, and rightly feared, disease. The main treatment was of course bed-rest, with the avoidance of draughts and attention to diet. So began Elizabeth's long imprisonment in her bedroom, in which she was to remain till Robert Browning encouraged her to leave it, and ultimately to escape from it for ever.

Elizabeth stayed in Torquay for three years. In 1840, her brother Sam died in the West Indies. And then on 11 July happened an event which had a profound influence on her behaviour. Her eldest brother Edward, 'Bro', was drowned while sailing. Not only was Bro her dearest friend, she also blamed herself for his death. As she told Browning later in one of her letters, she had asked her aunt to write to her father requesting permission for Bro to stay on. In doing so her father said he considered it very wrong of Elizabeth to exact such a thing. 'These words were burned into me as if with fire,' Elizabeth told Browning years later. That autumn she wrote to Miss Mitford:

Notwithstanding this trembling hand I am better and stronger —and more tranquil as to my thoughts. I suffered from what was called *congestion of the heart*—and was (?) in so singular and frightful a state of weakness as not to be able to sleep for five minutes together without *fainting*. For weeks they watched me in their kindness night after night—only ascertaining the transition by a sigh, or the sudden coldness of cheek and forehead. And now I can sleep for an hour or more at a time—and the faintings are almost quite gone. Dearest Miss Mitford—I do truly love you. Love me a little. You understand so well—and will—besides—that I want them all to go and leave me here with my maid for the winter. I should be far easier and happier if they would—*far easier* but I fear they won't go,—dear things! . . .

Her guilt and loneliness occasioned by Bro's death increased her dependence on, and love for, her father to whom she dedicated her poems in 1844. The dedication ends:

And my desire is that you, who are a witness how if this art of poetry had been a less earnest object to me, it must have fallen from exhausted hands before this day,—that you, who have shared with me in things bitter and sweet, softening or enhancing them, every day,—that you, who hold with me over all sense of loss and transiency, one hope by one Name,—may accept from me the inscription of these volumes, the exponents of a few years of an existence which has been sustained and comforted by you as well as given. Somewhat more faint-hearted than I used to be, it is my fancy thus to seem to return to a visible personal dependence on you, as if indeed I were a child again; to conjure your beloved image between myself and the public, so as to be sure of one smile,—and to satisfy my heart while I sanctify my ambition, by associating with the great pursuit of my life its tenderest and holiest affection. Your E.B.B.

Elizabeth returned to Wimpole Street in September 1841 in a patent invalid carriage 'with a thousand springs'. She wrote at once to Miss Mitford.

I write only a line. I am tired of course, with a sense of being thoroughly *beaten*,—but bad symptoms have not occurred—at least the spitting of blood increased *very* little in proportion to what might have been expected—and the whole amount of God's mercy to me is told in the fact of my being *here*. 'How great is the sum of it'! Here—with Papa—in the midst of all left! No more partings—nor meetings which were worse—almost *much* worse sometimes. I thank God for the undeserved mercy.

The grief stricken bedridden invalid was now installed in the household presided over by Edward Moulton Barrett. He had become a dominant, domineering and thoroughly unreasonable father. Despite his wife having herself produced twelve children for him he had become fanatically opposed to the idea of a sex life for his remaining children. None married without his consent. None, although all over twenty years of age, were allowed guests to dinner without his consent. Fortunately he could be depended on to be absent in the city dealing with Jamaican trade and his two ships from noon to six or seven in the afternoon.

Some idea of the way she lived is given in this extract from a letter to Miss Mitford dated 4 May 1843,[6] five years after her illness began:

I have come into Papa's room, the adjoining room to mine, for the first time today, to have the windows opened and a little dusting done . . . which will make me cleaner and more exemplary tomorrow. The consequence of living through the winter in one room, with a fire, day and night, and every crevice sealed close, . . . you may imagine perhaps by the help of your ideal of all Dustlessness, latent and developed. At last we come to walk upon a substance like white sand, and if we dont lift our feet gently up and put them gently down, we act Simoom, and stir up the sand into a cloud. As to a duster or a broom, seen in profile even, . . . calculate the effect upon us! The spiders have grown tame—and their webs are a part of our own domestic economy,—Flush eschews walking under the bed. The result of which is that I am glad May is come, that I yield to that necessity at once.

Though she rarely left her room, the invalid was not idle. Some of her best poetry dates from this period. Her letters, particularly her sustained literary gossip with Miss Mitford, indicate how much she read and with what critical perception. All the living facts are reviewed. But her letters, unlike those of Proust, make no more mention of her illness than any other relevant topic. Browning appears for the first time in a letter of 1 April 1842 (Isn't it *spring?*): 'Certainly Mr Browning does speak in parables—and more darkly than . . . even . . . some others of your friends. But he is a true poet. I estimate him very highly—and so do you—and so must all who know what poetry is and turn their faces towards its presence willingly.' By 14 December 1842 she writes: 'I admire Mr Browning; and recognise him always as a true original poet whenever I consider, and that is not seldom,—how great a thing it is to be one . . .' The respect deepened with each new experience.

In *Lady Geraldine's Courtship*, published in 1844, she wrote:

Or from Browning some 'Pomegranate', which, if cut
deep down the middle,

Shows a heart within blood-tinctured, of a veined humanity.

Robert Browning, who was at that time much less famous
than Elizabeth Barrett, was delighted to receive such appreciation and from such a source. He wrote on 10 January 1845:

I love your verses with all my heart, dear Miss Barrett,—and
this is no off-hand complimentary letter that I shall write,—
whatever else, no prompt matter-of-course recognition of
your genius, and there a grateful and natural end of the thing.
Since the day last week when I first read your poems, I quite
laugh to remember how I have been turning and turning again
in my mind what I should be able to tell you of their effect upon
me, for in the first flush of delight I thought I would this once
get out of my habit of purely passive enjoyment, . . . I do, as
I say, love these books with all my heart—and I love you too.

Thus began a correspondence which rapidly ripened into
friendship and, perhaps not unnaturally with such literary
talent, became one of the most delightful collections of love-
letters in the world. The problem was to meet, for Elizabeth,
imprisoned in her room, was guarded not only by the customs
of the house, but by her own well-established habits. But the
desire grew. In March she wrote to Miss Mitford:

Ah—Mr Chorley. But you know, I cannot exchange him quite
for Mr Browning. Mr Browning and I have grown to be
devoted friends I assure you—and he writes me letters praying
to be let in, quite heart-moving and irresistible. In the summer
I must see him—and Mr Chorley too. I shall like to see *both*.
And then for Hyères and everybody! You see what Mr
Chorley says of Paracelsus? You see it is not merely a dream
of mine!—he is full of genius. And then he writes letters to me

with Attic contractions, saying he '*loves*' *me*. Who can resist *that*?

John Kenyon, the mutual friend of both poets, and accepted
visitor to 50 Wimpole Street, arranged the meeting. Elizabeth
wrote to Miss Mitford on 26 May 1845:

Mr Kenyon has not returned yet,—but will, I suppose, at the
end of this week, or the beginning of next —— and oh! did I
tell you in my last letter that I had seen lately (*now I beseech
you to keep my counsel and not tell Mr Horne—and not tell Mr
Chorley!*) Mr Browning? He said in his courtesy more, in the
way of request, than the thing was worth,—and so I received
him here one morning, and liked him much. Younger looking
than I had expected—looking younger than he *is*, of course—
with natural and not ungraceful manners,—and full of his art,
which he is destined, I believe, so worthily to sustain. He is
kind enough to promise to read my new Prometheus for me,—
and we shall be good friends I hope.

Browning had stayed an hour and a half and made a deep
impression. 'I had a sense of your presence constantly,' Elizabeth told him later. He wrote at once hoping he had not stayed
too long, expressing his happiness and asking her not to
humiliate him by calling him kind. She wrote back impulsively
that there must be no restriction on their vocabulary and inviting him again in a week's time and again when he liked. A day
later he wrote intemperate things, an open declaration of love.
Her agitated reply urged him to forget at once and for ever
what he had written.

It is not difficult to understand how upsetting it must have
been to the invalid recluse. She was thirty-nine and had been
apparently gravely ill for seven years. This handsome talented
young man, already beloved by her as a poet, must have had a
cataclysmic effect by his appearance in the flesh and precipitate
declaration of love. She later confessed 'I could not sleep night
after night,—could not,—and my fear was at nights, lest the
feverishness should make me talk deliriously and tell the secret

aloud.'⁷ The passionate friendship continued for some weeks to run into the stormy waters of misunderstanding. But mutual affection, sympathy and common interests gradually asserted themselves. Browning knew that he wanted this tiny pallid-faced woman with the big eyes for his wife. There were three obstacles, her health, her father, and money. They kept their weekly interviews as far as possible secret, except from her father who, though he did not over-value poetry, seems to have been proud of the visits as testimony to his daughter's growing reputation as a poet. He certainly did not suspect the true nature of their friendship.

On 8 July, Elizabeth ventured not only out of her room but out of the house, going for a short drive in her carriage. She repeated this, walking, as she told her brother George, 'as well as most children of two years old'. Robert encouraged her: 'Never, pray, *pray*, never lose one sunny day or propitious hour to "go out and walk about".' 'But do not surprise *me*,' he added boldly, 'one of these mornings by "walking" up to me when I am introduced . . . or I shall infallibly, in spite of all the after repentence and begging pardon—I shall . . .'.

The possibility of her going to the Mediterranean for the winter was discussed between them and Mr Kenyon. Malta became the focus. But Mr Barrett was unhelpful. A little later it was Pisa, recommended now by Dr Chambers. Her brother and sister were to have accompanied her. But the Pisa project also fell through, wrecked again on the unyielding rock of Edward Moulton Barrett.

The mutual affection between Robert and Elizabeth had now got as far as to enable them to discuss the possibility of marriage. On 16 September 1845, Elizabeth wrote of the barrier God had put between them. 'As dear Mr Kenyon said to me today in his smiling kindness . . . "In ten years you may be strong perhaps."' Browning, however, did not despair. The winter came and went. With spring Elizabeth was out again. With the coming of autumn the advisability of wintering in the south was raised again, but the intention now was not that Elizabeth should go with her brother and sister, but that she should go with Robert as man and wife. Pisa was to be the goal.

Browning had hitherto lived on an allowance from his father. His poems brought him in nothing. Elizabeth had a small private fortune: £8,000 in the Funds, an investment in the Eastern Railway and a share in the ship, the *David Lyon*, brought in a little under £200 a year. She drew £40 a quarter which did not represent her whole income. She spent it, but not all on herself. Her dress never exceeded £20 a year. 'My greatest personal expense lately has been the morphine. Still the money flows out of the window and the door. You will understand how it flows like a stream.' The fact is that Elizabeth was extremely generous and was always sending her friends like Miss Mitford gifts of salmon, oysters and similar delicacies.

The plans for Pisa were eventually perfected. Wilson, Elizabeth's maid, and Flush, her dog, a present from Miss Mitford, were to go too. Wilson was to smuggle the luggage, in advance, to Nine Elms Station, whence they were to take the train, cross the channel, go to Paris, and thence to Pisa. Browning made the necessary arrangements. On the morning of 11 September, Elizabeth and Wilson slipped out of the house at 11 o'clock. Robert and Elizabeth were married at St Marylebone Parish Church with Wilson and Browning's cousin, James Silverthorne, as witnesses. At 11.30 Browning left, while Elizabeth returned to the cab and drove to Boyd's house in St John's Wood, where she had lunch with him and her sisters. In the afternoon they drove to Hampstead Heath and so home. On 19 September between 3.30 and 4 o'clock, Wilson and Elizabeth left Wimpole Street carrying only small bags of necessities and Flush. Outside Hodgson's, the bookshop, they met Browning and entered a cab for Nine Elms Station. They were just in time, for on the 21st Mr Barrett had arranged to take his family to Little Bookham, so that Wimpole Street could be redecorated. Elizabeth had posted letters to her father and sisters on the morning of the 19th, but they had not arrived when Henrietta told her father of Elizabeth's flight. Mr Barrett

was standing on the stairs holding a heavy book. In his amaze-
ment he dropped the book. Henrietta, terrified, slipped and fell.
And so the legend started that on hearing of the flight of his
eldest daughter, Mr Barrett threw her sister downstairs. A note
of the marriage, giving no date, was inserted in the leading
newspapers. Mr Barrett never referred to Elizabeth again. Her
correspondence with Miss Mitford came to an end.

Travelling in the mid-nineteenth century was by no means
easy. The journey from Dieppe to Paris took nineteen and a
half hours. Nevertheless, Elizabeth survived without mishap
other than fatigue. Her old friend Mrs Jameson persuaded them
to stay a week in Paris at her hotel. In Orleans letters from home
awaited them. Those from Mr Barrett and brother George were
curt and angry, those from her sisters Henrietta and Arabella
warm and friendly; from that day on they had Robert's deep
affection. The Brownings stayed some months in Pisa where
they became bored and then moved on to Florence which was
to be their home till Elizabeth's death.

After her marriage Elizabeth had become a different creature. As Mrs Jameson said: 'You are not improved, you are
transformed.' She wrote to Mrs Martin: 'I was buried and that
was the whole . . . a thoroughly morbid and desolate state it
was which I look back now to with a sort of horror with which
one would look back to one's graveclothes if one had been
clothed in them by mistake during a trance.' Browning persuaded her to go for long walks and on expeditions into the
mountains. Almost at once she became pregnant, much to her
surprise; this miscarried at five months. Their only child,
Robert Wiedeman Barrett (Pen) was born in 1849. She had
two further miscarriages, losing 100 ounces of blood with the
second in July 1850 which left her very weak. Given the state of
medicine and therapeutics at the time, this must have left her
with a profound iron deficiency anaemia which would account
for her subsequent pallor and bouts of lethargy. How they
spent their lives may be gleaned from Elizabeth's letter to
Henrietta in April 1855. 'Robert's poems are magnificent and

will raise him higher than he stands. We are up early working, working. Penini's lessons I never neglect—then I write. Then dinner—then I criticise Robert's MSS. Altogether I have scarcely breath for reading. . . . Everybody admires at me for looking so well. How can I hope to be pitied when I am always dying and it makes no difference.'

Living in Italy was wonderfully cheap and they had managed to keep Wilson and employ other servants on Elizabeth's small income, augmented by £100 a year from Mr Kenyon after Penini's birth, and by the £11,000 left to them by Mr Kenyon after his death.

At first neither Elizabeth nor Robert wrote much. Then they began and in 1855 each wrote 8000 lines of poetry. Elizabeth's publications included *Sonnets from the Portuguese* in 1850, well received but written mostly before her marriage, *Aurora Leigh*, 1857, a long poem which shocked proper Victorians, and *Poems before Congress*, 1860.

Her father died in 1857. Elizabeth was deeply distressed. She would not leave the house. After a month, Robert wrote: 'She shall if I have to carry her, before the week is out', and he did succeed in bringing his wife back to life, even if not to so full a life as he had provided before. After her marriage, Elizabeth's health at first was wonderfully good. But the chest trouble returned. In 1856 a London fog brought on a cough and difficult breathing. She did not recover until she had returned to Florence. She continued to get attacks which steadily weakened her, and made her more breathless. By the summer of 1859 she could not climb the steps to the cathedral in Siena. In June 1860 she 'caught cold through sitting in a draught'. Her doctors found signs of consolidation of a lung and suspected an abscess. At first Robert carried her during the day into their sitting-room, later a bed was put up for her there. She began to sleep heavily. She died in Browning's arms on 29 June 1861.

It may be in doubt whether Elizabeth's best poetry was written when she was an invalid recluse, or before that, or afterwards. There is no doubt that she was creative in all three periods. I can see no evidence for supposing that her creativity was dependent on her period of invalidity, though her experiences during that time must have affected her art, and may have refined her feeling. Moreover, one would expect that when she was febrile, breathless, and spitting blood, she would not write poetry. Commenting on the influence of her illness on her poetry, she herself wrote (to Robert Browning):[7]

I have lived only inwardly; or with *sorrow*, for a strong emotion. Before this seclusion of my illness, I was secluded still, and there are few of the youngest women in the world who have not seen more, heard more, known more, of society, than I, who am scarcely to be called young now. I grew up in the country—had no social opportunities, had my heart in books and poetry, and my experience in reveries. My sympathies drooped towards the ground like an untrained honeysuckle—and but for *one*, in my own house—but of this I cannot speak. It was a lonely life, growing green like the grass around it. Books and dreams were what I lived in—and domestic life only seemed to buzz gently around, like the bees about the grass. And so time passed, and passed—and afterwards, when my illness came and I seemed to stand at the edge of the world with all done, and no prospect (as appeared at one time) of ever passing the threshold of one room again; why then, I turned to thinking with some bitterness (after the greatest sorrow of my life had given me room and time to breathe) that I had stood blind in this temple I was about to leave—that I had seen no Human nature, that my brothers and sisters of the earth were *names* to me, that I had beheld no great mountain or river, nothing in fact. I was as a man dying who had not read Shakespeare, and it was too late! do you understand? And do you also know what a disadvantage this ignorance is to my art? Why, if I live on and yet do not escape from this seclusion, do you not perceive that I labour under signal disadvantages—that I am, in a manner, as a *blind poet*? Certainly, there is a compensation to a degree. I have had much of the inner life, and from the habit of self-consciousness and self-analysis, I make great guesses at Human nature in the main. But how willingly I would as a poet exchange some of this lumbering, ponderous, helpless knowledge of books, for some experience of life and man.

THE NATURE OF MISS BARRETT'S ILLNESS

The data that I have been able to find regarding Elizabeth's first illness are meagre. There seems no doubt that spinal disease, and possibly Potts disease or tuberculosis of the spine, was suspected, and there seems no doubt that, after it, the carefree tomboy never rode her pony again and was disposed to treat herself, and be treated by her family, as having to lead a protected life. Her prolonged illness with cough, fever and the spitting of blood was most probably pulmonary tuberculosis or, much less likely, bronchiectasis. However, there is no doubt that when Robert Browning entered her life she was not so ill as she seemed. She improved rapidly under his guidance and management. Their life after marriage was by no means without its hardships. There were many expeditions into the mountains together and they travelled a good deal. Although over forty, she bore a child and had three miscarriages, in one of which she bled freely. At length the cough began to return intermittently. She became breathless. Eventually, after a new infection, her state was suggestive of a lung abscess and this attack killed her at the age of fifty-three.

We may thus presume that Elizabeth had a chronic lung affliction, beginning acutely in her early thirties, becoming dormant, even during four pregnancies, and finally killing her at the age of fifty-three. Considering the era in which she lived, pulmonary tuberculosis is by far the most likely, leading perhaps to a more chronic fibrosis of the lung with a terminal acute infection.

By the time Robert Browning came to know her, Elizabeth's lung infection was in a dormant phase. She was no longer febrile and her cough is not mentioned. She was an invalid confined to her room because her doctors considered it necessary; they were still concerned about her pulse (see p. 249). In this they were greatly encouraged by her father. Was Miss Barrett ill at this stage of her life? In the eyes of the world she certainly was; in the opinion of her doctors and her father she certainly was. As there is no evidence that her illness had any longer an organic basis, we would have to call it a psychoneurosis. In this respect, Elizabeth's illness falls into the same category as that of Charles Darwin and Florence Nightingale. But here the resemblance ends. In both Charles Darwin and Florence Nightingale the illness arose from an inner conflict due to cirumstances which lasted for many years. The illness developed and persisted as an attempt to resolve the conflict. The doctors undoubtedly helped the psychoneurosis to develop and to persist, but their role was secondary. Miss Barrett's case was quite different. Indeed, I am doubtful whether at this phase of her life she had a psychoneurosis, or indeed whether she was ill at all. Her invalidism was a pattern of life left over from a previous organic illness, a pattern which was maintained, not for her own needs, but because of the fears of her doctors, encouraged by the desires of her fond but possessive and authoritarian father. Hence Robert Browning's astonishing success in transforming her life from that of an invalid recluse to that of a normal member of society. But there was one aspect of her illness that he could not cure. She had become a morphine addict or perhaps we should say, morphine dependent.

ELIZABETH'S MORPHINE ADDICTION

It is probable that Elizabeth's doctors prescribed opium very early in her illness. It was effective in producing sleep, subduing cough, arresting haemorrhage and allaying apprehension and therefore a common remedy in pulmonary tuberculosis. Be that as it may, Elizabeth was an addict by the time that Robert entered her life and remained so with brief intervals until her death.[3] It did not interfere with her activity and she was not ashamed of it, except in so far as Robert was. It is evident therefore that she had come to terms with her addiction. She was a well-balanced addict, as I for one am, or hope I am, in relation to alcohol and tobacco.

In 1974, drug addiction is an ingravescent social problem of horrifying proportions. Those who become addicted have personality defects. They seek the 'adventure' of pot, amphetamine, and finally morphine, or heroin, because it is an 'experiment', though heaven knows that it is an experiment so often made that one might have thought that the results were so well-known as to make repetition somewhat tedious. The drug makes them 'feel good', and so it is sought again.

Such is the fear with which doctors now view morphine addiction, that it was withheld from one of my pupils who was allowed to go through agony for weeks from painful spasms of his bladder afflicted by a cancer; I also endured agony for 24 hours after receiving a new hip because morphine was withheld. As a physician, I fortunately belong to an era when we used morphine with wisdom and understanding, to the comfort of our patients and our own peace of mind.

Elizabeth did not originally seek morphine to satisfy her desire for adventure, or to make her 'feel good'. She was given it to help to heal her, and she grew to depend on it. That was all. But because doctors now fear morphine so much, and on the whole justly, the well-balanced addict is extinct. Elizabeth has left us a picture in her letters to Miss Mitford,[6] which is thus of great contemporary interest.

January 1840: '. . . Can anything grow anywhere or anyway with this terrible wind? The temperature of my bedroom is kept up day and night to 65 and I am not suffered to be moved from the bed even for its making—and yet the noxious character of the air makes me very uncomfortable and sleepless. I took two draughts of opium last night—but even the second failed to bring sleep. 'It *is* a blessed thing!'—that sleep! —one of my worst sufferings being the want of it. Opium—

opium—night after night—! and some nights, during east winds, even opium wont do, you see! . . .'

The next letter gives the clue as to why her doctors prescribed opium:

Jan. 15, 1840: 'The spitting of blood has never intermitted from last March twelvemonth, and my voice has never been able to lift itself above a whisper since October. There has been by Dr Scully's desire, a consultation lately with a physician high in authority in Exeter whom I was ensnared into seeing, and they agreed that after all I was likely with care to get through the winter safely, and to be better in the warmer season. I made an enquiry whether it was considered medically possible for me to be *ever* quite well—and the answer modified my 'quite well' into a tolerably well —— such a degree of health as would admit of my creeping about again with some comfort and independence; and this is considered both possible and probable. I heard it thankfully.'

Jan. 20, 1842: 'Well—but how did you try this opium. I quite agree in the wisdom and propriety of giving it a fair trial, and I venture to suggest another attempt by way of *morphine*. The muriate of morphine is what I take—what I call my elixir, and I take it in combination with aether and something else. Aether is highly antispasmodic. I suggest a mixture of the morphine with the aether—only of course you wouldnt think of giving either without a direction as to quantities from your medical adviser. Do speak about it—do try it, if it is not advised against. My elixir has a sort of ubiquitous influence upon all parts of my system—quiets my mind, calms my pulse—warms my feet—spirits away any stray headache—gives me an appetite—relieves my chest—to say nothing of the bestowment of those sudden pleasant feelings belonging by right to better health and extreme youth—to say nothing of causing me to grow all at once, as young at least . . . as Miss Pardoe!! Now I recommend my elixir . . . you know I never tried it upon cramp—but I believe in its ubiquitous infallability, and recommend it. I chalk it up on your walls, wherever there's a blank one from creepers, at your village of Three Mile Cross! as MY ELIXIR! . . .'

Dec. 21, 1842: 'My beloved friend, you were magnanimous in not adding to the opium—far more so than I should be. I say nothing against opium. It would be mere hypocrisy if I did. Under the denomination of morphine, I take life and heart and sleep and calm from opium, and praise it gratefully whenever there is room for my voice—and am persuaded that it not only assuages the spirits but in my particular case does positive *good* to the lungs by equalising the general circulation. Vivat opium! And may you and I live by its means!—moderation which is good in all things, say the copy books—being very particularly good, we must admit, in this.'

When Robert Browning first met her, he was shocked to learn that 'sleep only came to her in a red hood of poppies'. He tried to oppose it, but she pointed out that she was only obeying doctor's orders. Her doctor one day, arriving early had, while she was talking quite cheerfully 'ordered it before the night hour . . . just for the need he observed in the pulse'. It was 'designed to give the right composure and balance to the nervous system'.

With Robert's help and encouragement, Elizabeth seems to have reduced her dependence on morphine and may have denied herself entirely on her best days. She gave it up entirely for some months before Pen's birth. However, she probably returned to it. Julia Ward Howe, furious on learning that the Brownings had criticised her poetry, wrote an attack on them which included the lines:

> I shrink before the nameless draught
> That helps to such unearthly things
> And if a drug could lift so high
> I would not trust its treacherous wings.

Elizabeth wrote calmly to Mrs Eckley in 1857 'As to the verses, there is nothing in them which has displeased me ever so little, except just the allusion to the nameless drug—which is called a "nameless drug" dear, and not morphine . . . Also the imputation is perfectly true so far, that life is necessary to writing, and that I should not be alive except for the help of my morphine.'

Thus it seems probable that many of Elizabeth Barrett Browning's best poems were written during the period in which she was a morphine addict. In this she joins S. T. Coleridge. But unlike Coleridge, she was so well adjusted to it, that it is unlikely that anyone not privy to her secret would have guessed.

Chapter 15
THE NATURE OF CREATIVITY

The history of man has been largely determined by a very few people whose thoughts and acts have been exceptional and have earned them undying fame. These people are sometimes called geniuses, because they are exceptionally gifted or creative. Because of what they have done, Keats called them 'Men of Achievement'. How they came to be what they were is a question of outstanding interest and importance.

Many today view with dismay the future of mankind. Man has succeeded so brilliantly in understanding and controlling the biological and physical worlds that he is now possessed of immense powers for good or evil. But he has been most unsuccessful in understanding his own behaviour as it occurs in individuals or, especially, in social groups. So far he has shown no sign of being able to control those social forces resulting in overpopulation, war, and pollution of the environment that seem likely to destroy mankind. If such an event is to be averted, it will probably be through the thought or action of one or two creative people. Would it not be comforting to be able to produce them, or at least to recognise, at an early age, those who make such a contribution and to help them on their way? Alas, we are very far from understanding what exactly are the ingredients for creativity, much less how to put them together in the correct proportions.

The scholarly study of genius began with Francis Galton's*

* Galton, Sir Francis (1822–1911), was Charles Darwin's cousin, and like him a medical student who never became a doctor. Galton is one of the founders of modern genetics and of statistics. He was much cleverer than his cousin Charles, though by no means so famous. Would he have been if he had been biologist on the *Beagle*?

book *Hereditary Genius*.[1] Galton studied the lineage of eminent persons, judges, statesmen, commanders, literary men, men of science, poets, musicians, painters and divines. He followed Samuel Johnson in defining genius as one who is endowed with superior intellectual power. Proof of eminence was derived from rank achieved, such as Prime Minister or Lord Chancellor, and from biographical lists of eminent men compiled by others. Eminence he regarded as not simply based on intelligence but on 'ability', 'zeal', and 'a capacity for hard work'. He argued that eminence is an adequate index to natural ability, since the truly able individual cannot be repressed by social obstacles. His investigations showed that in all these professions, those who achieved eminence had a much greater than average number of eminent relatives. Moreover, the more eminent the person, the more probable that he had eminent relatives. Thus of thirty Lord Chancellors of England, twenty-four had eminent relatives, while of two hundred and fifty-six judges, only ninety had eminent relatives.

> The general uniformity in the distribution of ability among the kinsmen in the different groups, is strikingly manifest. The eminent sons are almost invariably more numerous than the eminent brothers, and these are a trifle more numerous than the eminent fathers. On proceeding further down the table, we come to a sudden dropping off of the numbers at the second grade of kinship, namely, at the grandfather, uncles, nephews, and grandsons. . . . On reaching the third grade of kinship, another abrupt dropping off in numbers is again met with, but the first cousins are found to occupy a decidedly better position than other relations within the third grade.

Galton concluded that his studies provided evidence that intelligence is inherited or, as we should now say, genetic. He concluded: 'I feel convinced that no man can achieve a very high reputation without being gifted with very high abilities and I trust that reason has been given for the belief, that few who possess these very high abilities can fail in achieving eminence.'

The advent of Sputnik in 1957 upset American complacency. Action was required if they were to regain scientific and technological ascendency. Was their educational system producing enough of the right kind of scientists and engineers, and, in particular, was it stifling originality or creativity? So began a spate of psychological researches on 'Creativity' (Vernon 1970).[2] In the main these researches are of little relevance to the problem we are concerned with here. But one conclusion is: namely that personality is at least as important as intelligence in determining an individual's creativeness. This conclusion was based on an analysis of eminent persons by Cox (1926), Roe (1952) and MacKinnon (1962). Cox subjected to analysis the biographical data of 300 eminent persons, eliminating those born before 1450 and those whose achievement could not be justified on grounds of ability, for example, those of aristocratic lineage. All her subjects proved to be of high intelligence; but personality was equally important. She remarked: '. . . high but not the highest intelligence, combined with the greatest degree of persistence, will achieve greater eminence than the highest degree of intelligence with somewhat less persistence.' Roe tested and interviewed sixty-four of the most eminent scientists in America. She agreed with Cox, and remarked: 'The one thing that all these sixty-four scientists have in common is their driving absorption in their work.' MacKinnon, studying eminent architects, concluded: 'Our data suggest, rather, that if a person has the minimum of intelligence required for mastery of a field of knowledge, whether he performs creatively or banally in that field will be crucially determined by non-intellective factors.'

These studies would seem to justify the following conclusion. A necessary ingredient of the really creative individual is high intelligence. Intelligence is partly inherited or inborn, and partly acquired. The proportions are now disputed, but my prejudice concurs with that of Galton in thinking that genius is largely inborn. Intelligence is not, however, enough. Other personal factors, particularly imagination, courage, drive, and the capacity for hard work, are also needed for creativity. Whether these are inborn or are acquired cannot even be guessed at. Nor is anyone equipped with the knowledge to say which child will achieve eminence and which not. I know from forty years' experience in selecting students, lecturers and professors for universities, that, even in assessing adults, gross errors in prediction are all too common.

Let us now turn to the process or act of creation. Arthur Koestler has recently written exhaustively on this theme, drawing extensively on modern physiological and psychological theory.[3] His answer is 'bisociative thinking'. I must confess that I find, after reading Koestler's book, that I emerge with no very clear idea of what this is. I share Cyril Burt's view, which is expressed in the foreword to the first edition: 'At the moment the views of professional psychologists still seem mainly to be in a state of bewildered confusion; and there is a crying need for an entirely fresh examination of the subject from top to bottom.'

One of the most lucid and informative accounts of the creative process is by Helmholtz, the great German physicist, given at a banquet in honour of his seventieth birthday.[4] He said that, after previous investigation of a problem '. . . in all directions, . . . happy ideas come unexpectedly without effort, like an inspiration. So far as I am concerned, they have never come to me when my mind was fatigued, or when I was at my working table. . . . They came particularly readily during the slow ascent of wooded hills on a sunny day.' He thought the creative process could be divided into three stages. The first is preparation, in which the relevant data are collected and worked at; the second is 'incubation', in which one is not consciously thinking about the problem; the third is that in which the 'happy idea' suddenly appears, the stage of illumination or inspiration. Then follows the hard work of verification.

The process described by Helmholtz seems to be common to most creative work in music, art, literature, mathematics and science. Although it is convenient for understanding to separate and distinguish his three phases, it is important to recognise that they are not always or usually separate in time. The collection of data is largely a conscious process. The next two stages take place largely in the subconscious mind from which they may emerge as dreams or daydreams. The subconscious process is nowadays termed free association. It results in numerous combinations of which one seems to be chosen because it fits. In art it produces the required shape and form; in science it provides the key to understanding the problem at issue. The emergence of this solution into consciousness is the moment of inspiration or 'the happy idea'.

All these stages are necessary components. Thus, creativity depends on hard work. But perhaps what distinguishes the greater from the lesser creators is the range and richness of association of ideas and the ability to choose rightly. In science the quality of such a solution, a scientific hypothesis, may be judged by the extent to which it explains data hitherto unexplained and the extent to which it is refutable.[5]

Let me illustrate from physics, mathematics, chemistry, physiology and music. Hiero, the tyrant of Syracuse, feared that his crown was made of adulterated gold. He consulted Archimedes, who knew that all other metals were lighter than gold. To weigh the crown was easy, but how to calculate its volume? While the problem occupied his mind, he got into his bath, and observed what he had, no doubt, observed many times before, namely that the water level rose. Here was the solution: obviously the body displaced its own volume of water. According to legend he jumped out of his bath crying 'Eureka'.

Poincaré has described a similar process in mathematics. He was concerned with what are known as Fuchsian functions. He wrote:

For fifteen days I strove to prove that there could not be any functions like those I have since called Fuchsian functions. I was then very ignorant; every day I seated myself at my work table, stayed an hour or two, tried a great number of combinations and reached no results. One evening, contrary to my custom, I drank black coffee and could not sleep. Ideas rose in crowds; I felt them collide until pairs interlocked, so to speak, making a stable combination. By the next morning I had established the existence of a class of Fuchsian functions, those which come from the hypergeometric series; I had only to write out the results, which took but a few hours.[6]

Kekulé's great discovery came to him in a dream, or dream-like state. He was concerned with the reason for the extraordinary stability of the 6-carbon hydrogen molecule called benzine. As he dozed in front of the fire

. . . the atoms were gambolling before my eyes. This time the smaller groups kept modestly in the background. My mental eye, rendered more acute by repeated visions of this kind, could now distinguish larger structures, of manifold conformation; long rows, sometimes more closely fitted together, all twining and twisting in snakelike motion. But look! What was that? One of the snakes had seized hold of its own tail, and the form whirled mockingly before my eyes. As if by a flash of lightning I awoke.[7]

So the answer became clear: the six atoms of carbon formed a ring.

The idea that the nerves of the autonomic or visceral system act by releasing noradrenaline or acetyl-choline at their nerve endings arose from the observed similarities in responses to nerve stimulation and to these substances. It was an idea entertained in a desultory way by many, but quite unsupported by evidence. One night in 1921 the idea of a crucial experiment came in a dream to Otto Loewi.[8] He woke and wrote it down on thin paper. In the morning he remembered he had had an important dream but was quite unable to read his scrawl. The next night, fortunately for posterity, the dream was repeated.

Loewi at once awoke, wrote it down, and went to his laboratory to do the experiment. He perfused two frog's hearts in series. Stimulating the vagus nerve slowed the first heart, as was known, but it also slowed the second heart which was perfused with fluid issuing from the first. Thus the hypothesis was vindicated.

In each of these instances of scientific discovery, what was decisive was not the event that triggered the discovery, it was the passionate interest of the discoverer in an answer to a question. As Pasteur remarked, 'Opportunity comes to the prepared mind'. The exhilaration of the moment of discovery provides the sublimest bliss which man can experience. One can almost recapture the joy with which Archimedes in his bath suddenly found the answer to his question and, springing out, cried 'Eureka'. Even Darwin's sober account of the three moments when the outstanding problems of the origin of species progressively fell into order shows the same exhilaration. It is this exhilaration which keeps a scientist on the alert. It is like a drug of addiction, once one has had the experience, one wants it again.

As Medawar has pointed out, a new idea in science gives the same pleasure to its begetter whether it proves to be valid or invalid.[9] The other great pleasures of research are the designing of elegant experiments, and the gathering of entirely new data.

In art, literature and music, dramatic episodes are less prominent in the creative process than they seem in science. Nevertheless, the mental processes involved seem to follow the same general pattern. In art, as in science, greatness is achieved only through extremely hard work, particularly in the perfection of techniques. The processes of incubation and inspiration tend to proceed together. The actual execution of the idea already formed is sometimes done in the most unlikely circumstances, as by the writers mentioned on p. 292 and in Mozart's case.

Here is Mozart's description of the process of musical composition:

When I am, as it were, completely myself, entirely alone, and of good cheer—say, travelling in a carriage, or walking after a good meal, or during the night when I cannot sleep; it is on such occasions that my ideas flow best and most abundantly. *Whence* and *how* they come, I know not; nor can I force them. Those pleasures that please me I retain in memory, and am accustomed, as I have been told, to hum them to myself. If I continue in this way, it soon occurs to me how I may turn this or that morsel to account, so as to make a good dish of it, that is to say, agreeably to the rules of counterpoint, to the peculiarities of the various instruments, etc.

All this fires my soul, and provided I am not disturbed, my subject enlarges itself, becomes methodised and defined, and the whole, though it be long, stands almost complete and finished in my mind, so that I can survey it, like a fine picture or a beautiful statue, at a glance. Nor do I hear in my imagination the parts *successively*, but I hear them, as it were, all at once (*gleich alles zusammen*). What a delight this is I cannot tell! All this inventing, this producing, takes place in a pleasing lively dream. Still the actual hearing of the *tout ensemble* is after all the best. What has been thus produced I do not easily forget, and this is perhaps the best gift I have my Divine Maker to thank for.

When I proceed to write down my ideas, I take out of the bag of my memory, if I may use that phrase, what has been previously collected into it in the way I have mentioned. For this reason the committing to paper is done quickly enough, for everything is, as I have said before, already finished; and it rarely differs on paper from what it was in my imagination. At this occupation I can therefore suffer myself to be disturbed; for whatever may be going on around me, I write, and even talk, but only of fowls and geese, or of Gretel or Bärbel, or some such matters. But why my productions take from my hand that particular form and style that makes them *Mozartish*, and different from the works of other composers, is probably owing to the same cause which renders my nose so large or so aquiline, or, in short, makes it Mozart's, and different from those of other people. For I really do not study or aim at any originality.[10]

The thrill of achievement is probably the same in the arts as in science. The ecstasy of a new intellectual experience is captured by Keats in his poem 'On First Looking into Chapman's Homer'. I believe that this ecstasy can be communicated. That he is able to impart this ecstasy is what distinguishes a great teacher or the founder of a great school of creative artists.

This exhilaration, or ecstasy, is related to the beauty of form of what has been newly created. I have no doubt that in their sense of form, the great commander, the great poet, novelist, artist, musician, philosopher, mathematician and scientist are essentially at one. The solution that emerges from their subconscious minds is one that passes an aesthetic test. It has beauty of form; it has style. What differs is the medium, not the quality of the product. I am most familiar with this in science and scientists. The new hypothesis which explains what was hitherto obscure has an elegant simplicity—why did we not think of that before? The new experiment, like the one carried out by Loewi, is so decisive that it at once resolves all reasonable doubts. And finally, the paper in which the great scientist describes his experiments and his conclusions is shapely, and well written. The creative person is thus distinguished by the quality of the choice with which he selects the possible combinations produced by free association.

In all the examples given, the reader will have been impressed by the extent to which the whole mind is occupied by the subconscious and conscious mental processes from which the great idea emerges. Those of us who pursue scientific research are familiar with this. Given a certain order of intelligence, the creative person is the person who has preserved his infantile curiosity, and the person who cares. The more passionately he cares, the more likely he is to be productive. Divine discontent and 'fire in the belly' are necessary assets of the creative individual.

The driving force, the urge to create, is thus probably the most important component in creativity. But though this can be recognised, we are very far from understanding it. Why was it, for example, that Athens in the fifth century B.C., and the City States of North Italy in the fifteenth and sixteenth centuries A.D., were crucibles from which came art, science, literature and thought, the like of which the world has not seen before or since? In his *History of Western Philosophy*, Bertrand Russell wrote:

The achievements of Athens in the time of Pericles are perhaps the most astonishing thing in all history. Until that time, Athens had lagged behind many other Greek cities; neither in art nor in literature had it produced any great men (except Solon, who was primarily a lawgiver). Suddenly, under the stimulus of victory and wealth and the need of reconstruction, architects, sculptors and dramatists, who remain unsurpassed to the present day, produced works which dominated the future down to modern times. This is the more surprising when we consider the smallness of the population involved. Athens at its maximum, about 430 B.C., is estimated to have numbered about 230,000 (including slaves), and the surrounding territory of rural Attica probably contained a rather smaller population. Never before or since has anything approaching the same proportion of the inhabitants of any area shown itself capable of work of the highest excellence. . . .

Most of Plato's dialogues are supposed by him to take place during the time of Pericles, and they give an agreeable picture of life among the rich. Plato belonged to an aristocratic Athenian family, and grew up in the tradition of the period before war and democracy had destroyed the wealth and security of the upper classes. His young men, who have no need to work, spend most of their leisure in the pursuit of science and mathematics and philosophy; they know Homer almost by heart, and are critical judges of the merits of professional reciters of poetry. The art of deductive reasoning had been lately discovered, and afforded the excitement of new theories, both true and false, over the whole field of knowledge. It was possible in that age, as in few others, to be both intelligent and happy, and happy through intelligence.[11]

Russell's account suggests that wealth was probably one factor; perhaps because it provided leisure and enabled some individuals to be spared the humdrum existence of acquiring the simple necessities of life, and to devote their whole beings to intellectual adventure. Wealth encouraged competition for excellence among craftsmen and designers. The peace of mind allowed by good government was probably another factor. No doubt, also, intellectual freedom and the consequent encouragement to entertain new ideas, and new art forms, was another. Vasari commented: 'The spirit of criticism: the air of Florence making minds naturally free, and not content with mediocrity.'[12]

Darlington has supposed that this remarkable rise and equally remarkable fall of Athens can be explained on a genetic basis.[13] The right constellation of genes for creativity had come together in the making of Athenian excellence, and had been dispersed in its eclipse. This is a bad scientific hypothesis, judged by Popper's[5] criteria, in that it is not capable of being refuted. Darlington is a geneticist. I am by way of being more catholic. My prejudice is that the remarkable achievements of Athens were not due mainly to their remarkable genes, but to the intellectual climate of the time, what Goethe termed the *Zeitgeist*. This is a characteristic which one generation also transmits to another but by behaviour or attitude and not by genes. In the same way, the Jews have preserved their unity through two and a half millennia of persecution, not through genes but through religion. For the return of the faithful to Israel in the last quarter century has shown that Jews coming from Poland, Morocco, Baghdad and the Yemen bring back a pattern of blood groups that is characteristic not of Jews but of the country whence they have recently come.[14]

The history of science abounds with examples of serendipity, of great discoveries being made by chance; or during the course of an entirely different search. This fact need cause no surprise; for it is the essence of a great discovery that what is discovered was before unknown and therefore could not be sought. The Lachine rapids on the St Lawrence River were so named by Jacques Cartier, who had reached the limit of his voyage into the unknown and liked to think that what he had discovered was China. Similarly Brazil was discovered by a Portuguese, Pedro Alvares Cabral, who was blown off his course in the South Atlantic when he was on his way around the Cape of Good Hope. There are hundreds of examples of the role of the unforeseen and unforeseeable in scientific discovery. To make my meaning clear I shall describe two in some detail, namely the discovery of X-rays by Röntgen, and of penicillin by Fleming.

In 1895 the Professor of Physics at Würzburg, W. K. Röntgen, noticed that a paper screen covered with barium platinocyanide began to fluoresce without apparent cause. In the same room he was studying the conduction of electricity through gases by means of a cathode ray tube enclosed in black cardboard. At that time no radiation was known that was able to penetrate this substance. However, the existence of invisible rays emitted by the tube and capable of penetrating the cardboard seemed the only possible explanation. Thus were X-rays discovered. Within a few weeks he had discovered that the rays were capable of passing through human flesh, thus outlining the bones as shadows on a luminous screen.

Fleming's discovery of penicillin happened in the following way. During the first world war, millions of young men in the prime of life died of war wounds. These got infected and it was the infection that killed. Thousands of distinguished scientists tried to find an antiseptic that would save the patient, and they failed. Alexander Fleming was one. But he had demonstrated to his own satisfaction why this was so. All antiseptics are more lethal to human tissues than to the bacteria invading them. So, with the prepared mind advocated by Pasteur, he was on the look-out for something more lethal to bacteria than to human cells. In 1928 he was engaged in the pedestrian task of typing a microbe called the staphylococcus, which he grew on a jelly called agar. After completing his examination of the culture plates, he took them out of the incubator so that they could be destroyed. But being a cautious Ayrshire farm boy, he kept his plates in case he wanted to look at them again. He found that one was contaminated with a mould, and round the mould the staphylococci had disappeared. Ninety-nine out of a hundred bacteriologists would simply have said confound that mould, and thrown the plate away. But Fleming was the exception. He preserved the plate and cultured the mould which proved to be a Penicillium. He found to his delight that the fluid on which the mould was growing killed staphylococci and many other virulent bacteria but was without effect on the scavenger cells of human blood. Alas, his chemical co-worker did not share Fleming's conviction, and so purification stopped when it got difficult. But when in 1940 Fleming spoke of it to a meeting on war wounds, I was so impressed that I wrote to the best biochemist I knew, urging him to isolate and synthesise it. But he knew that already Florey and Chain had started to do just that, in which they were brilliantly successful. Penicillin has been so effective that it has completely altered the structure of society. Hitherto an old person breaking his hip, or confined to bed for any reason, died of bronchial pneumonia, the old man's friend, as Sir William Osler used to call it. Penicillin stopped all that and thus is a contributory cause of the world population problem in which the old may form the largest fraction of society.

As I explained in the first chapter, I began to explore the relationship between illness and creativity because the subject was previously unexplored and because my interest in it had been aroused. But I always had another consideration at the back of my mind. A causal relationship between psychological illness and creativity seemed so unlikely that if there were one, then a consideration of its nature might throw some light on the factors necessary for a great creative act. This thought gave an added spice to the venture.

Bearing these considerations in mind, we may now review the subjects whose lives and illnesses have been considered in detail. They were selected on two grounds, that their achievements were enough to bring them lasting fame, and that they had an illness which might be psychological in origin. Inquiry was directed to a possible relationship between the two and to its nature.

Great creative works are only achieved if two conditions are satisfied. First, there must be an original idea which fills a need in the contemporary world. Second, that idea must be fully developed or executed. The capacity to develop or execute an idea is much less common than the capacity to formulate one. Darwin was not the first to conceive the idea of evolution. His achievement was to provide such massive evidence that henceforth the idea was seriously entertained by all educated folk. If psychological illness and creativity are related, then that relationship may lie in the formulation of an idea, or in its execution, or in both.

In the case of Charles Darwin the evidence is clear. He got his idea before he became ill. His illness was in fact a result of the conflict between, on the one hand, his desire to develop the idea and to provide solid evidence for it, and, on the other, the demands made on his time by social intercourse with friends and fellow scientists. And so he became an invalid and a recluse. The illness solved his problem and enabled him to accumulate a mass of evidence relating to his idea, evidence which he was forced to publish, as he thought prematurely, because of Wallace's letter containing precisely the same idea but without the wealth of evidence.

Miss Nightingale's case closely resembles that of Mr Darwin. She got her idea to improve the lot of the British soldier through reforming the War Office when she had to share the suffering and injustice inflicted on him in the Crimea. And she fell in love with the common soldier as a mother with her children. In this way she became possessed by a passionate urge to carry out her purpose. It was when she met the indifference of statesmen and politicians and the obstruction of bureaucrats to her reforming zeal that she first became ill. And it was the persistent demands made by her mother and sister which forced her to become bedridden, unable to see her relatives or other unwanted visitors. All her business assumed a new urgency because it was thought that her life hung on a thread. Accordingly she relentlessly worked her collaborators into their graves, while she lived till she was ninety. As with Charles Darwin, her illness provided neither the idea nor the passionate desire to execute it. It conserved her time and her energy by protecting her from the trivialities of social intercourse.

There were two other circumstances of great relevance to their achievements. They both had wealth and an assured social position, and both were served by devoted acolytes. It is arguable that their driving force would have found its expression even in poverty, as happened in some others of our characters, but in the England of their day social position made the start of their task easier. Again disciples seem to be inevitable for those dedicated to an idea or possessed by a purpose. It is part of their charisma. But for Charles Darwin and Florence Nightingale, willing slaves to provide their particular needs seem to have been available from the start. What each needed and each got was the opportunity for unremitting toil and the relentless pursuit of an object which was known to them from the outset.

In Joan of Arc, Mary Baker Eddy, Sigmund Freud and Marcel Proust, the role of illness was quite different. Joan's illness revealed to her the solution for France's miseries under the yoke of England. Inspired by this revelation, she led Charles to victory and ultimately to coronation. Mary Baker Eddy's agony of mind, expressed in her disabling illness, vanished when she began to sense what was to be her great contribution to thought and religion, namely the effect of mind upon health. The process began with the cure by Phineas Quimby, and was completed when she cured herself in Lynn, and Christian Science was revealed to her while she was in a state of ecstasy, or so she said. The most remarkable feature of her case was, however, that she was no less than forty-five years of age, penniless and rejected by her family, when she conceived her great idea. She was fifty-four when *Science and Health* was first published, and she was eighty-seven when she founded the *Christian Science Monitor*. In my view Christian Science was a form of mental catharsis which was part of the cure of her illness. What a powerful process it was to bring lasting fame during that time of life when in most people the flame is going out.

Freud's case was rather similar. As Ernest Jones pointed out, many of his greatest ideas occurred to him when he was suffering from psychoneurotic symptoms: his most original work was done when his neurosis was at its height.[15] It was at this time that he began the self-analysis; a search for the causes of his own often very distressing symptoms, which led to his magnum opus *The Interpretation of Dreams*,[16] and later to the idea that infantile sexuality, and the Oedipus complex in particular, was the essential cause of psychoneurosis. In Freud's case, the illness provided both the idea and the drive by which Freud made it acceptable to others.

Mary Baker Eddy and Sigmund Freud share many other remarkable features. They were both over forty when they conceived and developed the idea that brought fame. In each case the idea came as part of the process of self-cure of the psychoneurosis. In each case the idea assumed the proportions of a religion. The founder was an autocrat whose word was law. Disciples were attracted and ruthlessly discarded, in one case for the practice of malicious animal magnetism, in the other for daring to hold opinions that deviated from the orthodoxy of the founder.

Proust's illness began as a reaction to his mother's death and his guilty fear that he might have been responsible for it. It converted him into an invalid recluse whose mind dwelt almost entirely in the past, pouring itself out into memories and fantasies that formed *À la recherche du temps perdu*. In these four, then, the agony of mind caused the illness and it was their reaction to this which made them famous.

It is not unlikely that similar periods of such mental agony are frequent in creative writers, artists, and musicians. Their own subjective descriptions often reveal this, though it may escape a cursory biographical examination. As with Freud, 'he continued with his daily work . . . and in all probability gave little sign of neurotic manifestations to his surroundings'. (See p. 221).

Finally we come to that extremely charming woman, Elizabeth Barrett. Of all the characters that I have analysed here, she would be my choice of a friend and companion. Her illness sat very lightly on her, and so Robert Browning found little difficulty in disposing of it. It played a correspondingly small part in her creative work. Elizabeth Barrett's flow of poetry seemed to be almost uninfluenced by her illness. She began to write poetry when she was very young, and she wrote it throughout her life, with very few interruptions. Unlike the other subjects considered, her illness, such as it was, was imposed from without by her doctors and her father, and was not generated from within. In fact, I doubt whether she was really ill in the latter part of her incarceration in her bedroom in Wimpole Street. She was kept there by her doctor's timidity and her father's protective and possessive passion.

Thus the part played by psychological illness in creativity is not always the same. It may apparently have no role, as in Elizabeth Barrett. It may provide both the idea and the drive that ensures its execution, as in Joan of Arc, Mary Baker Eddy, Sigmund Freud, and Marcel Proust. In the last three of these, their creative work was, so to speak, a mental catharsis, an essential part of the cure. Finally the illness may provide neither the idea nor the drive to execute it; it may have, rather, a protective function, as in Charles Darwin and Florence Nightingale, whose illness relieved them from the dissipation of their time and energy which would have defeated their purpose.

Chapter 16
CREATIVITY
AND ILLNESS

We have seen how, in six of the seven characters considered in this book, psychological illness played a decisive part in the creative work which brought fame. Indeed, without that illness, the great work would never have been done, though 'The Lady of The Lamp' would still adorn history books for the young. The reader will ask: are these examples of a general relationship, or are they exceptions to the rule; and if exceptions, why are they exceptions? The reader will also ask whether there is a relationship between creativity and illness in general or only with mental illness. To the more general problem we may now proceed.

For our purpose, illness can be divided into three kinds: organic illness, by which is meant disease of one of the organs of the body; psychosis, by which is meant disorder of the mind severe enough to produce insanity in its legal sense; and psychoneurosis, by which is meant a lesser degree of mental disorder.

Organic or physical disease is not, to my knowledge, in general an aid to creativity. Vigour is essential to creativity. Many organic diseases are associated with pain, discomfort, fever, and lack of energy. Many, too, give rise to fear, which tends to monopolise the mind and to displace productive activity. It has been suggested that fever may occasionally contribute to creativity. We have seen how Alfred Russel Wallace was confined to his hut in Ternate with relapsing fever when the sequence of ideas raced through his mind that led to his paper on evolution by natural selection. Wallace had previously made a great contribution when he was confined for some days in a hut in Borneo alone with his cook. He himself considered that on each occasion it was his enforced solitude and the unimpeded opportunity for free association rather than the fever that was decisive.

It was at one time thought that infection of the lungs with tubercle bacilli also improved the quality of the mind. Keats and Robert Louis Stevenson were possible examples. But there are other circumstances in addition to fever to explain these occurrences. The invalid with pulmonary tuberculosis used to be put to bed, and tended assiduously. Rest, good food, and protection from the more exacting affairs of life, were the established treatment. In fact, they had imposed on them the kind of environment that Florence Nightingale and Charles Darwin found so helpful to their own missions. Most patients, according to my inquiries, found it a stultifying, rather than a stimulating, experience. For Thomas Mann incarceration in a sanatorium produced *The Magic Mountain*: for most of his fellow inmates it afforded only spiritual impoverishment and despair. But Thomas Mann produced other notable works in other circumstances. The sanatorium provided the theme, not the essential conditions for creative work.

René and Jean Dubos have made a special study of the relationship between consumption and genius.[1] They considered that some consumptives may have been driven to achievement by their fear of dying, as was Miss Nightingale, though the death she feared was from a different cause. At the end of their lives they experienced that pathetic frustration expressed by Keats: 'Oh! what a misery it is to have an intellect in splints!' The Duboses concluded: 'There is no evidence that tuberculosis breeds genius. The probability is, rather, that eagerness for achievement often leads to a way of life that renders the body less resistant to infection.'

The idea that genius is closely related to madness goes back to classical times. Plato thought there were two forms of delirium—insanity and inspiration. He wrote: 'I have observed this about poets. It is not by taking thought that they create what they create; it is owing to a natural disposition and when ecstatically possessed.' Aristotle said that no mind of any eminence is free from a streak of madness. Burton wrote: 'All poets are mad.' Shakespeare wrote:

> The lunatic, the lover and the poet
> Are of imagination all compact.

In *Absalom and Achitophel*, Dryden subscribed to the idea:

> Great wits are sure to madness near allied;
> And thin partitions do their bounds divide.

However, not all past writers are agreed. Charles Lamb, in his essay on the *Sanity of True Genius*, wrote:

So far from the position holding true, that great wit (or genius, in our modern way of speaking) has a necessary alliance with insanity, the greatest wits, on the contrary, will ever be found to be the sanest writers. It is impossible for the mind to conceive of a mad Shakespeare.[2]

Thus opinions concerning the association between mental illness and genius have been sharply divided. Let us now look at the problem more closely.

The psychoses are, as we have seen in Chapter 2, associated with mental deterioration at least in their advanced stages. At that stage those afflicted are not creative even though they may have been earlier. Schumann was either a manic depressive or suffered from dementia paralytica (a form of tertiary syphilis). Slater and Meyer[3] studied his case thoroughly and showed that in his later years his output varied with his mood, being absent when he was depressed; his later works were without merit. He tried to drown himself in the Rhine and died in a mental hospital. Van Gogh was certainly psychotic in later life and spent much of his time in a mental hospital. His paintings display his changes of mood. Louis Wain, who painted cats, was a schizophrenic and his paintings display the evolution of his illness. Virginia Woolf was a manic depressive who drowned herself when depressed. She herself thought her illness contributed to her art:

> If I could stay in bed another fortnight (but there is no chance of that) I believe I should see the whole of 'The Waves' . . . I believe these illnesses are in my case—how shall I express it?—partly mystical. Something happens in my mind. It refuses to go on registering impressions. It shuts itself up. It becomes a chrysalis. I lie quite torpid, often with acute physical pain—as last year; only discomfort this. Then suddenly something springs.[4]

There are other candidates for inclusion in this list, Nietzsche, Swedenborg, Dostoevsky, but they have been insufficiently studied from this point of view. Strindberg appears to have been a schizophrenic exhibiting paranoid symptoms who wrote a book about his own case.[5] He thought that he wrote best in hallucination. He wrote: 'Not everyone is capable of being mad; and, of those lucky enough to be capable of madness, not many have the courage for it.' (My comment would be that he had remarkable insight for a psychotic.)

As mentioned earlier, swings in mood from elation to dejection are not uncommon, and are frequently conspicuous in creative people of all disciplines. Winston Churchill was a well-known example. Handel seems to have been another. But this falls well short of the full manic depressive psychosis.

Turning now to the psychoneuroses, we meet substantial difficulties. The boundary between normal behaviour and a psychoneurosis is a tenuous one and would be differently drawn by different authorities. Moreover, the available evidence concerning many personalities is incomplete. I, for one, would never have suspected, from what I knew of Freud's work and writings, that he was the victim of a psychoneurosis. We owe this information to the unusual circumstances that his biographer was not only a close friend and disciple, but also a psychiatrist of great distinction. A further difficulty is that achievement may at once be the result and the cure of a neurosis.

There is, as far as I know, no convincing evidence of exceptional creativity among psychoneurotics in general. At the present time, the psychoneuroses are some of the commonest diseases affecting society. Exceptional creativity, on the other hand, is very rare. Nor is there any evidence that there is a correlation between intelligence and psychoneurosis, though the question has not been submitted, as far as I know, to rigorous scientific scrutiny. However, the impressions of most psychiatrists would be that psychoneurosis occurs with all levels of intelligence and that in a given population of psychoneurotics, there is no preponderance of the highly intelligent.

Approaching the problem from the other direction, is there any evidence that men and women who have achieved distinction through their own creations are unusually prone to psychoneuroses? Ernest Jones seemingly thought so when he remarked: 'Neurotics are the torchbearers of civilisation.'

In looking at this problem more closely, we may begin with the scientists. I happen to be acquainted with many of the most distinguished of living scientists. I have known personally, or known a good deal about, the Presidents of the Royal Society during the last forty years. None of them had, as far as I know, a psychoneurosis. Certainly none of them had a psychological illness severe enough to interfere with their way of life, as it did in all the characters that I have analysed here, with the exception of Sigmund Freud, who, as I have emphasised, would not have been so diagnosed but for exceptional circumstances. I am less well acquainted with the Nobel Prize winners, but those that I do know have not suffered from a psychoneurosis. Looking back into the great scientists of the past, there is only one that I know of, apart from Darwin, who suffered in this way. This was Isaac Newton, whose case will receive further notice (see p. 300).

Artists, as we have known about them in the nineteenth and twentieth centuries, have tended to behave oddly. This is probably related to their rejection of the ideas of current society and the technique of classical art and the foundation of revolutionary new schools. I know of no informed work on the extent to which they have been afflicted by mental illness: and it is important to maintain a distinction between non-conformity and mental illness if we are not to fill our mental hospitals with those who criticise society. Freud wrote of them:

> The artist is an incipient introvert who is not far from being a neurotic. He is impelled by too powerful instinctive needs. He wants to achieve honour, power, riches, fame and the love of women. But he lacks the means of achieving these satisfactions. So like any other unsatisfied person, he turns away from reality, and transfers all his interests, his libido, too, to the elaboration of his imaginary wishes, all of which might easily point the way to neurosis. A great many factors must combine to present this termination of his development; it is well known how often artists especially suffer from a partial inhibition of their capacities through neurosis. Apparently their constitutions are strongly endowed with an ability to sublimate and to shift the suppression determining their conflicts. The artist finds the way back to reality in this way.[6]

The great musicians have shown no special proclivity to disease in general, or to mental disease in particular. Eric Blom, in *Some Great Composers,*[7] studied fifteen. One, Verdi, died at eighty-seven; three, Haydn, Handel and Wagner, died in their seventies; four, Berlioz, Bach, Dvorak and Brahms, died in their sixties; two, Beethoven and Tchaikovsky, in their fifties; one, Schumann, in his forties; and four, Chopin, Purcell, Schubert and Mozart, under the age of forty. Of the four dying young, Chopin died of tuberculosis, Purcell of a chill, Schubert of typhus, Mozart of uraemia. Tchaikovsky was probably a manic depressive, though when he died at the age of fifty-three, it was of cholera. Schumann, as we have noted, was a psychotic in his later years. Handel had a partial paralysis when he was fifty-two, but he wrote the Messiah afterwards, and died at seventy-four, quite blind. Beethoven became totally deaf but continued to compose music which is highly esteemed. Some of these, for instance Beethoven, Berlioz, Schubert, Tchaikovsky and Wagner, were certainly unusual characters by the standards of their own or any other day.

The lot of a musician in the seventeenth and early eighteenth century was hard. Mozart and his father were employed by the Archbishop of Salzburg. They ranked with the cooks and the valets. Despite his amazing genius and the extremely large output of beautiful compositions, Mozart lived his thirty-five years in poverty. When he died he was buried in a pauper's grave at the public expense. It would seem that in the past a musician had to be tough to be successful. Serious illness might often have imposed an insurmountable obstacle to his achievement.

In his Lloyd Roberts Lecture for 1947,[8] Harold Nicolson studied the health of authors. He showed that the popular idea that all creative writers, and especially all poets, are of weak bodily constitution and as such liable to premature death, was erroneous. He selected the thirty-two most famous British poets who lived between the middle of the fourteenth and the end of the nineteenth centuries. Ten lived beyond the age of seventy; nine died between sixty and seventy; seven between fifty and sixty; two between forty and fifty, and only four under the age of forty. He suspected that if we examined the lives of thirty-two famous clergymen, lawyers or merchants living in the same period, they might show no higher average of survival.

Of the four mighty poets who died young, Keats died of consumption at twenty-six; Shelley and Marlowe due to accidents, Marlowe in a tavern brawl and Shelley by drowning; Byron's death at the age of thirty-six has been attributed to the excessive blood letting practised on him by the doctors of that time. Reading his medical history, which is revealed in his collected letters,[9] he probably died of some mismanaged

Mediterranean fever—possibly typhus, typhoid or malaria: but before this his oddities of behaviour, and, in his last years, his occasional epileptic fits may have been due to some localised disturbance of the temporal lobe of the brain.

Nicolson examined carefully the idea that poets are frequently mad and convinced himself that it was a fallacy, and that the legend was to a very large extent the fault of the writers themselves. 'All writers, and especially all poets, feel it dull to be thought completely normal. They thus divulge and even display their eccentricities.'

Of the thirty-two famous British poets whom he had selected, only two became demonstrably insane. William Cowper was a manic depressive who became suicidal at least twice. He composed his poetry during his interludes of perfect sanity, in which he was happy in a quiet, 'tea-party' sort of way. Swift, thoughout his life, was haunted by the spectre of insanity, yet senile dementia did not supervene until he was seventy-four years of age. However, several of the other poets were very odd. Tennyson was a convinced hypochondriac throughout most of his life. He died at eighty-three. Johnson was also an outstanding hypochondriac and cherished many strange delusions, such as that he would get drunk if he ate an apple. He was obsessed by the dread of losing his wits. He entrusted his secret to Mrs Thrale, and any time he felt that madness was approaching, he would persuade her to lock him in his room, place gyves upon his legs, and even to whip him with a rod. Although he was unhappily convinced of his own impending mental collapse, he maintained his sanity till he died of dropsy at the age of seventy-five.

Shelley was also a hypochondriac. Nicolson remarks: 'All creative writers are hypochondriacs, since those of them who do not worry about the state of their bodies are certain to worry about the state of their minds.' Shelley seldom regarded himself as mentally afflicted, but he persistently regarded himself as very ill. He was at one time obsessed by the belief that he was consumptive, and after that had various other imaginary diseases. He also suffered from spectral and auditory hallucinations. Nicholson remarks:

It is customary for very gifted writers to see spectres and to hear voices calling. After all, even Goethe (who assuredly was a man of the most Olympian calm and sanity) once met himself riding along a road on horseback. Shelley's hallucinations were vivid and detailed. On one occasion, while walking near Pisa, he saw a man coming slowly towards him dressed in a long cloak and with a hood or cowl hiding his face. When the man was only a few yards distant he raised his hood, and Shelley was much startled to see that the man was in fact himself.

The difficulty in generalising about writers is exemplified by the circumstances in which they write most convincingly. Oswald Sitwell and J. C. Masterman found hotel bedrooms the most conducive. Thackeray found that his ideas flowed most freely in the congested atmosphere of the Athenaeum Club. Mozart preferred to write out what he had already composed amidst the hum of general conversation, in which he sometimes participated. Schubert wrote one of his lyrics on the back of a menu while he was listening to a band in a beergarden. Some were at their best in the early morning, others, like Balzac, Byron, Dostoevsky and Conrad, wrote best at night. Some, like Elizabeth Barrett Browning and Edith Sitwell, wrote best in the recumbent position. Voltaire did most of his dictating from his bed. Dr Johnson's ideas flowed most freely to the movement of a carriage. Victor Hugo composed on the top of a bus between Passy and the Bourse, Trollope in a railway carriage. Milton said he could only write really well between October and March. Tennyson was more inspired during spring and summer. Thackeray, Mme de Stael and Southey found the ideas would come only if they had a quill or pen in their hands. Such examples may seem to indicate the frequency of what one might call obsessional neurosis, yet there are few of us who are immune. In fact, most of my acquaintances in medicine and university education exhibit, in greater or lesser degree, similar traits.* Nevertheless, Nicolson concludes that

> the creative writer, the poet and the artist do possess a certain special nervous sensibility, which manifests itself not merely in their receptivity to inspiration but also in certain, apparently morbid, eccentricities. When poets and writers contend, as they so invariably do contend, that 'inspiration' reaches them from outside they are describing an experience which is in no way abnormal but perfectly natural. It is true that these sudden and transitory intimations reach them from outside the area of their consciousness; they reach them from their subconscious; there is no need at all to drag in the supernatural phenomena of muses and daimons. Genius, in spite of Buffon and Carlyle, is not either a 'great aptitude for patience' or 'a transcendent capacity for taking trouble.' It is a *spontaneous* activity of the cells and fibres of the brain whereby new combinations of impressions are constantly being formed.

Nicolson concludes that the legend of madness or of mental instability amongst poets arose because 'No writer, however feeble he may be, can be of any value unless he possesses a powerful imagination; and powerful imaginations, as Shakespeare assures us—and he ought to know—are apt to play one tricks.'

The artistic temperament has unusual sensibility as one of its components. One might imagine then that such people would be unusually prone to drug addiction, to opium in the nineteenth century and to alcohol in the twentieth. It is easy to illustrate this by outstanding examples. It is equally easy to find examples of the contrary. No survey has been made, to my knowledge,

---

* Nearly all my nine grandchildren, when aged between two and five, have required certain conditions to be fulfilled before they would happily go to sleep. The conditions are intensely individual, a toy, a piece of cloth, an animal, a light on, etc. Such an obsession is so frequent amongst the very young that it cannot be regarded as abnormal.

which establishes whether either is more frequent than would have been expected in populations of similar age, sex, social and educational status. It is, of course, a great comfort to the victims and their friends to believe that their addiction is necessary for their art. I suspect that this is the essence of the relationship.

The relationship between opium addiction and romantic writing is the subject of an enthralling book by Alethea Hayter.[10] It seems strange to us nowadays that derivatives of opium were so freely available and so widely consumed by the public in the nineteenth century. Many of the cordials given to induce sleep· and alleviate cough contained opium. Laudanum was freely available to anybody at the local chemist. Even such a pillar of reforming morality as William Wilberforce, the emancipator of the slaves, was an addict. He first had recourse to opium for a serious digestive illness, which it cured, but he was never able to leave off taking it for the last forty-five years of his life. He got nothing from it; it was neither sedative nor stimulant. The effects only began when he tried to stop taking it. Other addicts were pillars of the Church, and some were leading doctors, like the great neurologist, Sir William Gowers,* or the pioneer of university surgery in the United States, Williams. Halsted.[11]

Amongst writers, opium taking was common. De Quincey's *Confessions* were the first to make the reading public aware of the pleasures of the initial stages, and the horrors of the late stages, of morphine addiction. De Quincey devoted a great deal of attention to dreams, and their effect on the romantic imagination. Lowes also made a detailed study of these.[12] The conclusion emerged that the content of a dream is greatly influenced by the dreamer's experiences, both actual and vicarious, through his reading. What opium does sometimes is to increase the vividness or intensity of the dream, and sometimes to alter its form. The most famous of the opium-induced poems was *Kubla Khan*, which Coleridge wrote down on

---

* As narrated by Dr James Collier M.D., F.R.C.P., in a paper to the Osler Club of London *c.* 1928.

awakening from a sleep induced by laudanum. His writing was interrupted by a caller and the poet could not recapture the state of ecstasy in which he wrote. Lowes showed that the content of the poem followed closely Purchas's *Pilgrimage*, which Coleridge had been reading immediately before he fell asleep.

The conclusions reached by more professional psychologists has been similar to that of the amateur.

The first attempt to study the frequency of mental disease in geniuses was made by Havelock Ellis in *A Study in British Genius*.[13] He selected 1030 names from the Dictionary of National Biography; 975 were men and 55 women. Only 44 (4.2 per cent) were demonstrably insane. He wrote:

> It is perhaps a high proportion. I do not know the number of cases among persons of the educated classes living to a high average age in which it can be said that insanity has occurred once during life. It may be lower, but at the same time it can scarcely be so very much lower that we are entitled to say that there is a special and peculiar connection between genius and insanity. The association between genius and insanity is not, I believe, without significance, but in face of the fact that its occurrence is only demonstrable in less than five per cent cases, we must put out of court any theory as to genius being a form of insanity.

Juda (1953) investigated the lives and medical histories of 113 artists and 181 men of science, chosen by experts in their fields of achievement.[14] She classified them as best she could. Her study, when compared with Ellis', illustrates both the attempt to impose 'scientific' attitudes in such investigations and their limitations in the appreciation of some important human attributes. She concludes:

> . . . in the artists, schizophrenia 2·8%, manic-depressive 0, unclear endogenous psychoses 2·0%, psychopathic personality 27·3%; in the scientists, schizophrenia 0, manic-depressive

4·0%, unclear endogenous psychoses 0, psychopathic personality 19·4%. Psychopaths were rarely 'erregbar' (excitable) or
'haltlos' (unstable), comparatively frequently 'Sonderlinge'
(eccentric) or 'Thymopathe'. There was then a little, but only
a little, more psychosis in both groups than could have been
expected if they had been members of the general population.
But in both groups there was about double the normal expecta-
tion of psychopaths.

Juda's study suffered from the difficulty both of classifying
subjects on most imperfect records, and of judging the frequency of the similar groups in the population at large. Moreover, the diagnosis 'psychopathic personality' is particularly
variable and ill-defined. However, Slater and Meyer[3] commented:

This is a decisive counter-demonstration to the vulgar belief
that men of genius are by and large mad or half-mad, and it
shows that not only is normality of personality compatible
with the highest achievement but also that the majority of men
of the greatest achievement are normal. It still leaves open,
however, as a problem requiring the closest study, the relationship of 'genius' with abnormality of personality.

This general survey suggests that there is no strong connection between mental illness and creativity. And yet my
characters remain. They are not particular examples of a
general rule. They are, rather, exceptions to the rule. This, however, does not in any way diminish their interest or importance.
Freud taught us this. In his beautiful essay on slips of the
tongue,[15] he pointed out that exceptions are also subject to the
law of causal sequence. He also showed us that when exceptions
are examined in this way, their explanation may be profoundly
enlightening. While, therefore, it is extremely unlikely that by
themselves the case histories will solve the problem of creativity, they may at least contribute to that solution.

Chapter 17

THE CREATIVE PERSONALITY

What is the essence of the relationship, which has been demonstrated in six of my subjects, between psychological illness and creativity? As we saw in the first chapter, all great creative personalities have been highly intelligent. So were all my characters. But high intelligence was not what made them famous. Indeed, in his youth, at a time when intelligence is commonly gauged, Darwin gave no sign of being unusually gifted.

Wealth was certainly a factor, possibly an essential factor, in making possible the great works of Darwin, Proust and Miss Nightingale. But it was conspicuously absent in Freud and Mary Baker Eddy at the time of their greatness, as it has been in many of the great artists, musicians, writers and scientists.

Range of free association and the ability to make the right choice from amongst this range are components of the creative process. They might be termed imagination and discrimination. They result in aesthetic sense, and the desire for excellence or style. A psychological illness may appear to increase the range of association of ideas, at least if that is judged by published dreams. Here, however, we must beware of biased evidence, since so much of it comes from the case books of psychiatrists, who have very few normal subjects to compare. On the other hand, a disturbance of the mind is in no way associated with wisdom, the ability to make a sensible choice.

Storr believes that many creative people have a schizoid character, i.e. they display a mixture of opposites.[1] He gives five ways in which the schizoid character aids creativity. First, most creative activity is solitary. Second, creative activity enables a schizoid person to retain at least part of his fantasy of omnipotence. Third, creative activity, for the schizoid person, reflects his own scheme of values in which the characteristic feature is that a greater importance is attributed to inner reality than to the external world. Fourth, certain kinds of creativity are peculiarly apt for overcoming the sense of arbitrary un-predictability. Fifth, creative activity can undoubtedly act as a defence against the threat which overhangs the schizoid person of finding the world meaningless. Storr illustrates the schizoid personality by Einstein and Newton.

A variant of the split personality is the possession of features more conspicuous in the opposite sex. He thinks that the evidence suggests that 'in the case of creative people, the contra-sexual side is closer to the surface, more in evidence, and less shunned than is the case amongst the average'.

In connection with the display of opposite characteristics in men of genius, Ernest Jones wrote: 'For there is every reason to suppose that men of genius are characterised by possessing exceptionally strong emotions and usually a correspondingly strong capacity for containing them.'[2] Einstein and Newton deserve further attention. Einstein was the son of Jewish parents who had become indifferent to religion. His son wrote that Einstein was 'a very well-behaved child. He was shy, lonely and withdrawn from the world even then. He was even con-sidered backward by his teachers. He told me that his teachers reported to his father that he was mentally slow, unsociable and adrift forever in his foolish dreams.'[3] Whilst he was still a schoolboy he himself emphasised his Jewish origin and went through a period of religious fervour which he described as his 'first attempt to liberate myself from purely personal links'.[4] At the age of twelve he freed himself from conventional religious belief. Later in life, as is noted on p. 308, he developed a more intellectually satisfying concept of cosmic religion, in which there was not an anthropomorphic god. He emphasised that God 'does not play at dice'. At this early age he found that Euclid transported him, and that 'Man was capable, through the force of thought alone, of achieving the degree of stability and purity which the Greeks, before anybody else, demonstrated to us in geometry.'[4] At the age of sixteen he went through a mental upheaval which was severe enough to enable him to obtain a certificate from the school doctor stating that he had a nervous breakdown and must take six months off school.

Einstein was not distinguished academically and became a clerk in the patent office at Berne, but he was then indulging, as he continued to do for the rest of his life, his two passions of music and mathematical physics. He held that it was as important for him to improvise on the piano as it was for him to work on his physics. He said: 'It is a way for me to be independent of people, and this is highly necessary in the kind of society in which we live.'[5] His favourite composer was Mozart.

His contributions to mathematical physics were made entirely by thought. The paper on the special theory of relativity, published in 1905, contains no references, and very little mathematics. This paper, and the ones that succeeded it, upset the conventional ideas of space and time. Two events that seem to the observer simultaneous may, in fact, be separated by thousands of years of time. This is so because if they are seen by the observer simultaneously then account has to be taken of the time that it has taken for the light to travel from a stellar object millions of miles away to the eye of the observer.

Einstein was unconventional and eccentric. He was quite indifferent to his physical appearance. In the course of ordinary conversation he would suddenly 'fall silent and stop listening to you. He would rise to his feet without a word, or remain sitting motionless. The effect would be the same. He would be unreachable . . . One never got rid of the feeling that his presence among us was only on temporary loan.'[4]

Storr does not discuss the nature of Einstein's illness at the age of sixteen, nor its possible consequences. Three things stand out in Einstein's personality. First, that he was not like most modern scientists, a university professor, but a patent clerk working in an office. Second, that he was very unconventional in almost everything. Not only in his behaviour. He refused to accept the concept of the Almighty that his forefathers had taken with them in their migrations for the last two and a half millennia, and devised his own concept of cosmic religion. In that intellectually lonely atmosphere of the Patent Office, he revolutionised physics. Finally, he was a passionate man, passionate in his love of music, passionate in his love of physics, and passionate in his love of humanity in general. He was one of those who were deeply disturbed by the atomic bomb.

To me, Einstein has always seemed a remarkably composed and harmonious man. He combined his passions for the exploration of the universe, for music, and for the best ideals of civilised society, with his own religious concept, which was not in conflict with his approach to the physical world. I suspect that his mental illness at sixteen was due to a conflict at that time unresolved. It may easily have been between belief and reason, and perhaps the concept of cosmic religion represented the resolution of that conflict. If that were the case it would represent another example of mental catharsis.

Storr's second example was Isaac Newton, perhaps the greatest genius in mathematics and physics of all time. It was he who devised the calculus. It was he who discovered the laws of gravitation, and the laws of motion, and thus brought together into one system the behaviour of the earthly and the heavenly bodies. It was he who elucidated the elementary laws of optics. All these he did before he was forty-five years of age, when his *Principia* was published. For my account of Newton, I have largely depended on J. M. Keynes,[6] for it was Keynes who acquired most of Newton's unpublished and unpublishable papers, over a million words mostly written during his intensely productive period. Keynes remarked how different he was from the conventional image of him. 'He was less ordinary, more extraordinary, than the nineteenth century cared to make him out.'

Newton's father died before Isaac was born, an event which happened at Woolsthorpe, Lincolnshire, on Christmas Day 1642. Thus he had his mother's undivided attention until she remarried and moved to another house just after he was three, and he was left in the care of his maternal grandmother. We know from his own account that he deeply resented this as a betrayal, and recorded later that he passionately wished to burn their house over his mother and step-father. When Newton was eleven, his step-father died, so his mother returned with two new step-sisters and a step-brother.

Newton was sent to the Grammar School at Grantham where he was not regarded as an outstanding scholar. He became a sub-sizar at Trinity College, Cambridge in 1661, did well enough to become a Scholar, and took his B.A. in 1665. He was sent away from Cambridge because of the plague in 1665–66 and while he was at Woolsthorpe he discovered the binomial theorem, differential calculus, integral calculus, computed the area of the hyperbola, and conceived the idea of universal gravitation. He returned to Cambridge in 1667 as a Fellow of Trinity, where he turned his attention to optics. In 1669 he was elected Lucasian Professor of Mathematics, and in 1672 a Fellow of the Royal Society. Keynes remarked:

In vulgar modern terms Newton was profoundly neurotic of a not unfamiliar type, but—I should say from the records—a most extreme example. His deepest instincts were occult, esoteric, semantic—with profound shrinking from the world, a paralysing fear of exposing his thoughts, his beliefs, his discoveries in all nakedness to the inspection and criticism of the world. 'Of the most fearful, cautious and suspicious temper that I ever knew,' said Whiston, his successor in the Lucasian Chair. The too well-known conflicts and ignoble quarrels with Hooke, Flamsteed, Leibnitz are only too clear an evidence of this. Like all his type he was wholly aloof from women. He parted with and published nothing except under the extreme pressure of friends. Until the second phase of his life, he was a wrapt, consecrated solitary, pursuing his studies by intense introspection with a mental endurance perhaps never equalled.

I believe that the clue to his mind is to be found in his unusual powers of continuous concentrated introspection. A case can be made out, as it also can with Descartes, for regarding him as an accomplished experimentalist. Nothing can be more charming than the tales of his mechanical contrivances when he was a boy. There are his telescopes and his optical experiments. These were essential accomplishments, part of his unequalled, all-round technique, but not, I am sure, his *peculiar* gift, especially amongst his contemporaries. His peculiar gift was the power of holding continuously in his mind a purely mental problem until he had seen straight through it. I fancy his pre-eminence is due to his muscles of intuition being the strongest and most enduring with which a man has ever been gifted. Anyone who has ever attempted pure scientific or philosophical thought knows how one can hold a problem momentarily in one's mind and apply all one's powers of concentration to piercing through it, and how it will dissolve and escape and you find that what you are surveying is a blank. I believe that Newton could hold a problem in his mind for hours and days and weeks until it surrendered to him its secret. Then being a supreme mathematical technician he could dress it up, how you will, for purposes of exposition, but it was his intuition which was pre-eminently extraordinary—'so happy in his conjectures,' said de Morgan, 'as to seem to know more than he could possibly have any means of proving.' The proofs, for what they are worth, were, as I have said, dressed up afterwards—they were not the instrument of discovery.

There is the story of how he informed Halley of one of his most fundamental discoveries of planetary motion. 'Yes,' replied Halley, 'but how do you know that? Have you proved it?' Newton was taken aback—'Why, I've known it for years,' he replied. 'If you'll give me a few days, I'll certainly find you a proof of it'—as in due course he did.

During the twenty-five years he lived and worked at Trinity

as a recluse, mathematics and astronomy were only a part, and perhaps not the most absorbing, of his occupations. Unpublished papers which emerge from this period fall into several groups. Very early in his life Newton had abandoned orthodox belief in the Trinity and become a monotheist.

> He arrived at this conclusion, not on so-to-speak rational or sceptical grounds, but entirely on the interpretation of ancient authority. He was persuaded that the revealed documents give no support to the Trinitarian doctrines which were due to late falsifications. The revealed God was one God.
>
> But this was a dreadful secret which Newton was at desperate pains to conceal all his life. It was the reason why he refused Holy Orders, and therefore had to obtain a special dispensation to hold his Fellowship and Lucasian Chair and could not be Master of Trinity.

For anti-Trinitarians were persecuted and excluded from public office.

Another large section of his writings was concerned with all branches of

> . . . apocalyptic writings from which he sought to deduce the secret truths of the Universe—the measurements of Solomon's Temple, the Book of Daniel, the Book of Revelations, an enormous volume of work of which some part was published in his later days. Along with this are hundreds of pages of Church History and the like, designed to discover the truth of tradition.

> The third section concerned alchemy—transmutation, the philosopher's stone and the elixir of life.

In these mixed and extraordinary studies, with one foot in the Middle Ages and one foot treading a path for modern science, Newton spent the first phase of his life, the period of life in Trinity when he did all his real work.

After the publication of the *Principia*, he was persuaded by his friends to abandon his studies, taking up university business and representing the University in Parliament.

With Pepys and Lowndes he became one of the greatest and most efficient of our civil servants. He was a very successful investor of funds, surmounting the crisis of the South Sea Bubble, and died a rich man. He possessed in exceptional degree almost every kind of intellectual aptitude—lawyer, historian, theologian, not less than mathematician, physicist, astronomer.

In 1689 his mother, to whom he was still deeply attached, died. Soon afterwards he suffered what Keynes called a 'severe nervous breakdown'.

Melancholia, sleeplessness, fears of persecution—he writes to Pepys and to Locke and no doubt to others letters which lead them to think that his mind is deranged. He lost, in his own words, the 'former consistency of his mind.' He never again concentrated after the old fashion or did any fresh work. The breakdown probably lasted nearly two years, and from it emerged, slightly 'gaga', but still, no doubt, with one of the most powerful minds of England, the Sir Isaac Newton of tradition.

In 1696 his friends finally persuaded him to leave Cambridge. He settled in London and set up house with his niece, Catherine Barton, who was probably the mistress of Newton's old friend Charles Montague, Earl of Halifax and Chancellor of the Exchequer. Newton became Master of the Mint, was knighted, and reigned as President of the Royal Society for twenty-four years. He put on rather too much weight. 'His pink face, beneath a mass of snow-white hair . . . is increasingly both benevolent and majestic.' He became the sage and monarch of the age of reason.

But he never concentrated, never recovered 'the former consistency of his mind'. 'He spoke very little in company.' 'He had something rather languid in his look and manner.'

And he looked very seldom, I expect, into the chest, where, when he left Cambridge, he had packed all the evidences of what had occupied and so absorbed his intense and flaming spirit in his rooms and his garden and his elaboratory between the Great Gate and Chapel.

Keynes acquired much of these unpublished and unpublishable papers, and remarked:

As one broods over these queer collections, it seems easier to understand—with an understanding which is not, I hope, distorted in the other direction—this strange spirit, who was tempted by the Devil to believe, at the time when within these walls he was solving so much, that he could reach *all* the secrets of God and Nature by the pure power of mind— Copernicus and Faustus in one.

Keynes's account leaves no doubt as to the correctness of Storr's view. Newton was the classical example of a man whose mind was split between an effortless unravelling of the mysteries of the physical world and a tortured profitless exploration of the occult. How much this was due to his peculiar relationship to his mother or to the illness which became manifest after her death, has not been explored. Nor is it possible to say whether or not his behaviour at the time of his great discoveries was sufficiently unusual to constitute a psychoneurosis. I suspect that it was, and that a more penetrating analysis of Newton's case, than I have been able to perform, would place him alongside Sigmund Freud.

Einstein and Newton display beautifully an outstanding characteristic of all truly creative persons. Their minds are so obsessed with the object of their passionate interest that they heed not what they regard as the little things of life. They tend to be neglectful of their personal appearance, their clothes, their eating habits. They often behave strangely being afflicted with seemingly unaccountable fits of absence of mind. They are different from their fellow creatures; they are eccentric; they are odd. As Keynes remarked 'Geniuses *are* very peculiar'. Oddity is a character which the genius shares with the psychopath. But the psychopath rarely shares with the genius high intelligence and intense devotion to a cause.

Perhaps the outstanding quality of the creative person is his driving force, once known as psychical energy to the psychologist, and as passion to everyone else. This characteristic was outstanding in the people described here. Darwin described himself as having a passion for shooting, for collecting, and finally for science, a passion which the daily routine at Down might seem to have hidden until one reads the succession of learned yet revolutionary works which issued from the study and garden of the invalid recluse. Florence Nightingale described herself as having a passionate nature, which was indeed displayed throughout her life, except when she wished to charm with sweet reason, and until she became a benign and slightly portly old lady. Passion also characterised Joan of Arc, Mary Baker Eddy, Sigmund Freud and Marcel Proust. Fisher wrote:

Florence Nightingale, a far nobler figure than Mrs Eddy, was not altogether the amiable tender creature of the Victorian legend, but, as Jowett once described her, 'very violent'; and equally violent and compelling was the will of the woman who founded the Christian Science Church. The image of a saintly healer, gentle, compassionate, penetrated with mystical devotion, thinking always of others, never of herself, and winning her way to influence by the magic of eloquence and virtue, is as far from the reality as are the photographs which give to Mrs Eddy the appearance of a finished lady of society.[7]

Of Freud, Jones wrote:

By nature Freud was endowed with unusually strong emotions; he could both love and hate passionately. But that gift went with an equally strong self-control, so that the emotions were hardly ever displayed to outsiders.[8]

Chesterton[9] deduced from her poems that Elizabeth Barrett too had passion but this was often concealed by her wit, her gaiety, and her kindness to her fellows.

The passion to which I refer is, of course, not physical passion or lust; it is what Havelock Ellis described as a passion of the soul.[10] He wrote: 'My work, I am often told, is cool and serene, entirely reasonable and free of passion, but without that devouring passion of the soul my work would have been nothing.' Ellis was singularly devoid of physical passion. Freud would consider the passion to which I am referring as a sublimation of the sexual urge; in other words, psychic energy is derived ultimately from the sex instinct.

Passion is to be distinguished from ambition. For whereas passion can be selfless, ambition is self. Christ was the embodiment of passion and the negation of ambition; so to a lesser extent were Miss Nightingale and Mr Darwin. Napoleon had both, and it is his and the world's great tragedy that passion was transformed by success to ambition.

How often is fame the spur? Amongst the more successful of my own contemporaries, I have no doubt that the desire for fame is the driving force in many. But fame tends to be Dead Sea fruit. Those who seek fame are often dissatisfied with the measure of it they receive. It is seldom enough, and the appetite is whetted for more. No cup is more bitter than the realisation that fame has eluded its pursuer. Amongst the personalities discussed here, there is no doubt that Charles Darwin was not unmindful of fame, though he did not ostentatiously seek it. Mrs Eddy, Marcel Proust and Freud were all intensely interested in their own reputation during their lifetime. I doubt whether Elizabeth Barrett Browning was. As for Miss Nightingale, she seemed to do her best to diminish and even to suppress the fame which she had won so worthily. 'F.N. born 1820, died 1910' is in character.

There is a relationship between passion and religion. No one has expressed this better than Einstein:

> . . . I maintain that cosmic religiousness is the strongest and most noble driving force of scientific research. Only the man who can conceive the gigantic effort and above all the devotion, without which original scientific thought cannot succeed, can measure the strength of the feeling from which alone such work . . . can grow. What a deep belief in the intelligence of Creation and what longing for understanding, even if only of a meagre reflection in the revealed intelligence of this world, must have flourished in Kepler and Newton, enabling them as lonely men to unravel over years of work the mechanism of celestial mechanics. . . . Only the man who devotes his life to such goals has a living conception of what inspired these men and gave them strength to remain steadfast in their aims in spite of countless failures. It is cosmic religiousness that bestows such strength. A contemporary has said, not unrightly, that the serious research scholar in our generally materialistic age is the only deeply religious human being.[11]

Of the creative personalities here considered, Joan of Arc and Mary Baker Eddy were religious leaders. So, according to my understanding of his life, and work, was Sigmund Freud.* So in a sense was Miss Nightingale for she regarded herself as having a mission; she had been called to do God's work, and referred to herself as 'this handmaiden of the Lord'. Darwin, I suspect, would not have dissented from Einstein. Elizabeth Barrett was an unselfish idealist. I get no feeling for religious ecstasy in Proust.

I have now completed the intellectual exercise, which I repeat was undertaken for its own sake, because my curiosity had been aroused and I wished to satisfy it. I hoped it might, as

---

* Though I suspect he would have been horrified by this.

a by-product, throw some light on the creative personality. I think it does. It emphasises the singlemindedness of many men of genius, their obsession with the object of their passion to the exclusion of the ordinary conventions of daily life. Geniuses are very peculiar. And the dividing line between the odd and the mentally ill is tenuous.

My study emphasises particularly the importance of passion, which is to be distinguished from ambition or the desire for fame. Passion is the chief characteristic that I can find which relates the psychoneuroses of the characters here described and the creative work which brought them fame. Psychoneurosis arises when there is a conflict between a wish and its fulfilment. The more passionate the desire the more likely is its frustration to lead to psychoneurosis. This in turn may make possible the fulfilment of the wish, or act as a spur to the mental catharsis which produces a great creative work. This seems to be the basis of the relationship between psychoneurosis and creativity.

In brief, a psychoneurosis represents passion thwarted, a great creative work, passion fulfilled.

Notes to Chapter 1

[1] D. Hubble, 'Charles Darwin and Psychotherapy', *Lancet*, vol. 1 (1943), 129.
[2] Lytton Strachey, *Eminent Victorians* (London: Chatto and Windus, 1918).
[3] C. Woodham-Smith, *Florence Nightingale* (London: Constable, 1951).
[4] S. Freud, *An Autobiographical Study* (London: The Hogarth Press, 1935).
[5] P. B. Medawar, *The Art of the Soluble* (London: Methuen, 1967).

Notes to Chapter 2

[1] M. M. Katz, J. O. Cole, and H. A. Lowery, *American Journal of Psychiatry*, vol. 125 (1969), p. 937.
[2] I. P. Pavlov, *Conditioned Reflexes*, trans. G. V. Anrep (Oxford: Oxford University Press, 1927).
[3] P. H. Wood, 'Da Costa's Syndrome', *British Medical Journal*, vol. 1 (1941), pp. 767, 805, 845.
[4] T. Lewis, *Diseases of the Heart*, 4th edn (London: Macmillan, 1946).
[5] Robert White, *The Abnormal Personality*, 2nd edn (New York: The Ronald Press Co., 1956).

Notes to Chapters 3, 4 and 5

The main sources from which the biography has been constructed are as follows:

[1] *Autobiography of Charles Darwin*, with two appendices, comprising a chapter of reminiscences and a statement of Charles Darwin's religious views, by his son, Sir Francis Darwin. The Thinker's Library, No. 7 (London: Watts and Co., 1929). (*Labelled (A) in text.*)
[2] *Autobiography of Charles Darwin*, edited by Nora Barlow (London: Collins, 1958). (*Labelled (A) in text.*)
[3] *Charles Darwin's Diary of the Voyage of H.M.S. 'Beagle'*, edited by Nora Barlow (Cambridge: University Press, 1933). (*Labelled (D) in text.*)
[4] Charles Darwin, *A Naturalist's Voyage round the World* (Journal of Researches into the Natural History and Geology of the countries visited during the voyage round the world of H.M.S. *'Beagle'* under the command of Captain FitzRoy R.N.) 1st edn 1839, 2nd edn 1845. Reprint of 2nd edn (London: John Murray, 1902). (*Labelled (J) in text.*)

⁵ Francis Darwin (Editor), *The Foundations of the Origin of Species.* Two essays written in 1842 and 1844 by Charles Darwin (Cambridge: University Press, 1909).

⁶ Francis Darwin (Editor), *The Life and Letters of Charles Darwin*, including an autobiographical chapter (London: John Murray, 1887).

⁷ Nora Barlow (Editor), *Darwin and Henslow: The Growth of an Idea*, Letters 1831–1860 (London: Bentham-Moxon Trust/John Murray, 1967).

⁸ H. E. Litchfield, *Emma Darwin: A Century of Family Letters*, vols. I and II (Cambridge: University Press, 1904) (privately printed).

Additional references are:

⁹ Wilma George, *Biologist Philosopher*, A Study of the Life and Writings of Alfred Russel Wallace (London: Abelard-Schuman, 1964).

¹⁰ D. Hubble, 'The Life of the Shawl', *Lancet*, vol. 2 (1953), p. 1351.

¹¹ W. C. Alvarez, 'Why the Nervous Ill Health of Charles Darwin?', *Modern Medicine*, vol. 38 (1970), 105.

¹² L. A. Kohn, 'Charles Darwin's Chronic Ill-Health', *Bulletin of the History of Medicine*, vol. 37 (1963), p. 239.

¹³ C. E. Dent, *British Medical Journal*, vol. 1 (1965), p. 1129.

¹⁴ S. W. Adler, 'Darwin's Illness', *Nature*, vol. 184 (1959), p. 1102.

¹⁵ G. de Beer, *Charles Darwin: Evolution by Natural Selection* (London: Nelson, 1963).

¹⁶ J. Huxley, and H. B. D. Kettlewell, *Charles Darwin and His World* (London: Thames and Hudson, 1965).

¹⁷ P. B. Medawar, *The Art of the Soluble* (London: Methuen, 1967).

¹⁸ A. W. Woodruff, *British Medical Journal*, vol. 1 (1965), p. 745.

¹⁹ Thomas Reid, *Essays on the Intellectual Powers of Man*, 1st edn 1785, in *The Works of Thomas Reid, D.D.*, edited by W. Hamilton, 4th edn (London: 1854).

²⁰ Gwen Raverat, *Period Piece* (London: Faber and Faber, 1952).

²¹ E. J. Kempf, *Psychopathology* (St Louis: C. V. Mosby Co., 1920).

²² R. Good, *Lancet*, vol. 1 (1954), p. 106.

²³ P. Greenacre, *The Quest for the Father* (New York: International Universities Press Inc., 1963).

²⁴ D. Hubble, 'Charles Darwin and Psychotherapy', *Lancet*, vol. 1 (1943), p. 129.

²⁵ A. Moorehead, *Darwin and the Beagle* (London: Hamish Hamilton, 1969).

²⁶ L. Eiseley, *Darwin's Century* (New York: Doubleday, 1958).

²⁷ 'Observations on the Nature and Importance of Geology', *Edinburgh New Philosophical Journal*, vol. 1 (1826), pp. 293–302.

²⁸ T. H. Huxley, *Darwiniana* (New York: Appleton, 1893), p. 252.

Notes to Chapters *6, 7, 8 and 9*

The main sources from which her biography has been drawn are:

1 Sir Edward Cook, *The Life of Florence Nightingale*, vols. I and II (London: Macmillan, 1913).
2 Zachary Cope, *Florence Nightingale and the Doctors* (London: Museum Press Ltd, 1958).
3 I. B. O'Malley, *Florence Nightingale 1820–1856*, A study of her life down to the end of the Crimean War (London: Thornton Butterworth Ltd, 1932).
4 Lytton Strachey, *Eminent Victorians* (London: Chatto and Windus, 1918).
5 Cecil Woodham-Smith, *Florence Nightingale* (London: Constable, 1951).

Additional references are:

6 *The Institution of Kaiserswerth on the Rhine for the Practical Training of Deaconesses, under the direction of the Rev. Pastor Fliedner, embracing the support and care of a Hospital, Infant and Industrial Schools, and a Female Penitentiary* (London: Printed by the inmates of the London Ragged Colonial Training School, Westminster, 1851).
7 Letter to Catherine Winkworth, quoted by Mrs Woodham-Smith.
8 Barbara Harmelink, *Florence Nightingale: Founder of Modern Nursing* (London: Franklin Watts, 1969).
9 Osler's *Principles and Practice of Medicine*, 9th edn (New York and London: Appleton, 1920).

Note to Chapter *10*

1 John and Isobel-Ann Butterfield, 'Joan of Arc: A medical view', *History Today*, vol. 8 (1958), p. 628.

Notes to Chapter *11*

The chief works of Mary Baker Eddy quoted here are:

1 Mary Baker Eddy, *Science and Health*, first published by Mary Baker Glover in 1875, present edition 1934 (Boston: published by the Trustees under Will of Mary Baker G. Eddy).
2 Mary Baker Eddy, *Retrospection and Introspection* (Boston: Trustees under Will of Mary Baker G. Eddy, first published 1891).
3 Mary Baker G. Eddy, *Miscellaneous Writings, 1883–1896* (Boston: Armstrong, 1904).

Biographies used are:

[4] Sibyl Wilbur, *The Life of Mary Baker Eddy* (New York: Concord Publishing Co., 1907).

[5] Robert Peel, *Mary Baker Eddy: The Years of Discovery* (New York: Holt, Rinehart and Winston, 1966).

[6] Robert Peel, *Mary Baker Eddy: The Years of Trial* (New York: Holt, Rinehart and Winston, 1971).

[7] Georgine Milmine, *The Life of Mary Baker G. Eddy and the History of Christian Science* (New York: Doubleday, Page and Co., 1909).

[8] Edwin F., Dakin, *Mrs Eddy: The Biography of a Virginal Mind* (New York: Scribner, 1929).

[9] E. S. Bates, and J. V. Dittemore, *Mary Baker Eddy: The Truth and the Tradition* (New York: Knopf, 1932). (Dittemore had access to Calvin Frye's Diary.)

[10] Adam H. Dickey, *Memoirs of Mary Baker Eddy* (London: Carter, 1927). (This was withdrawn soon after publication and is now extremely rare. Only two copies are known to me: in the British Museum and the Library of Congress. The New York Public Library has a photocopy of that in the British Museum.)

[11] Allen Johnson, In *Dictionary of American Biography* (New York: Scribner, 1930).

[12] H. A. L. Fisher, *Our New Religion* (London: Watts, 1933).

Other works quoted:

[13] *Christian Science Journal*, June 1887.

[14] P. B. Beeson, and W. McDermott, *Cecil and Loeb's Textbook of Medicine*, 13th edn (Philadelphia: Saunders).

[15] Mark Twain, *Christian Science*, with notes containing corrections to date (New York and London: Harper, 1907).

Notes to Chapter 12

My account is largely based on

[1] E. Jones, *Sigmund Freud—Life and Work*, vols. I–III (London: The Hogarth Press, 1958).

with additional information from

[2] V. Brome, *Freud and his Early Circle* (London: Heinemann, 1967).

Other references are

[3] S. Freud, *Introductory Lectures on Psychoanalysis* (London: George Allen and Unwin, 1922).

[4] S. Freud, *Collected Papers* (London: The Hogarth Press, 1948).

[5] S. Freud, *An Autobiographical Study* (London: The Hogarth Press, 1935).

[6] C. G. Jung, *Memories, Dreams and Reflections*, trans. R. and C. Winston (London: Collins and Routledge and Kegan Paul, 1963).

[7] Karl Popper, *Conjectures and Refutations* (London: Routledge and Kegan Paul, 1963).

Notes to Chapter 13

[1] Marcel Proust, *Remembrance of Things Past*, vols. I–XI translated by C. K. Scott Moncrieff, Vol. XII by Stephen Hudson (London: Chatto and Windus, Uniform edition, 1941).

[2] André Maurois, *The Quest for Proust*, translated from the French by Gerard Hopkins (London: Jonathan Cape, 1950).

[3] George D. Painter (Editor), *Marcel Proust—Letters to his Mother*, translation (London: Rider and Co., 1956).

[4] George D. Painter, *Marcel Proust—A Biography*, vols. I and II (London: Chatto and Windus, 1966).

[5] Georges Rivane, *Influence de l'asthme sur l'oeuvre de Marcel Proust*, Preface by Henri Mondor (Paris: La Nouvelle Edition, 1945).

Notes to Chapter 14

[1] A. Hayter, *Mrs Browning: A Poet's Work and its Setting* (London, Faber and Faber, 1962).

[2] G. K. Chesterton, *Robert Browning* (London: Macmillan, 1903).

[3] Maisie Ward, *Robert Browning and his World: The Private Face 1812–1861* (London: Cassell, 1968).

[4] D. Hewlett, *Elizabeth Barrett Browning* (London: Cassell, 1953).

[5] P. Kelley, and R. Hudson (Editors), *Diary by E.B.B. The Unpublished Diary of Elizabeth Barrett Browning, 1831–1832* (Athens, Ohio: Ohio University Press, 1969).

[6] E. B. Browning, *Elizabeth Barrett to Miss Mitford*, Letters edited and introduced by Betty Miller (London: John Murray, 1954).

[7] Robert Browning, *Letters of Robert Browning and Elizabeth Barrett Browning 1845–1846*, vols. I and II (London: Smith Elder, 1899).

Notes to Chapter 15

1 F. Galton, *Hereditary Genius* (London: Macmillan, 1869).

2 P. E. Vernon (Editor), *Creativity* (Harmondsworth: Penguin Books, 1970).

3 A. Koestler, *The Act of Creation* (London: Hutchinson, 1964).

4 Helmholtz, quoted in P. E. Vernon (reference 2), p. 91.

5 K. R. Popper, *Conjectures and Refutations* (London: Routledge and Kegan Paul, 1963).

6 H. Poincaré, *The Foundations of Science*, trans. G. B. Halstead (Science Press, 1924).

7 A. Findlay, *A Hundred Years of Chemistry*, 2nd edn (London: Duckworth, 1948).

8 O. Loewi, In *A Dozen Doctors*, edited by D. J. Ingle (University of Chicago Press, 1963).

9 P. Medawar, *The Art of the Soluble* (London: Methuen, 1967).

10 E. Holmes, *The Life of Mozart*, including his correspondence (London: Chapman and Hall, 1878).

11 Bertrand Russell, *History of Western Philosophy* (London: George Allen and Unwin, 1946).

12 Vasari, quoted by Kenneth Clark, in *Civilization* (London: B.B.C. and John Murray, 1969).

13 C. D. Darlington, *The Evolution of Man and Society* (London: George Allen and Unwin, 1969).

14 M. Prywes, *Medical and Biological Research in Israel* (Jerusalem: The Hebrew University, 1960).

15 E. Jones, *Sigmund Freud—Life and Works*, vols. I–III (London: The Hogarth Press, 1958).

16 S. Freud, *The Interpretation of Dreams*, translated by J. Strachey (London: George Allen and Unwin, 1954).

Notes to Chapter 16

1 René and Jean Dubos, *The White Plague: Tuberculosis, Man and Society* (London: Victor Gollancz, 1953).

2 Charles Lamb, 'Sanity of Genius' in *The Last Essays of Elia* (London: Oxford Clarendon Press, 1951).

3 E. Slater, and A. Meyer, 'Contributions to a Pathography of the Musicians: I. Robert Schumann', *Confinia Psychiatrica*, vol. 2 (1959), pp. 65–94.

4 Quentin Bell, *Virginia Woolf: A Biography*, vols. I and II (London: The Hogarth Press, 1972).

[5] August Strindberg, *A Madman's Defence*, edited by Evert Sprinchorn (London: Jonathan Cape, 1968).

[6] S. Freud, *A General Introduction to Psychoanalysis* (New York: Boni and Liveright, [1920]).

[7] Eric Blom, *Some Great Composers* (Oxford University Press, 1944).

[8] Harold Nicolson, 'The Health of Authors', *Lancet*, vol. 2 (1947), p. 719.

[9] Lord Byron, *Letters*, edited by R. G. Howarth, Everyman's Library (London: Dent, 1936).

[10] Alethea Hayter, *Opium and the Romantic Imagination* (London: Faber and Faber, 1968).

[11] Wilder Penfield, 'Halsted of Johns Hopkins', *Journal of the American Medical Association*, vol. 210 (1969), p. 2214.

[12] J. L. Lowes, *The Road to Xanadu*, 2nd edn (London: Constable, 1951).

[13] Havelock Ellis, *A Study in British Genius* (London: Hurst and Blackett, 1904).

[14] A. Juda, *Höchstbegabung: Ihre Erbverhältnisse sowie ihre Beziehungen zu psychischen Anomalien* (Munich: Urban and Schwarzenberg, 1953).

[15] S. Freud, *Introductory Lectures on Psychoanalysis* (London: George Allen and Unwin, 1922).

Notes to Chapter 17

[1] Anthony Storr, *The Dynamics of Creation* (London: Secker and Warburg, 1972).

[2] Ernest Jones, *Sigmund Freud. Four Centenary Addresses* (London: Tavistock Publications, 1956).

[3] V. and M. G. Goertzel, *Cradles of Eminence* (London: Constable, 1964).

[4] Antonia Vallentin, *Einstein* (London: Weidenfeld and Nicolson, 1954).

[5] Peter Michelmore, *Einstein. Profile of the Man* (London: Frederick Muller, 1963).

[6] John Maynard Keynes, *Essays in Biography* (London: Rupert Hart-Davis, 1951).

[7] H. A. L. Fisher, *Our New Religion* (London: Watts, 1931).

[8] E. Jones, *Sigmund Freud—Life and Work*, vols. I–III (London: The Hogarth Press, 1958).

[9] G. K. Chesterton, *Robert Browning* (London: Macmillan, 1903).

[10] H. H. Ellis, *My Life* (London: Heinemann, 1940).

[11] K. Seelig, *Albert Einstein* (Zurich: Europea Verlag, 1954).

Index